ANDREAS VESALIUS

Publication No. 6

HISTORICAL LIBRARY
YALE MEDICAL LIBRARY

℮

Other Publications
ISSUED UNDER THE AUSPICES OF THE
HISTORICAL LIBRARY

ANDREAS VESALIUS

The well-known contemporary portrait of Vesalius which appeared in the *Fabrica* of 1543, the *Epitome* of 1543, and the China-root Epistle of 1546. Although still fresh in 1546 (and in 1555), the block had been chipped in the upper left corner. This is the only authentic portrayal of Vesalius.

A BIO-BIBLIOGRAPHY OF

ANDREAS VESALIUS

BY

HARVEY CUSHING

NEW YORK · SCHUMAN'S · 1943

TO

MORITZ ROTH

EDOUARD TURNER

AND

F. M. G. deFEYFER

STUDENTS OF
VESALIUS

ᶎ

EVEN the skeletal figures seem miraculously alive. The spirit of the Lord had set the prophet of old in the valley of dry bones and asked, "Son of man, can these bones live?" There was an earthquake, and the bones came together, bone to bone; and lo, there were sinews upon them, and flesh came up, and skin covered them above; and the breath came into them, and they lived, and stood upon their feet. So wherever Vesalius taught, he articulated a skeleton, set it up above or beside the corpse that lay on the table, and invited his students to take the muddy vesture of decay which he anatomized before them, reknit its parts, made clean and sweet again, project it in imagination on to those dry bones, and breathe again into its nostrils the breath of life. But it must have been a rare student, even in the renaissance, for whom the miracle came to pass at the master's word. What the word could not evoke, the craft of artist, engraver and printer enacted in the *Fabrica*.

From Max H. Fisch's "Vesalius and his book"
Bull. med. Libr. Ass., 1943, 31:208-221.

❧ PREFACE ❧

IN Dr. Cushing's copy of the 1543 *Fabrica,* a note occurs in his handwriting stating that he had acquired the volume in 1903; however, his interest in Vesalius, stimulated by Osler, dates from 1898 or possibly even earlier. In the impetuous Vesalius, Harvey Cushing saw a vigorous and indefatigable character with a stormy temperament similar to his own—a man with artistic leanings who gave unremitting attention to detail—all of which aroused Cushing's admiration and caused him to follow Vesalius with instinctive determination and persistence. During the forty years from 1899 until his death on October 7, 1939, Cushing pursued the trail: he collected everything conceivable relating to him, including the writings of a host of less gifted followers who copied the Vesalian text and figures; he corresponded with nearly every Vesalian scholar in this country and Europe, and his greatest delight was to uncover a new fact concerning the man or his work.

As indicated in the *Apologia* which follows, Dr. Cushing had for at least twenty years contemplated publishing a Vesalian bibliography and he spent the last year of his life assembling the materials in final form; indeed, when the end came in October 1939, the family dining-room, which he had confiscated during the summer for bibliographical ends, was completely occupied with books and papers relating to the bibliography. Had he lived a few months longer, he would no doubt have finished the work to his own satisfaction. But unfortunately only the introductory matter and Chapters I to V approached completion. Chapters VI and VII were partly drafted, but Chapters VIII, IX and X were untouched.

There had been certain misgivings in Cushing's mind concerning the wisdom of his undertaking a full-length bibliography. He felt that his Latinity was short and that he had had too little first-hand experience with the detail of technical bibliography. His gay disregard for bibliographical conventions and need for consistency has indeed left a heavy burden to his editors; but it has also left a freshness of approach and vigour of literary style that put vibrant flesh on the Vesalian bones, and it makes him live again at a time when anatomy as Vesalius knew it has become an almost forgotten discipline—except possibly to those who are attempting to restore the human wrecks of modern warfare. In 1544 Vesalius had followed the victorious army of Charles V into the valley of the Marne and the Argonne to Château Thierry, Soissons, and indeed to the very walls of Paris itself. He was thoroughly familiar with battle casualties, even as

Cushing came to know them when struggling on the same terrain in 1915-1918; and because of his knowledge of anatomy Vesalius undoubtedly found himself better equipped to deal with war injuries than many of his contemporaries, excepting of course Ambroise Paré who, like many surgeons of 1943, had learned anatomy the hard way—in the field of battle. For these, and many other reasons, we have persevered in bringing out the Vesalius bio-bibliography in 1943, at a time when physicians on every battle front will undoubtedly welcome a reminder of the man who at the early age of twenty-eight years first adequately portrayed the fabric of the human body. When the lights burn low and tradition falters, we must carry the torch of remembrance until it can flame again and brighten the paths of learning and free thought for those who now "sit in darkness and in the shadow of death."

Cushing's remarks about his shortness of latinity stem in part from modesty, for as an undergraduate at Yale he had good grounding both in Latin and Greek. Among his notes, however, I find the following amusing passage borrowed from Geminus, evidently designed for use in his preface: "Wherunto forasmuch as I am not my self so perfeict and experte in the Englishe tounge that I dare waraunt or trust myne owne dooynges, I have used the studious peines of Nicholas Udall and certain other learned men whose exercise in translations and penying in this tounge hath ben not without some frutte to the common weale." Cushing no doubt intended to quote this in offering his thanks to those who helped him render many difficult passages of Vesalian Latin into English, especially his friend, George L. Hendrickson, Professor Emeritus of the classics at Yale, the late Miss Ethel Gladstone of San Francisco, and Mr. Leon Nemoy of the Yale University Library, all of whom gave substantial assistance during a period of some eight years. He also felt much indebted to Prof. C. U. Clark who in 1905 had translated the full text of the Venesection Epistle for him.

Dr. Cushing had confidently expected to issue the bibliography in 1943 in commemoration of the 400th anniversary of the *Fabrica*; and although it would have gained immeasurably from the final touches which he could have given it, it has seemed essential to publish now what he had assembled rather than hold it until greater completeness could be attained. Dr. W. W. Francis, who in a sense has been a co-editor, has shouldered much of the burden, particularly in revising Chapters IV, V, VI and VII. He has also read all of the copy and all of the proofs. We have also been most fortunate in having the enthusiastic assistance of Dr. Arturo Castiglioni, who has examined the whole manuscript in detail, and we are particularly indebted to him for preparing the scholarly chapters on Fallopius and the Consilia. Dr. Edward C. Streeter has also read the manuscript and, as with Dr. Castiglioni, has given it the benefit of his intimate knowledge of Vesalius and Italian medicine. Mrs. John P. Peters has compiled and verified Chapter X on Vesaliana, and Miss Madeline Stanton, Dr. Cushing's secretary, has systematized and verified the main bibliographical entries, and she also undertook the stern task of preparing copy for the press. I have taken the responsibility for general editing, but I have attempted as far as possible to leave the text of the manuscript untouched except where matters of fact were involved, or when Dr. Cushing had left unanswered a question that could be settled from sources readily available. I am also responsible for the conventions of bibliographical description, including the decision (which Dr. Francis regretted) to transcribe all titles in the exact spelling of the original, with medial V's set down as v's (rather than as lower-case u's). The war has precluded a thorough census of foreign copies. The indices have been compiled by Miss Stanton and Mrs. Peters. Due to existing paper limitation, the figures have been printed on both sides of the sheets and folded in with the main gatherings. This has caused a number of dislocations in Chapters VI, VII and IX. The position of any given illustration can readily be found, however, from the list on the next page.

We are also much indebted to Mr. Carl P. Rollins for valuable advice in matters typographical and to Mr. Schuman, the publisher who, like Oporinus, has had the courage to commit himself to a formidable undertaking. To Mr. A. Colish, the printer and designer of this book, we owe much, and we feel particularly beholden to him for his patience—and also for his fonts of Poliphilus and the Blado italic.

JOHN F. FULTON

November 21, 1943

❧ ILLUSTRATIONS ❧

❧ CONTENTS ❧

KEY TO LIBRARY ABBREVIATIONS*

Amsterdam	University Library
Belt	Library of Dr. Elmer Belt, Los Angeles, California
BM	British Museum, London
BN	Bibliothèque Nationale, Paris
BNed	*Catalogus van de Bibliotheek der Nederlandsche Maatschappij tot Bevordering der Geneeskunst, in Bruikleen vereenigd met de Bibliotheek der Universiteit van Amsterdam. Amsterdam (1930).*
Breslau	University Library
Brunet	*Manuel du libraire et de l'amateur de livres,* par J.-C. Brunet. Paris, Dorbon-Aine (n.d.). 7 vols.
Brussels	Royal Library
Budapest	University Library
CaMM	McGill University Library, Montreal
CaMM-Os	Osler Library, McGill University, Montreal
CaTAM	Academy of Medicine, Toronto
Clendening	Library of Dr. Logan Clendening, Kansas City, Missouri
CSmH	Henry E. Huntington Memorial Library, San Marino, California
CSt-L	Lane Medical Library, San Francisco, California
CtY	Yale University Library, New Haven, Connecticut
CU-M	University of California, Medical Center Library, San Francisco, California
Cushing	Library of the Author, now in the Historical Library, Yale University School of Medicine, New Haven, Connecticut
DLC	Library of Congress, Washington, D.C.
DSG	Army Medical Library, Surgeon General's Office, Washington, D.C.
F	Feyfer, F. M. G. de, Die Schriften des Andreas Vesalius. *Janus,* 1914, 19:435-507
Fisher	Library of Dr. O. O. Fisher, Detroit, Michigan
Fulton	Library of Dr. John F. Fulton, now in the Historical Library, Yale University School of Medicine, New Haven, Connecticut
Ghent	University Library
Glasgow	Hunterian Library, University of Glasgow
Harvey	Library of Dr. S. C. Harvey, New Haven, Connecticut
H.C.	*See* Cushing
ICJ	John Crerar Library, Chicago, Ill.
ICN	Newberry Library, Chicago, Illinois
ICU	University of Chicago
IEN-M	Northwestern University Medical School, Chicago, Illinois
Königsberg	University Library
Leningrad	State Library
Leyden	University Library
Louvain	University Library
LNHT	Howard-Tilton Memorial Library, Tulane University, New Orleans, Louisiana
MB	Public Library, Boston, Massachusetts
MBM	Boston Medical Library, Boston, Massachusetts

*The abbreviations used for libraries in the United States are from the *Symbols used in the Union Catalog of the Library of Congress,* rev. ed., Washington, Govt. Printing Office, 1936.

MdBJ-W — Welch Medical Library, Johns Hopkins University Medical School, Baltimore, Maryland

MdBM — Medical and Chirurgical Faculty of the State of Maryland, Baltimore, Maryland

MH — Harvard University Library, Cambridge, Massachusetts

MH-M — Harvard Medical School Library, Boston, Massachusetts

MiU(Crummer) — University of Michigan (from the collection of the late Dr. LeRoy Crummer), Ann Arbor, Michigan

MiU(Pilcher) — University of Michigan (from the collection of the late Dr. Stephen J. Pilcher), Ann Arbor, Michigan

MnU — University of Minnesota, Minneapolis, Minnesota

Munich — University Library

NBMS — Medical Society of the County of Kings and Academy of Medicine, Brooklyn, New York

NIC — Cornell University Library, Ithaca, New York

NjP — Princeton University Library, Princeton, New Jersey

NN — Public Library, New York

NNC — Columbia University Library, New York, New York

NNC-M — Columbia University Medical Library, New York, New York

NNNAM — New York Academy of Medicine, New York, New York

NPV — Vassar College, Poughkeepsie, New York

OClM — Cleveland Medical Library, Cleveland, Ohio

Oxford — Bodleian Library, Oxford

PPCP — College of Physicians, Philadelphia, Pennsylvania

PU — University of Pennsylvania, Philadelphia, Pennsylvania

RCP — Royal College of Physicians Library, London

RCS — Royal College of Surgeons Library, London

RPM — Rhode Island Medical Society, Providence, Rhode Island

Stuttgart — Royal Library

Trent — Library of Dr. J. C. Trent, Durham, North Carolina

van Wagenen — Library of Dr. Gertrude van Wagenen, New York, New York

Vatican — Vatican Library, Rome

Venice — Library of San Marco, Venice

Vienna — Staats-Bibliothek, Vienna

ViRA — Richmond Academy of Medicine, Richmond, Virginia

W — Wellcome Historical Medical Museum, London

Waller — Library of Dr. Erik Waller, Stockholm

Wynne-Finch — Library of the late Heneage Wynne-Finch, London

"THERE, now! What do you say to this copy of Joannes de Ketam, Venice, 1522? Look at these woodcuts,—the first anatomical pictures ever printed, Doctor, unless these others of Jacobus Berengarius are older! . . . Take a look, too, at my Vesalius,—not the Leyden edition, Doctor, but the one with the grand old original figures,—so good that they laid them to Titian. And look here, Doctor, I couldn't help getting this great folio Albinus, 1747,—and the nineteenth century can't touch it, Doctor,—can't touch it for completeness and magnificence,—so all the learned professors tell me! . . . Did you ever read the oldest of medical documents,—the Oath of Hippocrates?"

OLIVER WENDELL HOLMES
The Guardian Angel, Chapter XI

1. APOLOGIA*

The effective, moving, vitalizing work of the world
is done between the ages of twenty-five and forty.
W. O.

AN INCURSION into bibliography has been compared to entering a dark forest full of unsuspected brambles in which even those with experience are prone to become entangled. One must not only step with care but have qualities of precision and alertness rarely possessed by those no longer young. Conrad Gesner, whom Osler so admired that he put him in his Bibliotheca Prima chiefly because he was "the father of bibliography," was only twenty-five when he began to collect the materials for his famous *Bibliotheca universalis* which was printed in 1545 by Chr. Froschouer in his native Zurich (169). Under the caption "Andreas Vesalius" on leaf 42 of this voluminous work, Gesner records all of Vesalius' publications that were then known to him and he ends his citation of the 1543 edition of the *Fabrica* by calling attention to the author's age as follows: "Scripsit autem Vesalius hos libros natus annos 28." As Gesner at the time was only 29 years old himself, he was naturally impelled to emphasize the age of the writer of this epochal work though far too modest to draw any further comparison.

When my personal interest in Vesalius was first aroused I am unable definitely to recall. It must have been nearly 40 years ago, for I find that I came into possession of Moritz Roth's remarkable biography (345) in 1900 which indicates that there must have been talk of the man probably at the Johns Hopkins Historical Club prior to that time. This may have been what led my colleague W. G. MacCallum, after a year of study abroad, to lug home and present to me in the autumn of 1903 an imperfect copy of the 1543 *Fabrica* which he had come upon that summer among some books for sale in the back of a blacksmith's shop in a side street in Rome.

That same summer Osler as usual had been brain-dusting abroad whence came the usual shower of postcards to the Baltimore stay-at-homes. On one of them postmarked Guernsey, July 17th, he exclaims: "I have bagged two 1543 Fabricas! 'Tis not a work to be left on the shelves of a bookseller." And again from the same place on July 25th: "Besides the two '43 Fabricas I have just

---

* The *Apologia* was published with an introductory note by Dr. W. W. Francis in the Klebs 70th birthday number of the *Bulletin of the History of Medicine*, 1940, *8*, 381-391. Numbered citations which follow in the text have reference to the entries in Section X of this bibliography (Vesaliana).

ordered a third. We cannot have too many copies in America & no medical library is complete without one. We are having a nice quiet time here . . ."

The upshot was that several copies of this historically important work were spread for comparison on his dining-room table one evening not long after the opening of the winter semester. The best of them he promptly inscribed as a wedding present for L. F. Barker. The next best he swapped with me for the MacCallum copy. A third (now in the Medical Library of the University of Missouri) was sent to W. J. Calvert, a recent graduate who had just been appointed Professor of Pathology at Columbia, Mo. This left him with the MacCallum copy and possibly two others (if there really were six) and his efforts to dispose of them are amusingly told in the introduction to his *Bibliotheca Osleriana* (310a), as follows:

"For some years Dr. Harvey Cushing and I had bought everything of Vesalius that was offered. One evening we had six copies of the first edition (1543) on exhibition. With the cash in pocket the book is impossible to resist, and I have distributed six copies to libraries. Forgetting what I had done, I took out a copy in 1907 to McGill, and showed it with pride to Dr. Shepherd, the librarian, who pointed out in one of the show-cases a very much better example presented by me some years before! Thinking it would be a very acceptable present to the Boston Library Association (in which I had a personal interest through Dr. James Chadwick and Dr. E. H. Brigham), I took the volume to Dr. Farlow, who looked a bit puzzled and amused. 'Come upstairs,' he said; and there in a case in the Holmes room, spread open at the splendid title-page, was the 1543 edition and, on a card beneath it, 'The gift of Dr. Osler.' I had better luck at New York, where the volume* found a resting-place in the Library of the Academy of Medicine."

Thus in the happy bygone Baltimore days those fortunate enough to come as latch-keyers under Osler's neighborly influence became inoculated with his bibliophilic spirit which has proved a solace for many of us in our later years even when it may not have developed into a hobby. Ere long a Vesalian club was organized, and though it was short-lived, an impromptu talk was given at its first meeting by Dr. Welch on the man and his works. This is well remem- bered, not only for what he said, but because a few days later Howard A. Kelly left at my door with his card a superb copy from his own library of the 1555

* Dr. Malloch informs me that on one of the foreleaves is written "Medical Faculty, McGill College, from Wm. Osler, October 29, 1903, the original edition of the greatest medical work ever printed."

Fabrica in contemporary stamped pigskin with clasps. So in those early days his-torically significant books might find their way to one's shelves, even though with an instructor's salary of $100 per annum there might be cobwebs in the purse.

In the effort that will follow to place the published writings of Vesalius in proper relation to those episodes of his life of which there is contemporary record, I am fully aware that to the perspicacious symptoms of the slowly pro-gressive though rarely fatal malady once vividly described by Thomas Frognall Dibdin will be disclosed. Dibdin, however, failed to point out that the Biblio-mania, while more commonly a masculine ailment, easily leads to difficulties because of an even more serious counter-disorder which is prone to affect the distaff members of the family, who usually control the majority vote. They show an uncontrollable tendency to accumulate odds and ends that go under the general name of antiques which mysteriously find their way into the house late in the day by way of the garage after all identification tags have been removed. On the other hand a new old-book, unmistakable in its brown paper parcel and bearing unfamiliar foreign stamps, is handed in openly at the front door by the postman, who must wait while the maid rummages round to find two cents for excess postage, thereby advertising its arrival from parlor to kitchen. Thus, while the advantages, as is quite proper, are all on the side of the antiquing distaffers, most collectors of books, in self-defense, after obliterating from their recent acquisitions such highly interesting records of provenance as pertain to their source of origin and purchase price, conceal them on shelves in their so-called dens, fully convinced that they have made a better investment for the long pull than has the party of the first part.

To provide an example of this, my first actual purchase of a Vesalian item from a bookseller's catalogue was made in 1905 from Boas of Berlin for 18 marks. It was a much used and annotated copy, bound in green vellum, of Vesalius' first publication—his thesis published at Louvain. While it was not the first issue of this tract, I have never but once since then seen another copy quoted. Of the first printing, so far as I am aware, but three copies survive, only one of which is in private hands. Because of this windfall, as I am bound to confess, I was lured twenty-five years later into the purchase of a rubricated fourteenth-century Rhazes manuscript which presumably came from one of the Austrian ducal libraries many of which were being sold at about that time. My tempter, the late Wilfred M. Voynich, wrote to say:

"It is interesting to recall that in the fifteenth century Eberhard de Wesalia, the grandfather of Vesalius, wrote commentaries on Rhazes which Vesalius had before him while working on his *Paraphrasis in nonum librum Rhazæ*. Since Eberhard became a doctor in 1433 and died young in his thirty-sixth year, *i.e.,* before the invention of printing, it follows that he was obliged to study the works of Rhazes from manuscripts. While I do not wish to imply that he ever had the present one in his possession, however, in view of the fact that it contains commentaries in various hands, some of which date undoubtedly from the early fifteenth century, one cannot overlook the possibility that Eberhard, etc., etc. . . ."

That proved an irresistible bait, though Mr. V. had conveniently forgotten just how the rare Rhazes MS. happened to come into his hands, even as I conveniently am obliged to forget just what was paid for it since manuscripts do not concern us here. It merely serves to show how one can be led by the nose from one thing to another.

Long before this concrete evidence of the fact that my resistance had completely broken down, I had begun to follow the footsteps of Vesalius and to seek traces of him in libraries, universities and art galleries whenever chance took me abroad, not to mention the perusal of auction sale-catalogues when at home. Notable among these sales was that of May 1911 when the library of Dr. Van den Corput (of Brussels) was auctioned at Muller's in Amsterdam, and when at a surprisingly low price excellent copies of the 1539 Venesection Epistle and —the tallest recorded one—of the 1546 China-root Epistle, along with twenty-five other items, were secured.* A Vesalian autograph letter for which Osler and I had submitted a combined bid was withdrawn from the sale as its genuineness had come under suspicion.

In August 1909 Sir John Stirling-Maxwell at Osler's request sent his father's copy of the *Tabulæ sex* to the Bodleian, where in the "Selden End" snapshots were taken of the separate sheets while the Regius Professor held the volume open. Curiously enough, L. F. Barker to whom that "best" copy of the 1543 *Fabrica* had been given six years before, happened to drop in, so Osler and his Baltimore successor were taken together flanking the exposed picture showing the venous circulation *à la* Galen (Fig. 1). It was learned at the time that not all of the thirty copies of the facsimile edition printed in 1874 for Sir William Maxwell had been distributed, and Osler saw to it that suitable habitats for the remainders were suggested, which accounts for the one in my possession.

During a short sojourn in Munich, on the way to the International Medical

---

* Actually 19 items containing 92 volumes in all.—Ed.

Congress at Budapest in that same year, fairly good copies of the 1543 *Epitome,*
both in Latin and in German, were purchased at a modest price from Ludwig
Rosenthal. Later at Basel the Vesalianum was visited and I was permitted by
the curator to mount a ladder and photograph in its glass case the skeleton with
bifid xiphoid process that Vesalius had prepared with his own hands while
awaiting proof sheets of the *Fabrica* as they were being struck off from the press
of Oporinus. While now incomplete, lacking the mandible and lower extrem-
ities, it is the oldest anatomical specimen with known provenance that has been
preserved, and above it in another sealed glass case are the skeletons of a female
child and of an ape that thirty years later were prepared by Felix Platter, then the
regularly appointed professor of anatomy at Basel. The tablet on the wall above
the cases bears in letters of gold on a dark green background this inscription:
"Skeletorum A. Vesalii nec non F. Plateri opera Basileæ annis p. Ch. n. 1543
et 1573 paratorum quæ supersunt." (Fig. 2.)

The Scuola del Bo', colloquially known as the "Bo'," at Padua was visited
more than once though there is not much now to see save Harvey's stemma and
the old precipitate oval well of Alessandro Benedetti's anatomical theatre which
was completed in its present form under Fra Paolo Sarpi's supervision while
Fabrizio d'Acquapendente was professor. Vesalius would doubtless have been
glad enough to have had such a room for his demonstrations though it was
scarcely to be compared with the idealized auditorium shown in Calcar's
frontispiece, which probably was intended to represent the dignified surroundings suitable, in the opinion of Vesalius, for such important events as public
anatomies. What his own makeshift quarters were probably like between 1537
and 1543 we can perhaps imagine from the account of the dissections held in
Bologna in a temporary shed which the auditors finally had to abandon late at
night because of the cold. Two hundred years passed before Bologna could
boast of an anatomical theatre worthy of the name, but even that which Ercole
Lelli finally saw erected would scarcely have held the 500 onlookers that are said
to have crowded around Vesalius during his demonstrations in the heyday of
his fame. There seems to be no possibility of identifying at Padua either the
house of Count Gabriel of Ortenburg where he wrote the epistle on blood-
letting in 1539 or the Casa degli Valli* (called "Cavalle" in the 16th century)

---

* This reference from Caius appears not to be exact. If *Valli,* as had been supposed, were a family name
(which seems unlikely), it would be written in Italian *dei Valli* or *de' Valli.* It appears, however, most likely
that the name refers to the *Prà della valle* (Meadow in the valley) which is to-day a centre of Padua and also
was well known in the 16th century. The fact that in Caius' reference *valli* is written with a small *v* bears
out this latter assumption.—Ed.

where for eight months he and the Englishman John Caius lived together, nor even the Ponte della Paglia near which it was supposed to have been located. Save for the other complete set of the *Tabulæ sex* which I have twice had an opportunity to study in the Biblioteca Nazionale Marciana, there is little to be found today in Venice, though one would like to know where Titian had his school, where Calcar lived, and where was the printing house of B. Vitalis.

I had long been accustomed to carry about a folder in which the muscle figures from the second book of the *Fabrica,* extracted from the back of Moritz Roth's biography, had been mounted serially so as to show their consecutive landscape-background to which Jackschath (212) in 1903 had first called attention (*cf.* Figs. 58-60). Professor Putti of Bologna had assured me that the region was familiar to him and could be easily found, but year after year we kept postponing our intention of trying to identify it. In 1932, however, Dr. Willy Wiegand, the Munich printer, was prompted to look into the matter and he succeeded in definitely locating the site as the region around Abano Terme, now a fashionable watering place in the Euganean Hills a short distance south by west of Padua—the countryside of Petrarch, as a matter of fact. There the site of the old Roman Thermæ shown in ruins in Calcar's sketch, the Bacchiglione river with the bridge over it, and the rugged trachytic rocks can all be easily identified. One can imagine Calcar making his way there on a free afternoon and amusing himself while resting on a hill by sketching, after the manner of Titian, the landscape panorama which he subsequently cut up and used as a background for the muscle figures.

Certain similarly alluring plans that were concocted were likewise postponed, I regret to say, until it was too late for them to be fulfilled. One was to trace the English ancestry of Isabella Crabbe, the mother of Vesalius, a task which the late Sir Walter Fletcher always insisted should present no great difficulty.

An opportunity came in the summer of 1912 to pay an all-too-brief visit to Brussels which, however, made possible a full day at Louvain. There on entering the ancient portal of "Les Halles universitaires" (Fig. 3), one passed beneath old stone arches to a broad flight of much worn stone steps which led up to the main floor where was the famous library. In the "Salle des promotions" (Fig. 4) nearby I had the fortunate experience of hearing two young medical aspirants defend in Latin before a board of examiners their graduation theses, much as Vesalius in February 1537 must have done. Subsequently in the library I was shown a copy of the rare Louvain edition of his *Paraphrasis* and also the vellum

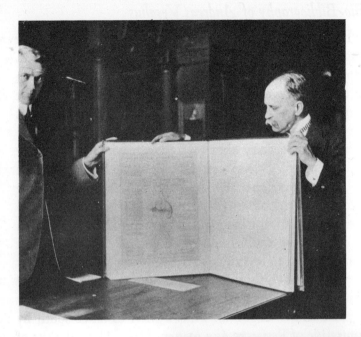

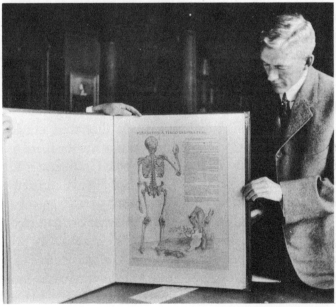

FIGURE ONE

Above: Dr. Lewellys F. Barker and Sir William Osler holding open the Stirling-Maxwell copy of the *Tabulæ sex*. Below: Dr. Barker and a close-up of the skeletal plate.

FIGURE TWO

The skeletons prepared by Vesalius and by Platter in the Vesalianum at Basel, photographed in 1909.

copy of the 1543 *Epitome* in which the figures of the last two sheets had been cut and superimposed according to the author's directions. Could I possibly have foreseen that in another two years the building would be in ruins, I would have taken more snapshots and made more careful notes of the visit.

Preparations by this time were already on foot to celebrate the four hundredth anniversary of Vesalius' birth by appropriate ceremonies to be held at Brussels in December 1914, together with the publication of a memorial volume of essays. For this occasion Osler had persuaded me to submit a study of the supposed portraits of Vesalius scattered through European museums, copies of which I had long been collecting and only eleven of which, most of them ascribed to Titian, had been enumerated in 1892 (345) by Moritz Roth. It was fortunately learned, however, that M. H. Spielmann, the Shakespeare iconographist, had been requested by Professor Heger, who had the program in hand, to undertake this contribution. Indeed before the outbreak of the war his illustrations and manuscript had been forwarded to Brussels and the photographs sent into Germany to be reproduced. Fortunately he had preserved duplicates of all his materials and long after the war, in spite of many vicissitudes, his incomparable *Iconography* (371) was finally published under the auspices of the Wellcome Museum in 1925. Many more posthumous portraits have subsequently turned up, most of them unquestionably based on the Calcar woodcut.

Personally I have a strong prejudice in favor of the portrait purchased for £39 by William Hunter at the sale in March 1754 of Richard Mead's effects, when it was specifically attributed to Titian. It is now in the Hunterian Collection at Glasgow, and though Mr. Spielmann passes over it lightly, it appears to me, taken in connection with the Glasgow Codex, to be the most likely contemporary portrait by Calcar in existence. It is beautifully painted and of course in the Titian manner which Calcar had learned skilfully to imitate. My second choice, for reasons to follow, would be the portrait in the Palazzo Pitti in Florence—of an older man, to be sure, with a heavier beard which is turning grey. He holds under his left arm a book which from its dimensions might well be a copy of the *Fabrica*. There could be no claim in this instance for Calcar who must have been long since dead, for this represents a man nearer 50 than 40 and if actually by the hand of Titian, as the catalogue states, it must either have been painted during some visit of Vesalius to Venice, or he conceivably might have sat for it at Augsburg where in 1550 Titian painted the portrait of Philip II that was sent to England as a lure—if the Habsburg chin could be so described—for Queen Mary. On my first visit to Florence, in 1909, 200 lire was all that a professional copyist who was at work in the gallery asked for making the copy which I still possess.

In following the footsteps of Vesalius one cannot escape from the shadow of Calcar, so closely are their reputations intertwined. In the University Library in Munich one may still see the original wood-blocks which at the end of their peregrinations from Basel in 1555 to Augsburg, to Ingolstadt, to Landshut, have finally come to rest there; and elsewhere in Bavaria one may find occasional *objets d'art* based on one or another of Calcar's drawings. There is, for example, the tomb of the physician behind the altar in the Stadtpfarrkirche at Landsberg marked by a life-size skeleton, cut in stone, in the position of Calcar's contemplative figure (314); also the carving on wood, designed after the portrait sketch and discovered in 1913 by Dr. A. C. Klebs (224), which decorates the façade of the Lemgo Ratsapotheke.

As December 1914 approached, my friend Dr. E. C. Streeter, who had a far better collection of books than I, proposed that we call attention to the date by an exhibit of Vesaliana for the spring meeting of the American Medical Association in Atlantic City. For this purpose we were allotted a booth and had a small pamphlet printed with a description of the books we had selected for display (4). It aroused little if any interest. We had arranged to alternate as showmen, Streeter in the morning hours, I in the afternoon. We met at lunch after the first morning and on my enquiring "How did it go?" he replied, "Well, only one old codger stopped long enough to read the sign VESALIAN EXHIBIT and said, 'Got any samples?'" Streeter asked "Samples of what?" He pointed to the sign and said, "Samples of Vaseline, of course." Sadder and wiser we returned to Boston with our "samples" at the end of the week.

The Brussels celebration was necessarily abandoned, but fortunately there was salvaged from the wreckage of those days a number of papers by Dutch physicians which appeared in the December 1914 issue of *Janus*. Among these was the notable Bibliography by Dr. F. M. G. de Feyfer of Geldermalsen which has been of the greatest possible service to the collectors of Vesaliana (130). After this invaluable contribution, together with Roth's scholarly and thoroughly documented biography (345) and Spielmann's notable Iconography (371), it would seem as though little could remain for anyone to say. It is, therefore, not with the vain expectation of improving on these three works that the present task has been undertaken, but rather with the idea that on their foundations a story of somewhat different sort might be strung together that would perhaps justify the effort.

I cannot leave this prefatory note without paying some sort of tribute to my many friends, past and present, in the book trade. I have already spoken of the late W. M. Voynich, to whom I owe much for his friendly advice about the purchase of books—not always to his own advantage. He had a scholar's love for books and usually read those in his possession, so that the biographical descriptions accompanying his sales were always both accurate and historically informing. The fine 1545 Geminus among my Vesaliana I owe to him; for knowing it would be snapped up quickly, he put it aside on the grounds that some day perhaps I could afford it and he meanwhile could afford to wait.

There was another old friend—that bearded Scot, L. J. Syme, whom I have had reason to bless while composing this book. I first stumbled upon him by accident one hot August afternoon nearly forty years ago during a forlorn six weeks' sojourn in Paris visiting hospitals in the morning, studying French the rest of the time, and sleeping in a room *au troisième* under the roof of a boarding house at 67 rue des Saints Pères. He was sitting in a rocking chair on the sidewalk before his shop in the rue des Beaux Arts indifferent to everything but his pipe—indifferent even to the chance purchaser, whom he curtly (in my case) told to come back tomorrow. Through the narrow door, which his chair blocked, one could see nothing but a tortuous passage between books piled to the ceiling. Having nothing better to do I stopped in the next afternoon on my way home, and he produced from under his chair seven slender volumes which in 1900, for it was then, meant to me nothing whatsoever, a fact he must promptly have realized. When I asked him what they were, he said: "Never mind about that, young man, you'll find out in due time, and when you do you'll have reason to thank L. J. Syme."

The seven thin books, unbound and untrimmed, were small folios each of which bore on the title-page the signature of "Franciscus Rossius Nöeus Chirurgus Parisiensis"* with his date of acquisition. They were: (1) the *Tabulæ quatuor* of Loys Vassé, Paris, 1553; (2) Galen's *De ossibus,* translated by Balamius, Paris, 1549; (3) the *Væsani cuiusdam calumniarum depulsio* of Jacobus Sylvius, Paris, 1551; (4) Ryff's *Anatomica omnium corporis partium descriptio,* Paris, 1545; (5) the *In Hippocratis et Galeni physiologiæ partem anatomicam isagoge* of Jacobus Sylvius, Paris, 1555; (6) Galen's *De usu partium* translated by J. P. Crassus, Paris, Wechel, 1548; and (7) the *De musculorum dissectione ex Galeno,* also by Crassus, Paris, Gazellius, 1548. As Mr. Syme foretold, I *have* good reason to bless him, for they not only have been useful to me these past few weeks, but any one of them today would fetch far more than he asked for the lot.

* François Rosse des Nœux, *fl.* 1552-84.

2. BIO-BIBLIOGRAPHY

OUR FIRST problem is to place Vesalius in the time and the circumstances that led up to the composition and publication of his several works, quickly culminating in the issuance of his masterpiece, the *Fabrica*—and as quickly falling away again. Born in Brussels at the turn of the year 1514/15,* it is commonly related that he showed a precocious interest in anatomy during his boyhood. However legendary this may be, it is known beyond peradventure that at an early age he matriculated in the nearby University at Louvain whose reputation in humanistic studies at the time rivaled even that of Paris. There he came under the influence of Johann Guenther of Andernach (Winter; Guinterius Andernacus) who was his teacher in Greek and of whom there will be more subsequently to tell.

This Guinterius, as he was commonly styled, was soon to become a teacher of anatomy in the tradition of Galen; and his young pupil, who ere long provided himself at Louvain with a human skeleton by robbing a gibbet, had a hankering for medicine in his blood as we shall shortly learn from his own words. Who may have suggested that he write a paraphrase of that popular mediæval compendium of medicine—the ninth book of Rhazes—for his graduation thesis is not apparent. Nor is it clear when it was composed. He probably began to work on it in Louvain whose famous library was celebrated for its source materials. Ten years later in the China-root Epistle he recalls with evident nostalgia:

"I rejoiced at preparing the paraphrase and in collating the Arabic writings with what Galen and the other Greeks had said in regard to those portions of the Art treated by Rhazes in his various works, especially because of my grandfather Everard, whose brilliant commentary on the books of Rhazes I possess, together with his annotations on the first four sections of the aphorisms of Hippocrates and several mathematical notes which show him to have been a man of great ability. Often have I heard my father [at time of *Paraphrasis* pharmacist to the Emperor Charles V] say that Everard died before he was 36 years old after he had taken the place of my great-grandfather John as physician to Mary, the wife of the Emperor Maximilian. John survived his son Everard for many years and taught medicine at Louvain in his later years when he was

* The horoscope of Vesalius cast by his contemporary, Jerome Cardan (70), is the authority for Vesalius' birth date. A translation of the horoscope is given in an appendix at the end of these introductory materials.—Ed.

xxiv

no longer fitted for life at Court. His father Peter was also a physician, as we know from his treatise on the fourth fen of Avicenna, and also from some volumes inscribed with his name which are among those still kept by my mother and in which we have all the works that were familiar to physicians of that time copied at great (and now useless) expense.

"The memory and traditions of my ancestors have become very sacred since visiting [recently] the tombs of the Witing family at Nimwegen and at the ancient and renowned town of Wesel in Cleves, the city from which our family came. Once I stayed quite a while in the latter place after leaving the Emperor on account of the illness of Navagerius [the Venetian Ambassador, Bernardo Navagero]."

In this account he says little of his father Andreas, one-time apothecary both to the Emperor Maximilian and to his son, the Archduke Charles; and when the Archduke in course of time became Emperor Charles V, this first Andreas was his constant attendant. We find them in 1517 at Valladolid, in 1521 at Mainz, and together during the third French War in 1536-38. It was at Nice in 1538 that he proudly showed the Emperor the six anatomical illustrations which Andreas his son had just had printed at Venice. At this time neither he nor his wife, Isabella Crabbe, who survived until 1546, could have foreseen that ere long their son would also be established at the Imperial Court.

With four generations of scholarly physicians back of him, Vesalius must have found it difficult to choose between a scholastic and a more practical career for himself. It may even be that the manuscript with his grandfather Everard's commentaries was in his hands when he decided to paraphrase the ninth book for his graduation thesis. However this may be, he took pains to give Greek synonyms for the terms in the 95 chapters *a capite ad pedem* which the treatise contains. In 1533, when eighteen years of age, he went to Paris with the object of more seriously pursuing his anatomical studies under the wing of his former teacher Guinterius, but more particularly under that of Jacobus Sylvius, previously a teacher of the classics at Amiens but now the most celebrated lecturer on anatomy in Europe. Of him another pupil, Loys Vassé, wrote in 1540: "From everywhere flocked to him Germans, English, Spaniards, Italians and others of all nations who all agreed that the like of this admirable and almost divine man was not to be found in the whole of Europe."(95)

To be sure, what knowledge of anatomy Sylvius and Guinterius possessed had been acquired from standard texts rather than through their own personal investigations and they both, naturally enough, had become confirmed Galenists who, as was then customary, simply read the texts from a raised seat—the cathedra—while barbers on the floor below made the dissection—far more often on an animal than a human cadaver. Against this custom the young Vesalius soon rebelled. As he says in the China-root Epistle, he spent hours digging bones in the Cemetery of the Innocents and at Montfaucon where he and a friend were once set upon by a pack of vicious dogs, on a mission similar to their own. He speaks most respectfully of his eminent teachers and more particularly of Sylvius in the preface to the *Paraphrasis,* and there can be no doubt that they in turn envied his industry and cleverness. Though Sylvius, as we shall see, attacked his anti-Galenism viciously in later years, Guinterius had just paid him in August 1536 a notable compliment in his edition of Galen's anatomical textbook (see Chap. III).

At about this time, in the late Autumn of 1536, Vesalius must have been making preparations to leave Paris and return to the Low Countries owing to the prospect of a renewal of war between those traditional enemies, Francis I and Charles V. Guinterius had good reason to miss such a clever pupil who could put his own hands to the work and observe things that had escaped others. And when five years later, in 1541, Vesalius meanwhile having made a name for himself in Italy, a second edition of the *Institutiones* was printed by Sebastian Gryphius at Lyon, Guinterius says in the expanded preface:

"In this work (of revising this book in the light of numerous dissections), not at all an easy one, I was helped, first by Andreas Vesalius—a young man, by Hercules, most diligent in anatomy, and a professor of pure medicine whom one need not at all be sorry for; only recently, in publishing this work of mine at Venice, he furnished an excellent piece of (editorial) work. Next to him is Michael Villanueva (Servetus), who in a friendly manner assisted me in dis-sections—a man who would be an ornament of any branch of letters, and who is second to none in the Galenical doctrine."

By 1541 the mention of Servetus begins to cast a foreboding shadow. And it must not be overlooked that the ebb and flow of the Reformation lay ominously in the background throughout the life of Vesalius. If Luther may be credited(269), his (Vesalius') great-grandfather John was a liberal Catholic, like Pico della Mirandola, Lorenzo Valla and Johann Reuchlin, who had been driven into opposition of the established church by its over-zealous persecution of heretics. Certainly Guinterius was similarly affected, and this may have been one reason not only for his transfer to Paris but for his later choice of printers in such comparatively safe places as Basel and Lyon.

What may have been the stand taken by Vesalius on these matters is not certain. He had controversies enough to face in his personal field of reformation, and it was by no means a joke to have been called the Luther of Anatomy. While he refrained from mixing physiology and theology, a trap in which Servetus was caught, it seems almost certain that he was a liberal Catholic to say the least, if we may judge from his Paris friends. Among them were not only Guinterius but Johann Sturm, Rutger Resch who was to be the first printer of his thesis, and Jodocus Velsius who subsequently in 1541 took his M.D. at Louvain. While still in Paris, this Velsius must have composed the Latin epigram for the *Paraphrasis* which roughly translated reads:

JODOCUS VELSIUS OF THE HAGUE

The dusty crowd of Arabs declares that learning aids us,
    While in olden times things barbaric were in favour.
Among these Arabs, Rhazes, the medical writer, is pre-eminent,
    An excellent man because of his service to mankind.
But having been badly translated, his work till now displeased
    Our countrymen, while henceforth it will be more esteemed.
This fact, Vesalius, we can attribute to you.
    Praise deservedly is yours. Do thou lead. I follow.

3. VESALIUS AND CALCAR

SHOULD EVIDENCE be sought to show that the blazing of new trails is a characteristic of youth, the romantic story of Vesalius would provide a striking example. As indicated in the portrait sketch by Calcar, soon to adorn the completed treatise that was to revolutionize our knowledge of the structure of the human body, he was at the time (*i.e.,* in 1542) but twenty-eight years of age. Yet for five years he had already occupied a chair in the world-famous University of Padua and with the publication ere long of this, his *magnum opus*, he like a rocket reached the summit of his distinguished career. Only eighteen years later, at the age of fifty, he was supposedly drowned in a shipwreck off the island of Zante on his return from the Holy Land where, according to rumour, he had been sent on a journey of expiation. By the time news of his death reached Europe and had spread to his native Flanders, he had already become an almost legendary figure.

Despite his brief and meteoric career and even though many details of his *curriculum vitæ* with its frequent changes of scene remain obscure, yet the living figure of Vesalius, the man at his prime, stands before us in Calcar's portrait, vigorous and undaunted among the few who for their contributions rank highest in the history of medicine—so few, indeed, that they may be counted on the fingers of a hand: Hippocrates, Galen, Vesalius, Harvey; and to commemorate the triumphs of modern surgery, Lister may at least be given the little finger, but perhaps deserves the more useful thumb. The first of them had lived in the Golden Age of Periclean Greece, the second five hundred years later in the heyday of Imperial Rome, and there had been ample time—some twenty centuries, in fact—for their hallowed example and teachings to become so thoroughly crystallized by a long succession of scholastic commentators that they were considered incapable of error and their writings thus transmitted were accepted as the final word.

Vesalius came on the scene at a time when the inviolability of tradition, whether ecclesiastical or scientific, was being widely questioned. What is more, ready at hand as if for his special purpose were newly discovered and highly perfected arts, that of printing by movable type and that of engraving on wood, both having reached in his day a level of excellence scarcely surpassed even in modern times.

To be sure, he was by no means the first or only one to grasp the opportunity of utilizing the graphic arts to illustrate a scientific text. An example had been

FIGURE THREE

Les Halles, Louvain, at the time of Vesalius (after Gramaye, 1606).

FIGURE FOUR
La Salle des Promotions, Louvain, 1912.

set by the medical botanists such as Otto Brunfels (58) as early as 1532 and Leonard Fuchs ten years later, the second edition in German of the *De historia stirpium* (149) having been printed by Isingrin at Basel in the very same year that the *Fabrica* appeared. Their problem, however, was a simple one compared to his. No doubt Henry Hüllmaurer and Albert Meyer, "pictores operis," and Rudolph Speckle, "sculptor," who were permitted to sign the works of Fuchs with their own self-portraits had worked in far pleasanter surroundings and under far less strain than did the artist-collaborator of an anatomist in his odoriferous dissecting room.

No such opportunity was given Calcar thus to sign his fellow Fleming's masterpiece, yet by a curious perversion of destiny it has come about that the very wood-blocks from which the prints were struck still survive, while the identity of the artist who drew the designs for them continues to be a matter of dispute. For the better part of two centuries, they were ascribed to Titian: by Bonavera, 1670 (47), Tortebat, 1667 (393), Maschenbauer, 1706 (VI.A.11), Ambroise Firmin Didot, *ca.* 1850 (111), etc. Only of late has the consensus of opinion accepted Calcar as the probable artist. The engravings from the first spoke the universal language of art which requires no translation, and they are still admired, copied and used, even after the passage of four centuries.

On the other hand, and in sharp contrast, the hurriedly composed Vesalian text, described by Garrison as "a torrent of mediæval Latin," which the anatomical figures were designed to illuminate, distorted, even calumniated by contemporary adherents of the Galenic tradition, remains unread and, save for a few fragments, untranslated to the present day. The author himself subsequently referred to it as a "youthful labor of love written in commonplace and amateurish style." Latin, then the universal language of scholars, was doubtless what Vesalius—himself a scholar—used in his public lectures, as well as for all of his published writings. But the time was near at hand when for medical texts to be avidly read, as those by Paré were soon to be, they must needs be written in the vernacular and printed in the smaller format which Aldus Manutius had popularized.

The author of the *Fabrica* was shrewd enough to realize that his ponderous tome would be too cumbersome for students to handle, possibly too expensive for them even to possess, and he made ready to issue coincidentally an *Epitome* of the complete work reduced, for more practical purposes, to what could be printed along with suitable illustrations on fourteen folio sheets. These sheets were soon so thumbed to pieces from excessive use that a complete set of them has become more rare than the work they summarize, and the fact that most copies of the *Fabrica* remain, in comparison, after four hundred years in a good state of preservation tells its own story.

To be sure, a small unillustrated two-volume pocket edition with textual revisions was printed in Lyon in 1552, but it could not have been popular since no second printing in this format was called for. Wanting Calcar's illustrations, it was not the same book; and there has developed indeed a modern tendency to ascribe more credit to Calcar than to Vesalius in the halo of reputation that still surrounds the folio editions of the work that came from the press of Oporinus at Basel (209, 210). That Vesalius had ventured to call attention to Galenic errors was abhorrent to those accustomed to read these texts as gospel from the high cathedra. That a young upstart from the Low Countries should ridicule this time-honoured custom by having an artist in an elaborately engraved frontis-piece depict the author making his own dissection surrounded by an eager audience in glorified surroundings was openly insulting.

So exasperated was his former Parisian teacher, Jacobus Sylvius, that he finally in 1551 when 73 years of age and a beaten man, let loose with a blast entitled: *Væsani cuiusdam calumniarum in Hippocratis Galenique rem anatomicam depulsio* (385), which in English may be rendered: "A repudiation of the calumnies of a certain madman* concerning Hippocratic and Galenic anatomy by Jacobus Sylvius, the Royal interpreter of things medical at Paris."

In his preface addressed to the Candid and Pious Reader after belaboring Leonard Fuchs who had taken sides with Vesalius, Sylvius proceeds to elaborate what in his opinion are the twenty-eight particular calumnies of Vesalius, and in the last of them he thus appeals to Charles V who by 1551 was in ill health and in no mood to dispute:

"I implore his Majesty the Emperor to punish severely, as he deserves, this monster born and reared in his own home, this most pernicious exemplar of ignorance, ingratitude, arrogance, and impiety; and to suppress him completely, lest he poison the rest of Europe with his pestilential breath. With his deadly spume, he has already infected certain Frenchmen, Germans, and Italians, but they, I believe, are ignorant of anatomy and of the other branches of medicine ... [etc.]"

And in conclusion he takes an unnecessary slap at Calcar's part of the work, as follows:

* *Væsanus*, usually spelled *vesanus*, playing on the similarity of the word to the name, Vesalius.

"But if, in that excessively verbose farrago by the calumniator, something fit to be read is found (for no writer is wholly vile), it is so small that it can be contained in a single sheet of paper, *provided that you disregard the illustrations, which are covered with shadows, and the letters appended to them. The whole method of employing such things is decidedly superstitious and obscure, and thoroughly useless, and you should consider both the illustrations and the letters a hindrance rather than a help,* especially to physicians, whose art is long, but whose life is short, and who should investigate the nature of all the parts of the human body, not in illustrations or in books alone, but by sight and by touch, in many anatomies. Certainly no ship-master, nor general, nor artisan of any kind is permitted to prepare for his craft by such contemplative training: and indeed, *Galen did not allow even plants to be depicted,* at the beginning of the sixth book, De facul. simpl. med."

The liberty has been taken of italicizing in the above quotation what Sylvius had to say of illustrations as something superstitious and obscure which might almost become emblems of worship whereas Galen was unwilling that even plants should be depicted. Such a suggestion could only have been made by a bitterly jealous man utterly blind to what art had already contributed to the medical sciences. Certainly could Galen have seen the superbly illustrated herbal of Leonard Fuchs which Isingrin had published only the year before the *Fabrica,* he would have felt warmly disposed toward it and perhaps even to the *Fabrica.* The objection that the illustrations and their shading and the appended letters were a hindrance rather than a help to the reader is interesting in view of the fact that in the second (1555) edition Vesalius had the woodcutter clear away the shading from around the letters to make them stand out more clearly on the muscle-men.

Though with less striking success, to be sure, occasional illustrations had been used in anatomical works, even in those of Galen prior to the time of Calcar and Vesalius. In the 1536 Basel (Cratander) edition of Galen's *Opera omnia* there occur in the *Liber de ossibus* excellent renderings of the front and back views of a skeleton along with a view of the base of the skull (apparently unknown to Choulant) that equal if they do not excel Calcar's first efforts in the *Tabulæ sex*; and the surgeons, like Dryander, had long been illustrating their books. What is more, Eustachius (1520-1574) had evidently for some time been preparing to illustrate an anatomy and many of his plates had been drawn long before he was called to Rome to the chair of anatomy. He very possibly was deterred, just as Canano was deterred, from his program by the appearance of the *Fabrica,* the very sight of which was enough to discourage any competitor.

Canano, a contemporary (1515-1578) of Vesalius, had issued at Ferrara about 1541 (66) an illustrated tract simply depicting the individual muscles of the upper extremity and he had doubtless intended to follow the same plan with other parts of the body. If Vesalius, as is not unlikely, stopped at Ferrara to visit his brother Francisco on his way to Basel a year later and carried a few samples of the woodcuts for the *Fabrica* that were passed around among his friends of the Faculty, Canano must have realized that here was a competitor far beyond his reach and have desisted from further efforts. Eustachius, on the other hand, had permitted the engraver of his *Tabulæ anatomicæ* to crowd together too much detail on his beautifully engraved figures which were smaller than those of Vesalius. How many of them, if any, were completed before 1543 is unknown, and they were not published until they came to light nearly two centuries later when the heirs of Eustachius permitted Lancisi to publish them at Rome in 1714, and there were several editions thereafter.

The publication of an illustrated book is not a task which concerns solely the man with the idea. Leonardo conceived the idea of an illustrated anatomy, but despite his rare talents it died unborn, for want of that sort of persistent drive to attain the end in view which characterized Vesalius. Nor is it a one-man job; for author, artist, engraver, printer and publisher must work together, and they are scarcely to be found in one person.

Not only were Vesalius and Calcar robbed of their just dues during their short tenures of life—for Calcar also died at an even younger age than Vesalius—but they have since been dogged by misfortunes which would have served to obliterate completely the memory of any pair of co-workers of lesser stature. Soon Calcar's portion of their combined labours came to be ascribed to his more celebrated master, Titian, under whose name, as in Domenico Bonavera's *Notomie di Titiano* published in the seventeenth century, many of the plates were engraved for the use of art students (VI.D.9). There is a possibility that the friendly relation of artist and author may have become strained during the hectic preparation for the publisher of the elaborate text and its multitude of explana-tory plates. Such things have been known to happen at other times and places. In the *Tabulæ anatomicæ* printed in 1538, five years before the *Fabrica,* Calcar's name appears in the colophon-shield of the last of the six plates. In the Venesection Epistle published the following year (1539), Vesalius writes to the same friend and patron, Nicolaus Florenas of Brussels, to whom his graduation thesis had been dedicated:

"As for writing anything further in regard to my systematic studies there is nothing for the present. We have now completed two plates of the nerves also: in the first the seven pairs of the brain are delineated; in the second the branches of the entire spinal cord are portrayed. I thought I ought to keep them till the time when I should undertake the plates of the muscles and all the inward parts. We have tried to make out a scheme of the dissections of this present year in the most convenient manner possible; but in view of the great crowd of spectators it proved altogether impossible to complete it."

And he concludes by saying: "So if I have a suitable number of cadavers, and Joannes Stephanus [Calcar] the most admirable artist of our time does not refuse his assistance, I shall not run away from the task." Did Calcar, preferring the atmosphere of Titian's studio to that of a dissecting room, refuse his further assistance, and was Vesalius obliged to engage someone of lesser merit from that time on, as Edouard Turner insists, or was Calcar persuaded perhaps against his will and were the drawings for the woodcuts really his? That is one of the many enigmas. Certainly nowhere in either *Fabrica* or *Epitome* is his name mentioned by the author who indeed expostulated in his preface over the delays in getting the illustrations ready for the printer. As a matter of fact, it is not known whether Calcar merely made the drawings which were then engraved on wood by someone else or whether he was both artist and woodcutter combined, a combination of talents which seems unlikely. The nearest contemporary allusions to Calcar are made by Vasari in his Lives of the Painters. Unfortunately in the 1550 Florentine edition there is no reference to him; and not until the second edition of 1568 (407), over twenty years after Calcar's death, the two following references, subsequently to be copied in all later-day editions, appear (408):

"Many young men have been with Titian for the purposes of learning; yet the number of those who may truly call themselves his disciples is not great, seeing that he has never given much instruction; yet all may learn more or less from the works of a master, once they have acquired the power of comprehending them. Among those about Titian meanwhile was a certain Giovanni, a Fleming,* who became a good master, whether for large or small figures, and in portraits was most admirable, as may be seen by his works at Naples, where he lived for some time, and where he ultimately died. By his hand, and they must do him honour to all time, were the designs for anatomical studies which the

* Johann Calcar, or Calker. See Lanzi, *Storia Pittorica*. See also Bryan, *Dictionary of Painters and Engravers*.

most admirable Andrea Vessalio [*sic*] caused to be engraved and published with his works."

"In the year 1545, I became known to, and contracted much friendship with Giovanni Calcar, a Flemish painter of great merit, who so successfully practised the Italian manner, that his works were not always perceived to be those of a Fleming; but he died at Naples, while still young, and when the fairest hopes had been conceived respecting his future progress. The anatomical drawings for the work of Vesalio [*sic*] were made by Calcar."

Ambitious students of art like Calcar flocked to Venice to get inspiration from Titian just as those interested in natural philosophy flocked to Padua some twenty miles away where Vesalius was at work on his book; and thanks to the *De libris propriis* (1570) of John Caius, who happened for a period of eight months to occupy the same house with him, we know the exact address: namely, the Casa de' valli near the Ponte della paglia. Such close collaboration must have been required to compose and illustrate a work such as the *Fabrica,* it would seem that author and artist must have worked elbow to elbow, which would have made it obligatory for the latter, were it really Calcar, to pass most of his time in Padua where the dissections were being made.

The first edition of Vasari's *Lives* was published in 1550; and if he became acquainted with Calcar in 1545, that was two years after the *Fabrica* was printed. Vesalius by then, smarting under the criticisms of the Galenists, had resigned from his chair, burned his manuscripts, and gone to join Charles V at the Imperial Court. As for Calcar, he is said to have died in Naples a year later, too soon to know or care what might happen to his anatomical drawings. He would doubtless have smiled could he have foreseen that for two centuries they would be ascribed to Titian and that an effort finally would be made even to pin them on Leonardo—a compliment indeed!

There are three lines of evidence by which we can with certainty associate Calcar with Vesalius: (i) the allusion to Stephen in the introduction to the *Tabulæ sex*; (ii) the occurrence of his name in the colophon of the last plate of the same work; and finally (iii) the signed figure of the young artist in the engraved frontispiece of the *Fabrica,* evidently a self-portrait with the figure, book in hand, overseeing the dissection. There is also a signed *croquis* of the *Fabrica* title-page bearing the name of Calcar (see Figs. 14 and 53). This fourth line of evidence is possibly more presumptive, but taken in association with the first three, it serves further to confirm their close relationship. That they must have been together in Padua most of this time seems highly probable, though the manuscript and woodcuts were finally forwarded in August of 1542 from Venice to Basel.

The few anatomical drawings found in various collections and dubiously ascribed to Calcar, or more often to the school of Titian, are as nothing compared to what we know of his capabilities from the pages of the *Fabrica*. As pointed out in Chapter VI, there have been preserved what appear to be preliminary sketches in various stages for the elaborate frontispiece: one in Stockholm, another in Glasgow, and a third formerly in the library of the late Dr. LeRoy Crummer, which the Munich printer, Dr. Willy Wiegand, regards as indubitably the final drawing from which the woodcutters engraved the block which of course reverses the drawing when printed.*

In the eighteenth century Calcar evidently was quite forgotten. Yet the beautifully painted Glasgow portrait (which in the writer's opinion is far and away the best of the many portraits of Vesalius in European galleries) may well enough have been by the clever brush of Calcar, naturally enough in the Titian manner. One can scarcely imagine the energetic Vesalius wasting his time to go to Venice to be painted by Titian any more than one can imagine Titian, then well along in years, being lured to Padua to paint a young anatomist. Calcar, on the other hand, must have had many opportunities and may well enough have felt the necessity of making a portrait in oil before undertaking the drawing for the woodcut portrait.

If this conjecture is credible, where both portrait and anatomical sketches may have lain hidden for two hundred years before they came into Richard Mead's omnivorous clutches (see Chapter VI) is another of the enigmas that envelop everything relating to Vesalius and Calcar. Though the existence of Mead's unique volume mentioned below in the footnote was unknown to Roth when he published his life of Vesalius in 1892, he subsequently was privileged to make a detailed study (349) of the codex with its 54 drawings and came to

---

* The Glasgow sketch which represents an intermediary stage of development is part of a codex that has an interesting provenance. Formerly in the possession of Dr. Richard Mead of London, it was purchased for £27 16s. 6d. by William Hunter on January 20, 1755 at the sale of Mead's remarkable collection of prints and drawings. It is cited in the catalogue, item 68, as "Vesalius's original anatomical drawings neatly bound in red morocco and gilt." Incidentally, Hunter purchased at the sale of Mead's pictures in March 1754, a portrait of "Vesalius, the great anatomist, by Titian" with the statement: "This is a capital picture by Titian who was an intimate friend of Vesalius and drew from the life Anatomical designs, which were engraved for his book of Anatomy of which a small but curious collection was purchased by Dr. Mead." This "curious collection" was of course the volume of drawings "bound in red morocco and gilt" with the inscription on the spine: *Desseins Origin. de l'Anatom de Vesale.* This volume together with the portrait of Vesalius previously purchased by Hunter are now in the Hunterian Museum at Glasgow.

the conclusion that along with the skeleton prepared with Vesalius' own hands while at Basel and the original wood-blocks in the University Library in Munich, it constitutes one of the three authentic relics of the collaboration of the two men that have come down to us.*

Vesalius states that on leaving Padua to join the Court of Charles V he destroyed all of his remaining manuscripts (see Chapter VII), and we may well believe this to be true in view of the few authentic scraps of his writing that survive. One such with his signature is reproduced in Burggraeve's biography (62); and another fragment, a letter in Latin from Toledo dated February 18, 1561, which was advertised in the sale catalogue of Dr. van den Corput's library (Muller: Amsterdam, 1911, No. 2843) was withdrawn from the sale without explanation as a presumptive forgery. Another Vesalius letter of August 28 (1556) written to Heinrich Petri is in the University Library at Basel (341). A manuscript in Madrid attributed to Vesalius has been described by Paul de Stevens (375). An occasional book carrying what is taken to be his signature has appeared from time to time, notably his copy of a book by his contemporary, Cornarius, with whom he was in disagreement, now in the possession of Erik Waller, formerly of Lidköping; but the authenticity of the other few volumes carrying a signature reputedly his is highly doubtful. All this is most peculiar, and when one takes into consideration the copious notebooks left by Leonardo that have come down to us, it merely adds to the Vesalian enigma.

Though a list of his publications occurs in the early biographies (*e.g.,* Gesner [169]), it was not until the nineteenth century that any serious attempts were made to analyse his life and his writings. The first of these was a volume published in Ghent in 1841 at a time when a resurgent Belgium was growing conscious of her more illustrious sons. It was written in French by Adolphe Burggraeve (62), then professor of anatomy at Ghent, and the larger part of the

* Sir Donald Macalister informed me in 1927 that it had long been the intention of Charles Singer in collaboration with the late Sir Grafton Elliot Smith to issue a facsimile of this precious codex—a plan that was unfortunately abandoned. The drawings by then had become greatly faded in comparison with their state in 1910 when I first saw them at which time photographs of all the plates were kindly made for me by the late John H. Teacher. A further example alluded to above in the Apologia of the way in which ill fortune has continued to pursue Vesalius even down to modern times was the interruption of the program under the chairmanship of Paul Heger of Brussels to celebrate in December of 1914 the four hundredth anniversary of his birth. The Great War had put an effectual stop to that and an invading army was already in Brussels, having destroyed on their way many precious records of Vesalius and his contemporaries, till then preserved, along with a presentation copy printed on vellum of the 1543 *Epitome,* in the Library at Louvain. For that occasion Sir William Osler and the writer had long planned to have the Oxford Press issue a new facsimile edition of the 1538 *Tabulæ sex* inherited by Sir John Stirling-Maxwell from his father, Sir William, who in 1874 had previously issued a facsimile edition.

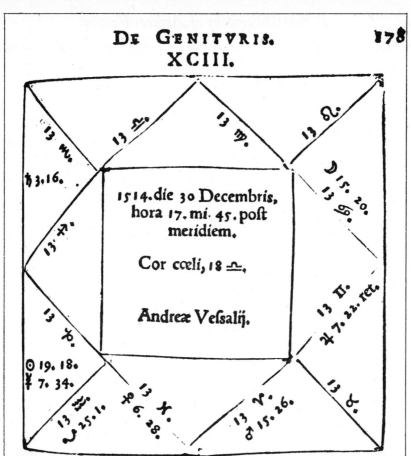

1514. die 30 Decembris,
hora 17. mi. 45. poſt
meridiem.

Cor cœli, 18 ♎.

Andreæ Veſſalij.

Hæc in diſſectione corporū admirabilis, antiquiscy merito cōparandus, opus prima inuenta ſcripſit, ſanè adeò egregiū, ut negotium penè totū abſoluerit, celebris in uita, iam nunc Cæſaris medicus, & poſt fata etiam celebris futurus. Si genitura hæc ſua eſt, ad amuſsim omnia conueniunt, nam Mars in quadrato Lunæ potentis in octaua, ſtudiū & agilitatē manuū præſtat, Mercurius in trino Iouis, & Venus in quadrato, ingeniū mirabile, & facundiam pro artis conditione, imo ſupra eam, decernunt. eſt enim medicus inſignis. Luna in oppoſito Solis, memoriā & ſcientiā, & multos dat hoſtes, clarū etiam facit: quia nocturna eſt genitura. Saturnus cū corde Scorpij, in ſextili Mercurij, ingeniū profundū, memoriā, ſtudiū. Spica Virginis in corde cœli, gloriā ex arte, quantā quiſcy alius. decet etiā animaduertere Martē aſpicere Solē in ſua exaltatione exiſtentē, tū Lunā in ſuo eſſe domicilio, hæc gratiā apud Principes decernūt. illud ſolum deeſt, quod nullus Planeta horuſcopi locū poſsidet, iuxta decreta noſtra.   yy ij

FIGURE FIVE
Horoscope of Vesalius (from Cardan's *Libelli quinque,* 1547).

PARA

PHRASIS, IN NONVM LI:
brum Rhazæ Medici Arabis clariss. ad
Regem Almansorem, de singularū
corporis partium affectuum
curatione, autore An-
drea Wesalio Bru-
xellensi Medi
cinę candi
dato.

Louanij ex officina Rutgeri Rescij.
Mense Februar.
1537.

volume was taken up with a critical analysis of the seven books of the *Fabrica*. Fifty years later, a far more comprehensive and thoroughly documented biog-raphy was written by Moritz Roth, the professor of anatomy at Basel, and published in German. It may well rank as the most scholarly life of a Doctor of Medicine ever written, although its author was devoutly prejudiced in favour of Vesalius and some of his opinions have proved highly controversial. Neither of these volumes has been translated, and though a biography in English by C. Louis Taylor was to have formed the last of the *Masters of Medicine* series (1877 *et seq.*), it was apparently abandoned and all that we have in its place is the sketchy monograph by James Moores Ball published in 1910 (26) for which Roth's notable volume was frankly admitted to be the basis.

As though it were insufficient penalty that Vesalius had been so calumni-ated by the Galenists in his lifetime, and that his great contribution to medicine was soon forgotten, the recent attempt in 1902 by a veterinarian of Tilsit, E. Jackschath (211) by name, to discredit altogether the authenticity of the work as nothing more than a gigantic plagiarism from the anatomical writings of Leonardo da Vinci who with Marc Antonio della Torre was supposedly in train to write a work on human anatomy, adds poignancy to the dramatic story. The details will be unfolded as we examine his individual works.

APPENDIX

CARDAN'S HOROSCOPE OF VESALIUS

DR. CUSHING had assembled a dossier concerning Cardan's (70) much discussed horoscope of Vesalius, but he had not as yet incorporated the material in the text of the bio-bibliography. Although the casters of horoscopes often selected dates and details best suited to their preconceived notions, there is reason, as Friedenwald (146) has pointed out, to give some credence to Cardan's birth date of Vesalius, since the two men were contem-poraries, and since Vesalius had in 1547 recommended Cardan as Court Physician to the King of Denmark. Cardan is also said to have written a life of Vesalius that appears to have been lost (146).

The horoscope appears on leaf 178*a* of the enlarged edition of Cardan's *Libelli duo* (1543) which appeared in 1547 as the *Libelli quinque* (70). The page in question is reproduced in Figure 5, and the horoscope itself has been translated as follows:

[Horoscope] of Andreas Vesalius.
[Born] December 30, 1514, 17.45 P.M. *[i.e., 5.45* A.M., *December 31st]**

"Most admirable expert in dissecting cadavers, comparable in merit to the ancients, he wrote a work which whilst his first yet is so excellent as to solve all difficulties; celebrated in life, now already Imperial physician, he is bound to be celebrated after his death. If this is his birth-date, everything in it is up to the measure, for Mars in the square of the mighty Moon in its eighth exhibits zeal and skill of hands. Mercury in the triple of Jupiter and Venus in the square exhibit an admirable mind and an eloquence not only up to the mark, but even above it—he is, indeed, an eminent physician. The Moon in opposition to the Sun gives memory and knowledge, and many enemies, indicating an illustrious person, seeing the birth-date is a nocturnal one. Saturn with the heart of Scorpio, in the sixth of Mercury, indicates a profound mind, memory, and zeal. Spica Virginis in the heart of the sky indicates a glory due to skill as great as anyone's. One must consider also Mars facing the Sun in his exaltation while the Moon is in her domicile—denoting favour with princes. The only thing missing, according to our decisions, is that no planet dominates the horoscope ['*possidet locum horoscopi*']."

In Dr. Friedenwald's copy of the *Fabrica,* there is an earlier version of the horoscope, said to be in Cardan's handwriting, which suggests that Cardan had obtained further information concerning his subject between the preliminary casting and the time of publication of the *Libelli quinque.*† This lends added reason for giving credence to the dates given in the final version of the horoscope.—Ed.

* See X.37, p. 58, col. 1.
† See Castiglioni, A. Gerolamo Cardano e Andrea Vesalio. *Rass. clin.-sci. Ist. biochim. ital.,* 1935, *13,* N.12.

The Writings of
ANDREAS VESALIUS

❧ CHAPTER I ❧

THE PARAPHRASE OF
THE NINTH BOOK OF RHAZES*

IT WAS a common university regulation in Europe, then as now, that a candidate's thesis should be printed before the granting of the degree and even before the public defence. And Vesalius, at 23 years of age, having returned to his home in Brussels after nearly three years' absence, induced his friend, Rutger Resch, to put the *Paraphrasis* in type at his press in Louvain. From a typographical standpoint it was not a very creditable production and within a short time a much more presentable edition was issued at Basel from the press of Robert Winter, who may conceivably have been a kinsman of Guinterius. On the title of the Louvain edition printed in February the author is called 'Candidate in Medicine,' this designation being omitted from the later Basel edition. While there are minor differences in the text of the two editions, the prefatory letter to Nicolaus Florenas, friend and patron of Vesalius and physician to the Emperor, bearing the subscription *February 1, 1537,* is essentially the same in both:

"The ancients, most learned Sir, have no doubt judged correctly of the importance attaching to the manner in which one pursues the arts and sciences, *i.e.,* does one use an exact method, proceeding from primary matters to secondary, thence to the next in the proper order, and in each instance does one express oneself clearly for everyone to show whether he is the primary or the secondary source.

"Of this you are by no means ignorant, and you knew several years ago that I was going to devote my labours to the study of medicine; furthermore, you deemed it worthy to prescribe for me a certain excellent and most useful method of studying the Hippocratic art. This method I have always persisted in, as far as I was able, and, wonderful to relate, have without difficulty and without any intricacies finally arrived at that branch of medicine which is called curative and which is in so far superior to others (which are taught for its sake alone) as it is of greater use in practice.

"And here I began to marvel much that the principles of combatting disease

---

*In what follows, de Feyfer's enumeration of the items in his excellent bibliography (130) will, so far as possible, be followed in order to lessen the confusion of those who have become familiar with the sequence he employed.

3

common to most of the physicians of our time varied so much from the methods of the learned Greeks, and remained so hopelessly and obstinately fixed in the very footprints, so to speak, of barbarians and Arabians.

"It appeared advisable to me, therefore, in order that nothing of the latter might escape us, to compare with greater diligence the pertinent works of the Arabians, along with those of the Greeks (whom, by virtue of your excellent judgment, you always used to prefer). This procedure is most often commended by the excellent Parisian physicians to their students, in the hope that soon the ancient art of medicine starting from Hippocrates will be, to the great advantage of mortals, recalled to their memory and will come to flourish, through the gradually increased labours of those who practise this art.

"Following in this manner your advice and that of my most eminent teachers, I put my hand first to Rhazes and examined him carefully with regard to the writings of the Greeks as the stone of the Lydians [*i.e.,* the touchstone], inasmuch as I have often heard from my preceptor and learned professor of medicine, Jacobus Sylvius, that he (Rhazes) was held to have been the most expert in the art of curing among all the physicians of his people. Which done, it seemed to me worth while that, cleansed of errors, and clothed in elegant Latin style, he should be made acceptable even to a reader possessed of a delicate ear, particu-larly since in that little treatise he deals with almost all local diseases, and does not differ, except in a very few points, from the writings of the Greeks.

"To be sure, some have tried to make out that this book was (really) trans-lated into Arabic from a Greek original, and was then inscribed with the name of Rhazes. Yet one can manifestly recognize both medicaments unknown to the Greeks, and the horrid and coarse style of expression in common use among the Arabians and totally different from the fine elegance of the Greeks; nor does it lend itself easily to translation into either Greek or Latin. Although I often thought of this, my mind was distracted with conflicting thoughts; now I would feel the urge to judge that I ought to undertake the work; then again, upon care-fully weighing the difficulty of it, I would feel deterred from it. For in the light of what was said above, can it be other than difficult to learn the identification of so many medicaments and of other terms most necessary in order to perform the work I had begun?

"Although you will find in the translation of this work some few remedies which are neither misspelled nor designated by obscure or even (native) Arabic terms, yet public utility must in the end prevail over private convenience (if avoid-ance of labour may so be called). There seemed, however, to be a not insignificant prospect of assistance from those who have engaged in the furtherance of that most difficult science of simple remedies.

"For almost twelve years some excellent medical minds have made attempts in that direction, not without success; so that there is scarcely a physician of any renown who has not attempted to bequeath to posterity something relating to that science. As a result they have all so far lightened the burden of my labours as to rid the druggists' shops of all barbarian words, if I may not say of all false drugs, and to restore them to their pristine integrity.

"Moved by these things and this example, I have started to revise the translation of Rhazes, both in order to liberate other candidates of medicine from immense labour, and to enable the author himself to reach men's hands henceforth cleansed of all barbarian names of medicaments unrecognizable to Latin ears, and with his entire mode of expression changed for the better; so that what was heretofore squalid and coarse and too obscure to be intelligible, will now be brightened, as far as possible, and will require the least exertion from the reader.

"It is true I did not always attempt to translate word for word, though perhaps a translator should do so; rather did I prefer to paraphrase, adding liberally what I judged to be necessary, and often explaining in a more profuse manner what seemed more obscure. I am therefore afraid my labours will not be at all safe from the bites of some fault-seekers, who do not wish to have anything cleansed and purified from its horrid barbarity, and do not value anything which they themselves did not learn. Having had some success with their work, they defend it ardently and, like Gryllus,* refuse to confess humanly their error, lest their bottomless ignorance should some day become widely and ignominiously known.

"For these reasons, most excellent Sir, I desire to have this youthful attempt of mine take the chance of appearing in print under the commendation of your celebrated name; hoping that perhaps it might thereby be safer from calumnies. Perchance, those haters of the success of others, standing in awe of your exceptional knowledge of Greek and Arabic medical literature, as well as of your rare and unheard-of erudition in matters philosophical and your other mental accomplishments, will cease to speak evil of attempts by students of the pure art of Hippocrates. To me you remain the foremost authority in medicine as well as in other good disciplines; may you not cease to urge me on with your most learned letters to pursue these studies, and to help me through, by your protection, which is everywhere most valuable.

* Gryllus, the presocratic philosopher, was the father of Xenophon.—Ed.

"I ask you, then, to defend this prelude of my studies with serene and smooth brow against quibblers, and to regard with benignity whatever you deem in it to be worthy, until such time as I shall produce something greater and more suit-able to your excellent learning. Farewell, ornament of all physicians; may you help our august Emperor Charles, whom at present the Christian world cannot afford to lose, to long and happy life."

The Louvain edition had evidently been printed in haste and in a small edition. The type was worn, poorly aligned, and contractures in the middle of words were frequent. Disappointed in its appearance, Vesalius must have set to work to prepare the elaborate subject index which precedes the text in the Basel edition in which the spelling is modernized, the errors corrected and the con-tractures largely resolved. But the chief difference in the two editions is shown by the marginal notes which are not only corrected and amplified but doubled if not trebled in number. All this, which was the author's chief contribution, must have required an expenditure of time difficult to crowd into the short month of February.

The text of each edition is followed by an explanatory Letter to the Reader, that in the Louvain edition having been dated *Mense Martio*, which is the date subjoined to Robert Winter's colophon to the Basel edition. To explain this puzzle, Mr. Leon Nemoy of the Yale University Library has suggested that Vesalius when in Brussels dated his dedication and postscript according to the civil year, whereas the ecclesiastical year, which began with March 21st, was employed by Winter at Basel. On this basis the second edition might really have been printed early in 1538 according to present reckoning. The Postscript which is essentially the same in both editions save for the omission of the date *Mense Martio* in the Basel edition reads as follows:

"I am afraid, dear reader, that I have not always been satisfactory to delicate ears, inasmuch as I have left sometimes in this paraphrase words commonly used by the Arabians and by almost all our contemporary physicians in matters medical, although they cannot be truly said to be Latin and have not been accepted by writers learned in the Latin tongue (such as Pliny, Celsus, Largus, Varro, and Columella). I must admonish you, therefore, that I have done it not always, but only at times and of necessity, in the case of names of some simple drugs unknown to these Greeks and other writers, and in some formulæ of compound medicines. Of this sort are some kinds of myrobalanum adopted by the Arabs, tamarind, camphor, julep, syrup, electuary, and possibly some similar

PARA-
PHRASIS IN NO.

NVM LIBRVM RHAZAE MEDICI ARA-
bis Clariſſ. ad Regem Almanſorem, de
affectuum ſingularũ corporis partium curatione, Andrea
Vveſalio Bruxellen-
ſi autore.

Rerum ac uerborum in hoc opere memo-
rabilium diligentiſſimus
I N D E X.

B A S I L E A E.

FIGURE SEVEN

Title-page of the revised second edition of the *Paraphrasis,* published by
Robert Winter at Basel in March 1537.

PARAPHRASIS
IN NONVM LIBRVM
Rhazæ medici Arabis Clariff. ad
Regem Almanforem, de affectuum fingularum corporis partium curatione, Andrea Vvefa-
lio Bruxellenfi autore.

*Rerum ac verborum in hoc opere me-
morabilium diligentiffimus*
INDEX.

**QVOD TIBI
FIERI NON
VIS, ALTERI
NE FECERIS.**

LVGDVNI,
Apud Ioan. Tornæfium, & Gu-
lielmum Gazeium.
M. D. L I.

PARAPHRASIS
IN NONVM LIBRVM
RHAZAE MEDICI ARABIS
clariff. ad Regem Almanforem,
de affectuum fingularum corporis partis
um curatione, ANDREA VVE-
SALIO Bruxellenfi
autore.

*Rerum ac verborum in hoc opere
memorabilium diligentiffimus*
INDEX.

VVITEBERGAE,
In Officina Cratoniana,
ANNO *1586.*

FIGURE EIGHT (*above*)
Title-page of the Lyon edition of the *Paraphrasis*.

FIGURE NINE (*below*)
Title-page of the Wittenberg *Paraphrasis,* 1586.

ones. In any case, I believe I have left no such instance, without explaining it as far as was necessary, either in the margins, where the reader was referred for consultation, or in the body of the book, and adding my own opinion on the matter. I am not unaware of the fact that some of these could have been rendered by a Latin or Greek term. But since there seemed to be too little agreement about them among authors, I was satisfied to leave them as I found them. Such are turbit, spodium of the Arabs, kanabel, cali, and possibly some kindred terms. I have taken care, however, to mark them, at least once, with *, while the mark † designates a variant reading. In addition to these you will find also the symbol § used in the text itself, which indicates that the passage marked by it is not by Rhazes.

"Although I have not always introduced everything which I added as a translator's licence, by means of these symbols, I have done so at least in such places, where because of prolixity or innovation I might be blamed by those of morose and petulant tongue. Even this is rather rare, for I have pursued the task of a paraphraser, rather than that of a translator.

"Farewell, candid reader, and think kindly of this labour of ours, which I was the first to undertake among those who have bequeathed something in medicine to posterity. In the year 1537, the month of March."

I.—1

PARAPHRASIS　Ed. princeps.　　　　　　　　*Louvain*, February 1537

Title (Fig. 6): [Ornament] Para [ornament] / phrasis, in Nonvm Li⁄ / brum Rhazæ Medici Arabis clariss. ad / Regem Almansorem, de singularũ / cor⁄ poris partium affectuum / curatione, autore An⁄ / drea Wesalio Bru⁄ / xel⁄ lensi Medi / cinæ candi / dato. / Louanij ex officina Rutgeri Rescij / Mense Februar. / 1537.

Collation: 8°. A⁄O⁸; 106, [6] *ll.*

Contents: A1*a* title; A1*b* blank; A2*a*⁄5*a* dedicatory preface to Nicolaus Florenas, dated Brussels, calends February 1537, followed by a poem by Jodocus Velsius; A5*b*⁄O2*b* (*ll.* 5*b*⁄106*b*) text; O3*a*⁄3*b* letter to reader dated March 1537; O4*a*⁄6*b* index; O7*a* errata; O7*b*⁄8*b* blank.

Note: Errors in numbering leaves are 02 for 20, 29 for 25, 80 for 71, 201 for 102. The type is old and worn and there are no ornamental initials or mar⁄ ginal notes.

Copies: Waller; London (BM) [lacking O8]; Vienna Staats Bibliothek [lacking O3⁄6 and O8]; [Louvain, lost in fire, 1914].

Copy used: Waller; measuring 14.1 by 10.6 cm. Paper shows watermarks, an hour⁄glass⁄shaped urn, at top of *ca.* every 8th leaf. De Feyfer cites the edition, evidently the Louvain copy.

I.—2

PARAPHRASIS   Basel, March 1537

Title (Fig. 7): [Ornament] Para-/phrasis in No-/nvm Librvm Rhazæ Medici Ara-/bis Clariss. ad Regem Almansorem, de/affectuum singularū cor-poris par/tium curatione, Andrea/Vvesalio Bruxellen-/si autore./Rerum ac uerborum in hoc opere memo-/rabilium diligentissimus/Index./Basi-leæ [ornament].

Colophon: Basileæ in Officina/Roberti VVinter./Anno/M. D. XXXVII./Mense Martio.

Collation: 8°. a⁸, b⁴, A-O⁸, P⁴; [12] *ll.*, 224 pp., [4] *ll.*

Contents: a1a title; a1b blank; a2a-4b dedication to Nicolaus Florenas dated at Brussels, calends Febru-ary 1537; a5a-b3a index; b3b poem by Jodocus Velsius; b4 blank; A1a-O8b (pp. 1-224) text; P1 letter to reader; P2a-3b chapter headings; P4a errata and colophon; P4b blank.

Note: This edition differs from that of Louvain in the presence of marginal notes. Errors in signatures are Q3 for a3, C4 for D4, and C5 for D5.

Copies: Amsterdam; Breslau; Leyden; London (RCP); Waller; Cushing; CaMM-Os; DSG; NNNAM (Streeter copy); Trent; Reynolds.

Copy used: H.C., measuring 16.7 by 11 cm. No watermarks. Purchased from Martin Boas in Berlin, 1905, for M.18.

I.—3

PARAPHRASIS   Basel, March 1544

Title: [Ornament] Abvbetri Rha-/zæ Maomethi, . . . opera exquisitiora, . . . Per Gerardum Toletanum medicum Cremonensem,/Andream Vesalium Bruxellensem,/Albanum Torinum Vitoduranū, latinitate donata, . . . Basileæ in Officina/Henrichi Petri.

Colophon: Basileæ per Henrichvm Pe/trvm Mense Martio, An-/no M.D.XLIIII.

Collation: Fol. a-d⁶, A-Z⁶, Aa-Zz⁶, AA-DD⁶; [24] *ll.*, 590 pp., [1] *l.*

Contents: a1a title; a1b "catalogue of all the books of Rhazes contained in this volume"; a2a-3b preface; a4a-d6a index; d6b blank; A1a-DD5b (pp. 1-590) text; DD6a colophon; DD6b printer's device.

Liber IX for which the Paraphrase of Vesalius is used occupies S3a-Z6a (pp. 209-275). Of these leaves, S3a-4a contain an index of chapters, the rest text. At the top of S4b (p. 212) occurs the heading: *Abvbetr iRha/zæ Maomethi Scientia Peritiaqve/in-signis Medici ad regem Mansorē liber nonus,/Andrea*

Vesalio Bruxellensi/Paraphraste.

Note: Text same as I.2 omitting preface, postscript and subject index. Preceded by chapter index as in I.2. Errors in numbering are 791 for 197, 109 for 209, 113 for 213, 161 for 261, 163 for 263, 174 for 374.

Copies: London (BM); Leyden; Waller; Cushing; Fulton (27.4 by 17.8 cm.); DSG; MH-M; NNN-AM; CSt-L; NBMS; NNC-M; MdBJ-W; MiU (Crummer); Fisher.

Copy used: H.C.; measuring 29 by 20.3 cm. Pur-chased from Günther, Paris (1907), for 70 francs. Bound in contemporary limp vellum.

I.—4

PARAPHRASIS
Lyon, 1551

Title (Fig. 8): Paraphrasis / in Nonvm Librvm / Rhazæ medici Arabis Clariss. ad / Regem Almansorem, de affe⁄ / ctuum singularum corporis par⁄ / tium curatione, Andrea Vvesa⁄ / lio Bruxellensi autore. / Rerum ac uerborum in hoc opere me⁄ / morabilium diligentissimus / Index. [Printer's device] Lvg⁄ dvni, / Apud Ioan. Tornæsium, & Gu⁄ / lielmum Gazeium. / M. D. LI.

Collation: 16°. a⁄p⁸; 212 pp., [14] *ll.*

Contents: a1a title; a1b blank; a2a⁄4b dedication to Florenas; a5a⁄o2b text; o3 epistle; o4a⁄p8a index; p8b Velsius poem.

Note: Text same as I.2.

Copies: London (RCS); Louvain; Cushing; Ful⁄ ton; MiU (Crummer); NBMS.

Copy used: H.C.; measuring 11.2 by 7 cm. Bound with another work by Jac. Sylvius from same printer (1554) in stiff white vellum covers with ties, stamped P.B.A.C. 1666. Purchased from Lier (1935) for $78.

I.—5

PARAPHRASIS
Wittenberg, 1586

Title (Fig. 9): Paraphrasis / in Nonvm Librvm / Rhazæ Medici Arabis / clariss. ad Regem Almansorem, / de affectuum singularum corporis parti⁄ / um curatione, Andrea Vve⁄ / salio Bruxellensi / autore. / Rerum ac verborum in hoc opere / memorabilium diligentissimus / Index. [Printer's device] VVite⁄ bergæ, / In Officina Cratoniana, / [rule] Anno 1586.

Collation: 8°. A⁄L⁸, M⁴, *⁸; 184 pp., [8] *ll.*

Contents: A1a title; A1b blank; A2a⁄M4b text; *1a⁄4a index of chapter headings arranged alpha⁄ betically; *4b brief statement to reader; *5a⁄7b index, with errata at end; *8 blank.

Note: Text same as I.2 with omission of dedication to Florenas and postscript to reader. Subject index greatly contracted. On *4b it states: "Since there remained a few blank pages we thought it useful to add an index of the principal auxilliary composites which occur in this book. They are called empiric already by many classical writers, having been partly so handed down and partly discovered by the author through long use."

Van der Linden does not mention this edition or the Wittenberg edition of 1592, but gives "Wite⁄ bergæ, apud Cratonem, 1587 in 8. Hic liber sup⁄ positicius, & à Vesalio non editus à quibusdam creditur."

Copy used: H.C.; measuring 16.3 by 10 cm. Pur⁄ chased from Lier (1911) for Swiss frs. 325, bound with several other Wittenberg books by the same printer. Paper badly foxed.

I.—6

PARAPHRASIS
Wittenberg, 1592

Cited by de Feyfer and others as 8°. No copy seen.

Copy: London (RCS). This copy could not be examined on account of the war.

❧ CHAPTER II ❧

THE 'TABULÆ SEX'

THAT BASEL, chief city of the Swiss Confederation, was a seat of learning where both Protestants and liberal Catholics might find, despite religious controversies, a reasonably comfortable habitat, must have been common knowledge in 1536 when Vesalius left Paris. Erasmus, who had just died there, had chosen it as his permanent residence, as was widely advertised by the fact that most of his works bore Basel imprints. Whether Vesalius went there in person in March of 1537 to oversee the printing by Robert Winter of the revised text of his *Paraphrasis* is not certain. Basel, however, was easily accessible from Brussels and on the direct route to Padua and Venice where in December 1537 Vesalius is next heard from;* and it would perhaps explain what was to happen in 1542/43 if in the Spring of 1537 he had come into personal contact with the scholars and printers—among them Oporinus—who lived in that picturesque and opulent university and cathedral city straddling the Rhine.

However this may be, he now betook himself (probably over the same trans-alpine route by which he was to retrace his steps four years later) to Italy where he hoped to find greater opportunity than in France to pursue his anatomical studies. In Venice he encountered his fellow countryman, Jan van Calcar, who for his own purposes, namely to study in the school of Titian, had likewise been drawn to that flourishing seaport. These two young and unknown Flemings, soon realizing that Venice was agog over the preaching of a Spaniard named Ignatius Loyola, may out of curiosity have joined those who flocked to hear him expound the word of God. Loyola and Vesalius were each in his own dynamic way a combination of dreamer, scholar and worker; and just five years later, in 1543, the one saw his great anatomy through the press at Basel, while the Society of Jesus founded by the other was officially recognized by the Pope and put in charge of the movement to stamp out heresy. Loyola and his followers had started out with the intention of carrying the gospel to Palestine—a plan from which they were diverted; Vesalius had ambitions of reforming anatomy which he succeeded in achieving, albeit he met his end when returning from Palestine

* It would appear that Vesalius had been in Venice for some months prior to his receiving the degree of Doctor of Medicine at Padua (December 5th). On December 6, 1537, he was appointed Professor of Surgery at Padua which carried with it the obligation to teach anatomy.—Ed.

10

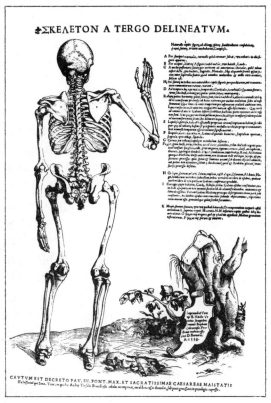

FIGURE TEN

Table VI of the *Tabulæ sex* showing below on the right an enlarged detail of the colophon making reference to Jan Stephan van Calcar. Compare the skeleton with those from Berengario and Balamio in the next figure.

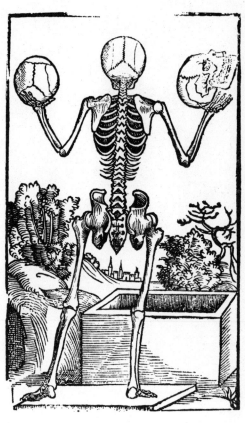

FIGURE ELEVEN

One of the first serious attempts to portray the human skeleton in a printed book. From Berengario's *Isagoge breves*, Bologna, 1522 (*l.* 70). The same plates had been used by Berengario in his edition of Mondino's Anatomy which had appeared in 1521.

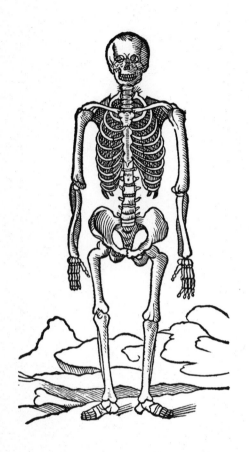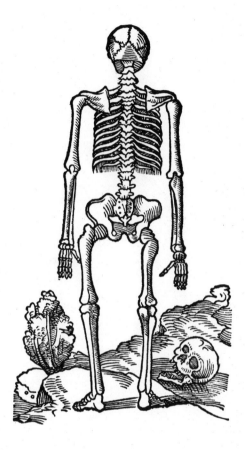

FIGURE TWELVE

The Balamio skeletons from the Latin translation of Galen's *De ossibus* issued at Lyon in 1535. A similar
skeleton re-engraved appeared in 1536 in Cratander's edition of Galen's *Opera omnia* issued at Basel (pp.
492-493) and in the Greek Galen of 1538 also published at Basel.

FIGURE THIRTEEN

Table I of Vesalius' *Tabulæ sex* showing portal system and liver, and other viscera. The reference to Calcar ("Stephanus") occurs in the opening paragraph.

where he had supposedly been sent by the Spanish Inquisition in expiation of some imagined heresy (98, 99).

Such progress in his studies did Vesalius make after reaching Venice that before the year was out, on the 6th of December 1537, just before his 23rd birthday, he received the celebrated appointment from the Venetian Senate enabling him to teach anatomy at the University of Padua. Before his transfer from Venice to Padua he had doubtless, in collaboration with Calcar, begun work on the six anatomical plates which were printed in Venice on April 1st the following year. It is debatable how much of the work was done independently by Calcar. Some (*e.g.,* Edouard Turner [402]), are inclined to believe that he drew only the three skeletal figures from a skeleton Vesalius is known to have prepared at this time, and that the other three drawings were designed by Vesalius himself. That would seem a fair division of credit and labour, but an anatomical artist is customarily shown by his chief just what is desired of him, and perhaps preliminary sketches were actually made by Vesalius. But when the plates came ultimately to be printed, Calcar evidently acted as the go-between with the printer, Bernardus, and paid the bills for Vesalius as indicated in the colophon (Fig. 10). Vesalius was well-to-do and it is improbable that the plates were printed "at the expense" (*sumptibus*) of Calcar himself. Curiously enough, the name of Vesalius occurs only twice: in the dedication on the first sheet and in the inconspicuous *privilegium,* thrice blessed by Pope, Emperor and Venetian Senate, at the very bottom of the sixth sheet.

The three skeletal plates are remarkable when compared with the cruder figures (Fig. 11) of Berengarius (1522). Less crude were the two engravings of a skeleton together with a rendering of the base of the skull which had first appeared in Ferdinand Balamio's 1535 octavo edition of Galen's *De ossibus* (Fig. 12) and in the following year were re-engraved and enlarged for the *Opera omnia* of Galen printed by Cratander in 1536 at Basel. Among the works printed by Cratander this item is not cited, and it must have been one of his last for he sold his press that year to the partnership of Winter, Oporinus, Platter and Lasius. When these plates came to the notice of Vesalius, he accused Balamio and Cardinal Rudolph of Capri of having deliberately withheld the book from him so as to prevent him from comparing Galen's account of bony anatomy with human osteology (345, p. 114). The Balamio skeletons also appear in many other works, *e.g.,* in the five-volume Greek *Opera Galeni* published in Basel in 1538, the same year that the *Tabulæ sex* appeared; and as late as 1665 they are mentioned in van Horne's (198) account of the Vesalius-Sylvius controversy.

These skeletal plates which seem to have been overlooked by Choulant show some obvious anatomical faults, such as the confusion between first and second ribs on the front view and the four instead of five lumbar vertebræ on the view from behind. Yet they are if anything better balanced than Calcar's figures and the pelvis hangs more securely on the sacrum. The *Tabulæ sex* were of course but a *ballon d'essai* for Vesalius, and not until five years later did he and his artist, whoever he may have been, come to show what they really could do. Even had his attention subsequently been called by his friends at Basel to the drawings in the 1538 *Opera Galeni,* it was too late for him to profit by them.

II.—1[A]

TABULÆ SEX Ed. princeps.   *Venice, April* 1538

Title: [Tabulæ Anatomicæ Sex.]

Colophon: Imprimebat Vene/tijs B[ernardinus]. Vitalis Ve/netus sumptibus/ Ioannis Stephani/Calcarensis. Pro-/strant [*sic*] vero in offi-/cina D. Bernardi./A. 1538.

Collation: Fol. max. Six separate sheets of water-marked paper printed on recto only, with colophon on shield of last table.

Contents: TABLE I. Above, Latin dedication which may be rendered as follows (Fig. 13):

"*To the eminent and famous Narcissus Parthenopeus, principal physician to His Imperial Majesty, his master and patron, Andreas Vesalius of Brussels gives greeting.*

"Not long ago, most learned Narcissus, when I was chosen to lecture on surgical medicine at Padua, and was occupied with the treatment of inflamma-tions, having in mind to explain the statements of the divine Hippocrates and Galen concerning revul-sion and derivation, I made on a sheet of paper a hasty sketch of the veins, thinking that I might be able to demonstrate easily in this manner what Hip-pocrates had meant to say by κατ'ἴξιν. You know what a tempest of dissensions and contentions this expression was the cause of, even among erudite men, with regard to venesection; some say Hippoc-rates had meant by this expression the correct arrange-ment [*consensum ac rectitudinem*] of the fibres. Others say he meant, I don't know what else. That delinea-tion of the veins, however, proved so pleasing to all the professors and students of medicine, that they strenuously urged me to supply a description of the arteries and nerves also. Since my teaching covered the field of anatomy, I had no right to refuse them, particularly as I knew that such outlines would be of

no little help to those attending dissections.

"To be sure, I think that it would be difficult, in fact quite impossible, for anyone to obtain the knowledge of parts of the body, or of simple drugs, from either pictures or formulæ alone; yet no one can deny that they are helpful in fixing things in one's memory. Inasmuch as many have vainly at-tempted to copy these outlines [by hand], I have committed them to the press, and have added new plates in which *Joannes Stephanus,* an outstanding artist of our time, has very fittingly expressed, in three positions, the skeleton which I have recently con-structed for the benefit of students, and for the great advantage of those who judge it not only honourable and proper, but also useful and necessary to examine the skill and artistry of the Supreme Maker, and to look into the interior of that which Plato calls the domicile of the soul.

"Moreover, we have appended to the individual parts their names, although this could not be done here as thoroughly as we might have wished it [*quamquam in præsenti negocio non admodum et sententia confici potuit*], and have kept barbaric words down to a minimum, although they still occur very often in the works of other authors. As for truthfulness, there is not one thing to be found here which those Paduan students who have attended this year's dissections could not testify to having seen me demonstrate—not to speak of my Parisian professors of great learning, and of the physicians of Louvain in whose presence I have more than once made public anatomical demonstrations.

"Now, then, in order that this new endeavour of ours might see the light under an auspicious protection and might more safely meet the double-edged judgment of critics, I have ventured to inscribe it to the fame of your name, partly because you possess an incomparable knowledge of various languages, and a remarkable command of anatomy, as well as of medicine and philosophy, so that you are spoken of by many erudite men of all nations, and deservedly, as the pride and ornament of the foremost and most expert physicians and litterateurs; and partly because you are esteemed among eminent men for such great prudence of mind, integrity, and outstanding gentleness and kindness that Charles V, the all-victorious and august Emperor, a most keen judge of character, not only assigned you the foremost place in caring for his health and nursing him after sickness, but also appointed you overseer for all the physicians and pharmacists of the Kingdom of Spain and Naples, although you are yet in the flower of your age, and has amply marked you with many honours and gifts, amongst many other eminent men.

"Accept therefore, most eminent Sir, this little gift on paper with the same graciousness with which you once received myself, when you declared yourself, with many tokens of benevolence, as most kindly disposed towards me. If it should prove pleasing to you and to students (in general), I shall some day do something greater than this. Farewell. *Padua, April first, 1538.*"

Below this dedication are four figures showing: (1) the five-lobed liver with gall-bladder turned back, also the spleen and the portal system of veins with its seven principal branches; (2) the male organs of generation; (3) the female organs of generation; and (4) the implantation of the seminiferous vessels. The two captions read as follows: [to left] The liver, the manufactory of the blood, attracts through the portal vein, called by the Greeks στελεχιαια, and by the Arabs [Hebrews] wārīd ha-shō'ēr, the chyle out of the stomach and the intestines, and pours the black bile into the spleen; [to right] Organs of generation, the male above, the female below. The third figure shows the implantation of the vasa deferentia. [*Subscription*] Galen enumerates seven principal branches of the portal vein.

TABLE II shows the five-lobed liver, the left kidney with vena cava, superior and inferior, and their 168 principal branches. On each side the figure

is flanked by a column of notes (*cf. infra*). [Caption] *Description of the hollow, hepatic vein* (vena cava, iecoraria), κοιλη, hāōrtē* hanābūb, *through which the blood distributes nourishment to all members of the body.* [*Subscription*] Some have counted 168 main branches of the vena cava.

TABLE III shows the heart and aorta with its branches including the rete mirabile. [Caption] *The great artery,* ἀορτη, hanābūb† haorti, *originating in the left sinus of the heart, carrying the vital spirit of the whole body, and tempering the natural heat by contraction and dilatation.* [*Subscription*] The noteworthy branches of the great artery seem to be 147 in number.

TABLE IV shows the front view of the skeleton with a single column of marginal notes. [Caption] *The bones of the human body, pictured from the front.* [*Subscription*] Some count 248 bones in the human body, others count a different number. I myself think there are 246 of them, not counting the hyoid, formed of six ossicles united by synchondrosis, nor the sesamoids. This number is contained in the distich on the following plate.

TABLE V shows the right profile view of the skeleton with a single column of marginal notes. [Caption] *Lateral view of the skeleton.* [*Subscription*] Distich containing the number of bones. Add to four times ten, twice one hundred, and six, and you shall have at once of how many bones you are constructed. (*Adde quater denis bis centum senáque, habebis / Quam sis multiplici conditus osse, semel.*)

TABLE VI shows the skeleton *a tergo* with a single column of notes to the right, and below a tree-stump with shield and colophon. [Caption] *The skeleton drawn from behind.* [Colophon] Printed at Venice by B. Vitalis, Venetian, at the expense of Joannes Stephanus Calcarensis. For sale in the shop of D. Bernardus. In the year 1538. [*Licence*] Warning is hereby given, in accordance with the decrees of Paul III, Supreme Pontiff, of his Sacred Imperial Majesty, and of the Illustrious Venetian Senate, that no one should print these tables of Andreas Vesalius, citizen of Brussels, or sell editions printed elsewhere, under threat of heavy penalties as specified in the privileges.

Copies: Until very recently only two complete sets (A and B) of these six tables had been known. One

---

* In Hebrew characters, and the wrong word! A transliteration of "aorta" is printed in this caption, while in that of Tab. III the word "hanābūb", hollow, is printed in Hebrew as the equivalent of "haorti", aorta.

† In Hebrew characters; see previous note.

of them [A] is bound together with the 1543 *Epi-tome* in a volume in the Library of San Marco at Venice. *Provenance.* On the flyleaf is inscribed *Exemplar Bibliothecæ Legatum ab Antonio Fantutio* [Fantuzzi?] *Medicinæ Doctore anno MDCCXC* [1790]. The leaves, somewhat cut, measure 50.5 by 37.7 cm. They had evidently once been folded in quarto, while the leaves of the *Epitome*, as is true of almost all copies, show signs of having been once folded transversely across the middle. Bound in is an extra print of Table VI, evidently a proof made before the lettering, as the colophon shield is blank, and the misspelled *Maistatis* in the privilege has been corrected to *Maiestatis.*

The second copy [B] was purchased in 1857 by the late Sir William Stirling-Maxwell for 60 Thalers from the *Kunstkatalog* of Rudolph Weigel of Leipzig, Pt. 24, No. 18707.* This copy (facsimiled in London, 1874, *cf.* II.2[B]) was inherited by Sir John Stirling-Maxwell, who presented it on May 25, 1929 to the Hunterian Library, Glasgow.

A third complete set is said to have been recently located in Prague by Dr. Wiegand, the Munich printer, but no details concerning it are available. In addition, two separate leaves have been recorded. One was formerly in the possession of the late Dr. Gustav Klein of Munich whose collection was purchased and presented after the War to the rebuilt University Library at Louvain. The plate in 1926 could not be found.

The other sheet, an example of Table V showing the skeleton from the side, turned up in 1931 at a shop in Bologna where it was mistaken for a stray leaf of the *Epitome*. It measures 51 by 34 cm., bears the telltale anchor-in-a-circle watermark (Figs. 14 and 15) and is in the collection of the late Professor Vittorio Putti. The coloured copy described by Choulant (80, p. 190) has disappeared without trace.

* It is lamentable that Sir William failed to secure for another 60 Thalers item No. 18708, which apparently contained among the "Convolut" of 14 broadsides the long-lost Macrolios plate described by Choulant (*cf.* II.8).

II.—2[B]

TABULÆ SEX Facsimile   *London,* 1874

Title: [upper scroll] Andreæ Vesalii / Tabvlæ anatomicæ sex. / [device] / Six Anatomical Tables of / Andrew [*sic*] Vesalivs. / [lower scroll] Venetijs / Imprimebat B. Vitalis, Venetus, sumptibus / Ioannis Stephani Calcarensis / M. D. XXXVIII. [on line below engraving] London: Privately printed for Sir William Stirling-Maxwell. / M.D.CCC.LXXIV.

The title-page bears a reproduction (nat. size) of the engraved frontispiece of the *Fabrica* (*cf.* VI.1); the upper scroll now carries the title of the present volume, the lower scroll the text of the colophon from the last of the skeletal plates; both are printed in red as is the imprint on the bottom line.

Collation: Large folio measuring 66.2 by 50.5 cm.; 14 *ll.*, first and last blank; the other 12 printed on recto only.

Contents: Fol. 1, blank.

Fol. 2. Presentation page: border from J. Weigel's *Trachtenbuch,* Nürnberg, 1577, printed in red.

Fol. 3. Title-page with imprint and colophon as cited.

Fol. 4. Contents with notes; devices in red above and below, the lower one containing initials of Sir William Stirling-Maxwell and his coat of arms.

Fol. 5. Portrait of Vesalius; die struck from *Epitome* on vellum in British Museum.

Fols. 6-7. Illuminated initial A in red; life of Vesalius; partial English translation of his letter to Oporinus, and many notes; terminal device in red.

Fols. 8-13. The six tables from II.1[B] in facsimile.

Fol. 14. Blank.

Copies: Of this gorgeously printed volume, as Stirling-Maxwell states, 30 copies were struck off, one on vellum, one on parchment, and 28 on paper. Examples may be found in the following collections: Surgeon General's Office, Bibliotheca Osleriana 581, Sudhoff's Institute at Leipzig, the Bodleian Library, the British Museum and the Royal College of Physicians, London.

Copy used: H.C., presented by Sir John Stirling-Maxwell, May 7, 1912.

As heretofore stated, a project was on foot to print another facsimile of the Stirling-Maxwell copy for distribution at the quatercentenary of Vesalius' birth to be held in December 1914 at Brussels. While this long-planned-for celebration was frustrated, recognition of the important anniversary was paid in many parts of the world. A "Vesal-Gedenkfeier" was to have been held under the auspices of the *Deutsche Naturforscher und Ärzte* at their Autumn congress in 1914, but the war prevented. No further meeting of this society was held until 1920, at which time the anatomist, Moriz Holl of Graz and Karl Sudhoff, the historian of Leipzig, published a facsimile edition, reduced to three-quarters natural size, of the copy II.1 [A] in the Library of San Marco at Venice (*Biblio-teca Marciana*):

II.—3 [A]

TABULÆ SEX Facsimile   *Leipzig,* 1920

Title: Des / Andreas Vesalius / sechs anatomische Tafeln vom Jahre 1538 / in Lichtdruck / neu herausgegeben und der / 86. Versammlung Deutscher Naturforscher und Ärzte / zur Feier der 400. Wiederkehr des Jahres seiner Geburt / dargeboten von / Moriz Holl (Graz) und Karl Sudhoff (Leipzig) / [Printer's mark] / 1920 / [Rule] / Verlag von Johann Ambrosius Barth in Leipzig.

Collation: Fol. 12 pp., 6 *ll.*

Contents: p. 1, title as above; p. 2, table of contents and apologia; pp. 3-4, Sudhoff's Historical Intro-duction; pp. 5-12, Holl's scholarly description of the six tables, comparing Vesalius and Leonardo to the former's disparagement. Tafel 1-6 collotype facsim-iles on recto only, as described under II.1[A].

Copies: Cushing; Fulton, etc.

II.—4 [A]

TABULÆ SEX Facsimile   *New York-Munich,* 1934

Title: Andreæ Vesalii / tabulæ anatomicæ / ad editionem anni MDXXXVIII / simulatæ.

Contents: f.[168a] title; f.[169a] tab. I; f.[170b] tab. II; f.[171a] tab. III; f.[172b] tab. IV; f.[173a] tab. V; f.[174b] tab. VI.

Note: This second facsimile of the Marciana copy by collotype process and of natural size is included without annotation as an afterthought in the *Icones anatomicæ* published under the auspices of the New York Academy of Medicine. Not only are the six tables reproduced, but also the duplicate proof which had been taken before letters of the colophon on the sixth leaf had been added. This proof is bound with the others in the Venice copy. (See VI.A.16.)

PLAGIARIES AND COUNTERFEITS

That the printing of these anatomical fugitive sheets made a great stir cannot be doubted. A set of them, forwarded to his father at Court, was presented to the Emperor who praised them highly, as reported in a letter of Nicolaus Florenas to the author (*cf.* p. 54). In the nature of things, it was not long before the Tables, despite the Imperial privilege, began to be copied, to the great vexation of Vesalius who four years later fulminated on the subject in his letter to Oporinus on the printing of the *Fabrica*:*

"But these privileges are often not worth the paper they cover, as I know but too well, from what happened to my *Anatomical Tables* published at Venice three years ago, the value of the decrees of sovereigns issued to printers and booksellers who swarm everywhere and have marred my works in putting them forth under pompous titles. In the edition of Augsburg the letter which I have written to Narcissus Vertunus, that model of physicians of our time, and first physician to the Emperor and king of Naples, has been suppressed and replaced by the preface of a German babbler who, unworthily decrying Avicenna and the Arabic authors, ranks me with the abridged Galens and, to cheat the buyer, pretends that I have put into six tables what in Galen fills thirty books.

"Moreover, he affirms that in his German translation he has used Greek and Latin terms, whereas he has not only suppressed these but has likewise omitted all that he could not translate and nearly all that gave value to my *Tables*; to say nothing of his wretched copies of the Venetian prints. He who has pirated them at Cöln has done still worse than his fellow of Augsburg; and although some anonymous scribe has written in praise of the printer that his plates are better than mine, they are in truth merely clumsy copies of rough sketches of my own which I had communicated to some of my friends during the progress of the work. At Paris they have copied the three first plates very well, but the others they have omitted, perhaps because they were difficult to engrave, though it was these first three which students could have best dispensed with. Worst of all, so far as science is concerned, at Strasburg, another plagiarist, whom Fuchs greatly blamed, thought fit to contract the size of the plates, which can hardly be too large, to daub them with ugly colouring, and to surround them with a text borrowed from that of the Augsburg edition, but put forth as his own. Envying this man's fame, another is publishing a book, compiled from all quarters and

* The passages from the Oporinus letter are taken from Stirling-Maxwell's rendering.

illustrated with prints taken from books printed at Marburg and Frankfort. Indeed I would gladly put up with and even welcome [the cost entailed on me by] the divine and happy Italian wits [whose works] deserve an appreciation from the doctors in Germany different from that which they have received from those who know them only as reproduced by the miserable slaves of sordid printers who, seizing upon any writing from which a little profit can be wrung, abridge it without discernment, or alter it, or merely copy it, and publish it under their own names as something new, and as if it were not protected by any privilege."

It would have been better for the author's later-day reputation had this portion of his famous letter to Oporinus been omitted. And doubtless could he have foreseen that four centuries later his admirers would still be puzzling over its significance in an effort to identify the persons to whom he had so disparagingly alluded, he would probably have blue-pencilled it in the proofs. Since he failed to do this, we have five plagiators (or counterfeiters) to account for: at (1) Augsburg, (2) Cologne, (3) Strassburg, (4) Marburg and Frankfurt, and someone less easily identified at (5) Paris. They may be taken up one by one for discussion in the order given.

(1) *The "babbler" of Augsburg.* The first of them, "the German babbler of Augsburg," was a certain Jobst de Necker, a woodcutter, printer and publisher who under the date of *June 1, 1539* issued a set of the six tables with plates so expertly engraved, line for line, as to be scarcely distinguishable from the originals were it not for the counterposed Latin and German texts. So few have survived they are almost as rare as the set printed in 1538 by B. Vitalis. It was obviously a direct piracy and yet one cannot but feel some slight sympathy for the perpetrator in view of his frank letter of explanation; and the severe castigation that he received four years later can only be condoned by assuming that Vesalius was then much on edge from overwork.

In their format the de Necker plates follow closely the original six sheets. The long German title and letter *Zum Leser* which have here been put into English occupy the upper one-third of the first table as did Vesalius' Latin dedication and letter to Narcissus Parthenopeus.

II.—5

JOBST DE NECKER   *Augsburg,* June 1539

Title: Ain gar künstlichs, allen Leyb vnd Wundärtzten, auch andrer kunsten
     Lyebha- / bern, hochnutzlichs werck, in sechs Figur gebracht, mit Innhalt

aller plütschlag vnd Flachssadern, sampt der gebaynen des gantzen Leybs, Vnd wie ain yedes seinen / vrsprung empfahe, vnd also ains auss dem andern volge, dem andern hilfs oder nacht hayle Bringe, Gar fleyssig vnd artlich Beschriben vnd anzaigt.

Collation: It would be unnecessarily repetitious to give a page-by-page collation of the six leaves. They differ from those of II.1 already given in detail only in the double rendering of the text by the translation of the original Latin into German. This has given each table when compared with the originals a somewhat crowded appearance; yet from a compositor's standpoint it must be looked upon as a most creditable performance for the printed area measuring *ca.* 47.5 by 33.5 cm. varies from plate to plate scarcely half a centimetre in the original and pirated issues.

Note: The paper bears no recognizable watermarks, and who the printer may have been does not appear. From the last of the three skeletal plates the Imperial licence granted to Vesalius has been omitted. In the shield which in the original gives the printer's name, place and date, there is printed the naive statement in German that to copy these figures in any wise is strongly forbidden by his majesty the Emperor (*cf.* Figs. 10 and 16). The text of de Necker's explanatory letter as translated by Georges Schaltenbrand runs as follows:

A very artistic work, highly useful to all physicians and surgeons, and also to the lovers of other arts, comprising six figures containing all the arteries, veins and bones of the entire body; demonstrating how each takes its origin, and how one follows another, aids it or hurries after it,—described and demonstrated, industriously and cleverly.

To the Reader:

My dear and friendly reader, Almighty God in His great wisdom and mercy has in our times not only loudly proclaimed His holy word to us, cleansed from all human obscuration but also sharpened, raised and enlightened human understanding, so much so that all even the poorest handicrafts have been raised to the highest and most artistic level, which has not occurred for many centuries. Also in all languages the elegant Latin orator has been brought into good use so that the lawyer begins to write and to speak the Latin in which the original texts were written and is no longer a barbarian like his scribes. Medicine, however, has been overlain and obscured especially because of the great handi-

cap of ignorance, as the majority of physicians did not know anything except what they had sucked superficially from official pandects; and they have for instance adored as an idol Avicenna who unworthily constituted himself an interpreter of the highly famous and intelligent Greek, Galen, and have used no judgment in their belief of him even in very coarse cases; and though they have professed that Hippocrates and Galen are noble and well founded teachers of medicine and are the only ones on whom a physician could entirely depend, among hundreds there is not one who has owned their original works, much less understood them; nevertheless it would have been endurable for them not to have owned or read Hippocrates or Galen in Greek if they had been translated into good Latin. Therefore, only the minority of physicians have read Galen, though occasionally someone has quoted him in a communication, a disputation, or on some other occasion. He has not taken from the original and from Galen's own works but has introduced, stated and used like any other writer a sentence often against his own reason. So those who have neither understood nor read Galen have quoted him without any real investigation of the original true understanding of Galen's books. And even though a few have obtained and read Galen in the old translation—as the minority have done—this former translation was so faulty and confused that no one could really understand it. Much is often omitted, and often forced and compelled into an opinion opposite to that of Galen himself so that he would not have recognized himself if he had read these his translated books. For in the above-mentioned translation not only has good Greek been transformed into bad and clumsy Latin, but the sense and meaning also have been fatally distorted and destroyed.

But in these times God has awakened many who have thoroughly studied Galen in his own language and have transcribed it into the best Latin, commutated and explained, so that others may also understand him as did the beloved and never-sufficiently praised Erasmus of Rotterdam, Linacre, Copus, Leonicenus and Manardus, and as Guinterius, Janus Comitius, Leonard Fuchs and Johann Agricola still do; as well as many others without mention.

FIGURE FOURTEEN (*above*)

Watermark from Calcar's "*Desseins originales*" (*sic*) in the Hunterian Library, Glasgow.

FIGURE FIFTEEN (*below*)

Watermark from Prof. Putti's single sheet No. V of the *Tabulæ sex*.

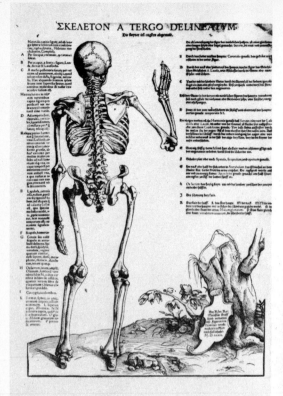

FIGURE SIXTEEN

Table 6 of the Jobst de Necker plates showing below the enlarged detail of the shield.

Detail of blank shield, one of the distinguishing marks of the second printing of the Jobst de Necker plates.

VENÆ CAVÆ, IECORARIÆ, ΚΟΙΛΗΣ, האורט HA=
NABUB DESCRIPTIO, QUA SANGUIS OMNIUM PARTIUM NUTRIMENTUM PER
UNIVERSUM CORPUS DIFFUNDITUR.

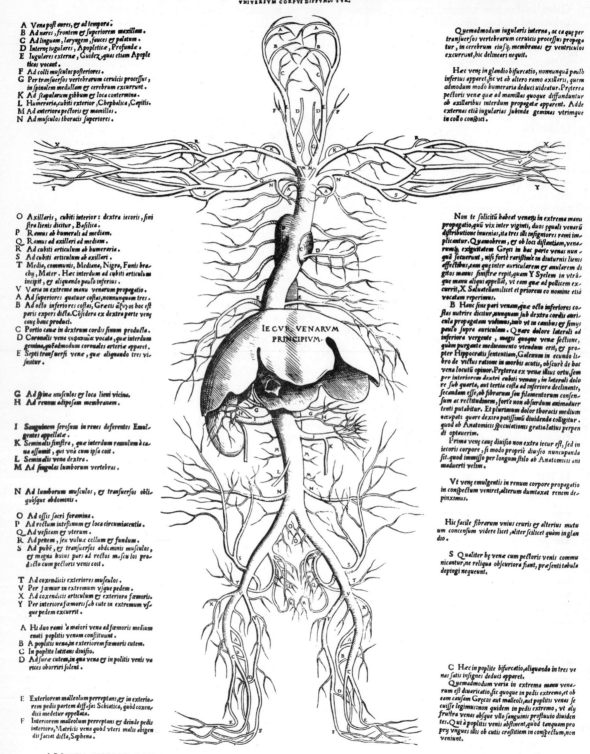

A Vena post aures, & ad tempora.
B Ad nares, frontem & superiorem maxillam.
C Ad linguam, laryngem, fauces & palatum.
D Internæ iugulares, Apopleticæ, Profundæ.
E Iugulares externæ, Guidez, quas etiam Apopleticas vocant.
F Ad colli musculos posteriores.
G Per transuersos vertebrarum ceruicis processus, in spinalem medullam & cerebrum excurrunt.
K Ad scapularum gibbum & loca conterminia.
L Humeraria, cubiti exterior, Chephalica, Capitis.
M Ad anteriora pectoris & mamillas.
N Ad musculos thoracis superiores.

O Axillaris, cubiti interior: dextra iecoris, sinistra lienis dicitur, Basilica.
P Ramus ab humerali ad mediam.
Q Ramus ad axillari ad mediam.
R Ad cubiti articulum ab humeraria.
S Ad cubiti articulum ab axillari.
T Media, communis, Mediana, Nigra, Funis brachy, Mater. Hæc interdum ad cubiti articulum incipit, & aliquando paulò inferius.
V Varia in extrema manu venarum propagatio.
A Ad superiores quatuor costas, nonnunquam tres.
B Ad octo inferiores costas, Græcis ἄζυγος hoc est paris expers dicta. Cōsidera ex dextra parte venæ cauæ hanc produci.
C Portio cauæ in dextrum cordis sinum productæ.
D Coronalis vena στεφανιαία vocata, quæ interdum geminæ, quéadmodum coronales arteriæ apparet.
E Septi transuersi venæ, quæ aliquando tres visuntur.

G Ad spinæ musculos & loca lieni vicina.
H Ad renum adiposam membranam.

I Sanguinem serosum in renes deferentes Emulgentes appellatæ.
K Seminalis sinistra, quæ interdum ramulum à caua assumit, qui vnà cum ipsa coit.
L Seminalis vena dextra.
M Ad singulas lumborum vertebras.

N Ad lumborum musculos, & transuersos obliquósque abdominis.

O Ad ossis sacri foramina.
P Ad rectum intestinum & loca circumiacentia.
Q Ad vesicam & vterum.
R Ad penem, seu vuluæ cellum & fundum.
S Ad pubē, & transuersos abdominis musculos, & magna huius pars ad rectos musculos productā cum pectoris venis coit.

T Ad coxendicis exteriores musculos.
V Per fœmur in extremum vsque pedem.
X Ad coxendicis articulum & exteriora fœmoris.
Y Per interiora fœmoris sub cute in extremum vsque pedem excurrit.

A Hi duo rami à maiori vena ad fœmoris mediūm enati poplitis venam constituunt.
B A poplitis vena, in exteriorem fœmoris cutem.
C In poplite latitans diuisio.
D Ad suræ cutem, in qua vena & in politis venis varices oborriri solent.

E Exteriorem malleolum perreptans, & in exteriorem pedis partem diffusa: Sciatica, quòd coxendici medetur appellata.
F Interiorem malleolum perreptans & deinde pedis interiora, Matricis vena quòd vteri malis abigendis faciat dicta, Saphena.

Quemadmodum iugularis interna, ac ea quæ per transuersos vertebrarum ceruicis processus propagatur, in cerebrum eiúsq; membranas & ventriculos excurrunt, hic delineari nequit.

Hæc venæ in glandio bifurcatio, nonnunquā paulò inferius apparet, sic vt ab altero ramo axillaris, quem admodum modo humeraria deduci videatur. Præterea pectoris venæ quæ ad mamillas quoque diffunduntur ab axillaribus interdum propagatæ apparent. Adde externas etiā iugularias subinde geminas vtrimque in collo conspici.

Non te solicitū habeat venæ; in extrema manu propagatio, quū vix inter viginti, duos æquali venarū distributione inuenias, ita tres illi insigniores rami implicantur. Quamobrem, & ob loci distantiam, venarum, exiguitatem Græci in bac parte venas nunquā secuerunt, nisi fortè rarissimè in diuturnis lienis affectibus, eam quæ inter auricularem & anularem digitos manus sinistræ repit, quam Y Syelem in vtráque manu aliqui appellant, vt eam quæ ad pollicem excurrit, X Salustellam: licet et priorem eo nomine etiā vocatam reperimus.

B Hæc sine pori venam, quæ octo inferiores costas nutrire dicitur, nunquam sub dextra cordis auricula propagatam vidimus, imò vt in cambus & simus paulò supra auriculam. Quare dolore laterali ad inferiora vergente, magis quoque venæ sectione, quàm purgante medicamento vtendum erit, & propter Hippocratis sententiam, Galenum in ecundo libro de victu ratione in morbis acutis, obscurè de bac vena locutū opinor. Præterea ex vena illius ortu, semper interiorem dextri cubiti venam, in laterali dolore sub quarte, aut tertia costa ad inferiora declinante, secandam esse, & sibrarum seu filamentorum consensum ac rectitudinem, fortè non obsurdum animaduertenti putabitur. Et plurimum dolor thoracis medium occupat; quare dextra potissimū diuidenda colligitur, quod ab Anatomicis speculationis gratia latius perpendi optauerim.

Prima venæ cauæ diuisio non extra iecur est, sed in iecoris corpore, si modo propriè diuisio nuncupanda sit, quod immisso per longum stilo ab Anatomicis animaduerti velim.

Vt venæ emulgentis in renum corpore propagatio in conspectū veniret, alterum dumtaxat renem depinximus.

Hic facile sibrarum vnius cruris & alterius mutuum concensum videre licet, aliter scilicet quàm in glandio.

S Qualiter bẹ venæ cum pectoris venis communicantur, ne reliqua obscuriora fiant, præsenti tabula depingi nequeunt.

C Hæc in poplite bifurcatio, aliquando in tres venas satis insignes deduci apparet.
   Quemadmodum varia in extrema manu venarum est duaricatio, sic quoque in pedis extremo, et ob eam causam Græcos aut malleoli, aut poplitis venas secuisse legimus: non quidem in pedis extremo, vt alij frustra venas absque vllo sanguinis profluuio diuidentes: Qui à poplitis venis abstinent, quod tanquam pro pry vngueis illis ob cutis crassitiem in conspectum, non veniunt.

IECUR VENARUM PRINCIPIUM.

ALIQVI VENAE CAVAE RAMOS INSIGNIORES CENTVM ET SEXAGINTA OCTO POSVERVNT.

FIGURE EIGHTEEN

The Vesalian scheme of the venous system, from the *Tabulæ sex*, 1538 (Tab. II). Compare this with the Ryff scheme shown in Fig. 19 opposite page 20.

Galen has thus been brought by translations of many writers and explanations of others into such use and understanding that many a man after having read Galen industriously compresses into one short figure all that Galen has written in many books, so that one is tempted to say that from one long Galen many short Galens grow and are born. So Stephan Intemplæus has reduced to six figures what Galen has dealt with in six whole subtle and highly useful books. And now Andreas Vesalius has brought together into six artificial but useful figures with beautiful understanding what has been written long and large by Galen in thirty or more books; which work has been written in Latin by Vesalius and then zealously printed by Bernard Vitalis, a Venetian, with the editing and arrangement of the artistic painter Johann Stephan. [In the undated set of plates (II.6), the text ends here.]

But because this artistic description of all the vessels and bones of the body is extremely necessary for every surgeon, and since in Germany surgeons only rarely understand Latin, I, Jobst de Necker, as a lover of the German nation have translated these artistic plates to the advantage of the Germans and have as far as possible transformed from good Latin into the unregulated German tongue the principal matters which never before have been described in German. I have then, with my art and not without great expense, copied the figures and had them printed, and allowed to go out the German with the Latin and for better understanding have put the one beside the other, occasionally adding the Greek and Hebrew so that one may better orient himself and see how one language is derived eventually from others.

Will you therefore, dear Reader, accept this work with gratitude from me and use it with zeal, so that God may be honoured and your neighbour improved in health with assistance, because only to this end shall my work be ordered and directed. Amen. Dated Augsburg, the first day of June, 1539.

Copies: The best known set is that in the Bayerische Staats-Bibliothek at Munich, catalogued as Rariora 748. In July 1926 through the kindness of Friedrich Müller, photostat copies of the six leaves were promised by the Director of the Library. Before they arrived in September, a set of the originals (wanting the last plate which was provided in facsimile) was purchased from Taeuber and Weil of Munich for $1000. The plates which have been cut close to the text measure 47.7 by 34 2 cm.; as remounted, 59.2 by 45.8 cm. The paper has no watermarks. They have no provenance and their source was not divulged. Another copy measuring 52.5 by 38 cm. from the library of Dr. Schmid of Berne was cited by Karl and Faber in their sale catalogue No. 44 for April 1931 (item 534) and was bought by R. Lier of Florence for Dr. Erik Waller, then of Lidköping.

Two years later, Sudhoff had the Munich set reproduced and published in facsimile (*cf.* II.7 *infra*). At that time he wrote to say that he was unable to find trace of the Darmstadt copy cited by de Feyfer. In 1926 while attempting to trace this copy myself, another set, an anonymous and undated variant of the de Necker plates, was located in Brussels of which photostats were secured. They are unmistakably the set described by de Feyfer as II.5.

II.—6

JOBST DE NECKER   Another ed.   *No place or date (c. 1540)*

Note: These six tables are essentially the same and evidently copies of those described under II.5. The wood-blocks, however, are obviously re-engraved. The type has been reset, less skilfully perhaps, but with certain corrections, *e.g., Ain* beginning the caption on Table I has been changed to *Ein.* The preface *Zum Leser* ends where indicated in the translation from the original above, so that the de Necker identification at the end with date is missing. The shield in the last plate is blank, so that all allusion to the original privilege is missing (Fig. 17).

Copies: The only recorded set is in the Royal Library at Brussels. A fragment of plate I containing the figure of the liver and kidney was obtained in 1942 for the Cushing Collection from Mr. H. P. Kraus of New York. Dr. Cushing had had both issues of Jobst de Necker photostated and mounted on facing pages in a volume designated "Jobst de Necker's Tabulæ".—Ed.

II.—7

JOBST DE NECKER   Facsimile   *Munich, 1928*

Title: Die anatomischen Tafeln / des Jost de Negker 1539 / mit 6 Tafeln und

2 Abbildungen im Text. Herausgegeben / von Geheimrat Professor Dr. Karl Sudhoff und / Museumsdirektor Professor Dr. Max Geisberg / [Rule] Hugo Schmidt Verlag München.

Collation: Fol.; 5 preliminary leaves of text followed by the 6 tables in facsimile, loosely attached to cardboard backs, measuring 55 by 40.3 cm.

Contents: Leaf 1*a* half-title; 1*b* blank; 2*a* full title with editors and printer; 2*b* copyright (1928) of collaborators, *e.g.,* Sudhoff, Geisberg and Schmidt; 3*a-b* Sudhoff's *Medizingeschichtliche Einführung;* 4*a* the Hela skeleton; 4*b* attached reproduction of skeleton sketched by Leonardo; 5*a-b* Geisberg's *Einige kunst-* geschichtliche Vorbemerkungen.

Note: The leaves are enclosed unbound in a pasteboard folder with front view of skeleton, title, and 'Hugo Schmidt Verlag München' on the front covers. The facsimile follows II.5 above. Sudhoff's preface makes the extravagant claim that Vesalius must have been a German!

Copy used: H.C., presentation, inscribed 'Sudhoff, Harvard, 8.x.1929'.

(2) *The pirate of Cologne (Macrolios).* In the Venesection Epistle printed in 1539 (*cf.* IV.1), Vesalius reports to his patron, Florenas, that he has taken a further step in his systematic studies with the completion of two tables of the nerves, in the first of which the seven pairs of the brain were delineated. By "systematic studies" he doubtless refers to the six anatomical tables described above (II.1) comprising three vascular and three skeletal figures printed in 1538 on separate sheets evidently for students. If, as Vesalius states, a seventh table, drawn either by himself or by Calcar to show the brain and cranial nerves, was completed in 1539, it does not appear under his authority in any publication prior to the *Fabrica.*

However, a copy of this drawing must somehow have been pilfered to be printed under the ægis of Ægidius Macrolios, the anonymous printer at Cologne in that same year, as stated in Vesalius' letter (1542, *cf.* p. 16) in which it is referred to as "an outline of the nerves, deplorably copied, which I had roughly sketched for one or two friends who had requested it pending publication by myself." Though Holl and Sudhoff in 1926 could find no trace of this plate at Dresden, so that there is no extant copy, one was seen, described and reproduced in 1852 by Ludwig Choulant (80, p. 51) who gives the following Latin title:

II.—8

[VESALIUS' TABLE SEVEN]   [*Cologne,* 1539]

Title: Ægidius Macrolios Cerebrum animalis facultatis fons et principium, sensum voluntarium per nervos communicans ab se et dorsali medulla enatos universo corpori.

Note: This is accompanied by an explanatory note which may be englished as follows:

"*Ægidius Macrolios, professor of anatomical medicine at Cologne, to students of anatomy.*

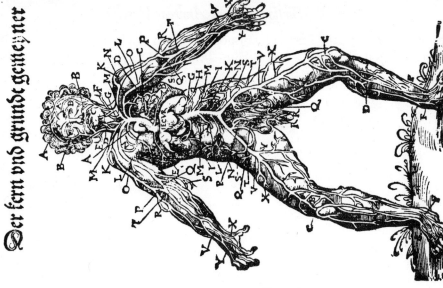

Anatomi / Contrafactur vnd beschreibung

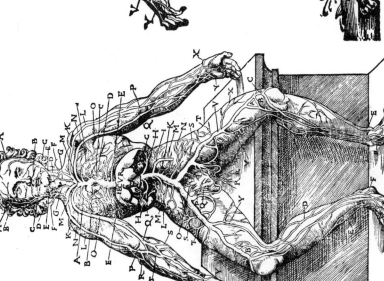

¶ Beschreibung des grossen lebers aber / Vena caua gnant / wie sy sich von der leber / als ghem vrspning / durch den ganzen leib erstrecke vnd außsthey ke / allen glidern narung zugeben. Diser aber fürnemlich ist / werden von etlichen acht vnd sechtzig zogn.

c

Der kern vnd grunde geineynet

FIGURE NINETEEN

Showing the evolution of Ryff's portrayal of the venous system in: A, his *Anatomi*, 1541; B, the *Tabulæ decem*, 1541; and C, *Die kleyner Chirurgi*, 1542 and 1551. Compare with Vesalius' venous plate from the *Tabulæ sex*, and note that the same lettering is used, Ryff having had the wit to superimpose the schema on a seated (A and B) or semi-squatting (C) body.

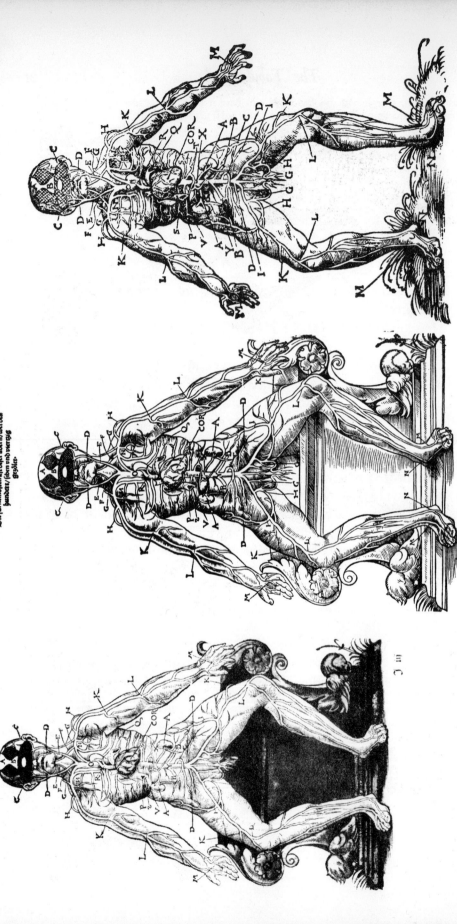

FIGURE TWENTY

Ryff's portrayal of the Vesalian arterial plate superimposed on the body, from: A, his *Anatomi*, 1541;
B, the *Tabulae decem*, 1541; and C, *Die kleyner Chirurgi*, 1542 and 1551.

"Andreas Vesalius, than whom no one since Galen has cultivated anatomy with greater diligence and correctness, has greatly contributed to the convenience of students who have not many autopsies at their disposal, by publishing several plates [*i.e.,* the *Tabulæ sex*] a year ago. But since the nature of a learned man abhors idleness, he proceeded forthwith to design with singular industry and elegance this plate also, which clearly exposes to the eye the sevenfold network ("syzygia") of nerves, those instruments and seats of the senses. Having obtained it not long ago,—in the shape of a mere outline, yet so elegantly done, that I believe the author would wish to have it become accessible to all—we have forwarded it to the printer, so that we might not, like so many envious people, be the only ones to enjoy such a treasure. Why should I not call a treasure that which expresses and teaches the ingenious machinery of nature? Nor do the foregoing six plates, which exhibit the images of the veins, the arteries, and the skeleton, contain anything so highly ingenious that they might be compared with this more important one—for that is how it ought to be styled, since it depicts the first principle of the human being. Farewell."

That Vesalius should have taken umbrage at this complimentary preface, if he indeed ever read it, suggests that his own "syzygia" had by now become somewhat frayed. So much for the plagiarists of Augsburg and Cologne at whose practices he expostulated.

(3) *The Strassburg plagiarist* (*Ryff*). It was unquestionably Walter Ryff whom "Leonard Fuchs so greatly blamed" for his plagiaristic tendencies. This, however, is really putting it mildly; for Fuchs more than "blamed," he excoriated Walter for his wanton thefts from others' works—"of all men the sun hath seen, the most shameless." Yet there may be something to say in behalf of even such a German pirate as he doubtless was; for though he did reduce the size of the Vesalian schemata which showed the arterial and venous systems separately (*cf.* Fig. 18), he was clever enough to superimpose them on seated male and female figures so that the relation of the vessels to the trunk and limbs of the human body was clearly apparent (Figs. 19 and 20). What is more, the vascular branches were all carefully marked with the same letters as those used by Vesalius so that they could be easily identified in the accompanying legends; and when the vessels had been delicately tinted, as in one of my copies, they give a surprisingly good idea, not furnished by the originals of the *Tabulæ sex*, of their anatomical topography.

Not only did Ryff in this volume thus alter the arterial and venous plates from the *Tabulæ sex*, but he used and modified Vesalius' diagram of the female organs of generation. He also drew freely for suggestions on the works of earlier Strasburgians, *e.g.,* Gersdorff's *Feldtbüch* (167) printed by Schott (1517) and Phryesen's (Fries') *Spiegel der Artzny* (147) printed by Grüninger (1518). He borrowed heavily from Rösslin's *Rosengarten* of 1513 (339) for obstetrical figures; and ended with nine plates re-engraved from Dryander's (116) recent *Anatomia capitis humani* (1536)—all without a shadow of acknowledgment.

While Ryff has a voluminous bibliography covering a variety of subjects, the only items which concern us here are those in which he has copied or modified for his own purposes some of the Vesalian figures. The first of these books, handsomely printed by Balthasar Beck of Strassburg the year before Vesalius' complaining letter was written, may be described as follows. The length of its German title, abbreviated here, is better shown in the reduced print of the page on which it appears.

II.—9

WALTER RYFF, Anatomi   *Strassburg, 1541*

Title (Fig. 21): Des aller fürtreff-/lichsten, höchsten vnnd adelich-/sten gschöpffs aller Creaturen . . . Das ist des menschen (oder dein selbst) warhafftige beschreibung oder Anatomi, seines/wunderbarlichen vrsprungs . . . erstmals inn Teutsche sprach verfasset vnd an tag geben . . .Durch M. Gualtherum Hermenium Ryff, Argentinum, Medicum. . . . M. D. XLI.

Colophon (final line, *l. 73b*): Zů Strassburg bey Balthassar Beck.

Collation: Fol. Goth. types. A-M⁶, N⁸; [6], 73 *ll.* + 1 blank.

Contents: A1a title; A1b side view skeleton after *Tabulæ sex;* A2-4 author's preface dated *Sept. 1, 1541;* A5a register; 25 full-page woodcuts (six repeated), 16 smaller woodcuts including birth figures (after Rösslin); schematic representation of eye (after Reusch); surgical instruments, etc.; 7 brain plates (redrawn after Dryander, 1537) and the three skeletal figures reversed from the *Tabulæ sex:* A1b *side view;* C4a repeated; C2b *front view;* C5b *back view;* also the plates of the vascular systems adapted from the *Tabulæ sex;* F1b venous plate (Fig. 19), J3a arterial plate (Fig. 20).

Copies: DSG; Cushing; MiU (Crummer).

Copy used: H.C., bought from E. P. Goldschmidt in 1926 for £90, measuring 30.8 by 19.5 cm.; provenance unrecorded.

In the same year (1541) Ryff issued, also from the press of Balthasar Beck, two sets of ten fugitive folio sheets, each printed on one side only, one with Latin and the other with German text* (Fig. 22). The first half-sheet of each set carries the introductory text; the other nineteen half-sheets all carry illustrations with brief captions. These fugitive sheets seem to have escaped Ryff's bibliographers. They represent nothing more than an illustrated epitome of the larger work which probably preceded them. They must certainly have come to the notice of Vesalius before his letter to Oporinus was written a year later. His renderings of Calcar's three skeletal plates are crude, though far less so than those in Dryander's *Anatomia Mundini* of the same year (*cf.* II.19); but he had exchanged them with friends in Paris, for they are obviously printed from the same woodblocks that were subsequently used in Tagault's *ed. princeps* of 1543, with whose

* It is possible that there may have been a French *Tabulæ decem* in 1541, but to date we have found no certain trace of it.

printer, Chrestien Wechel, Ryff was to have open dealings two years later (*cf.* II.15, 16).

II.—10

WALTER RYFF, Tabulæ decem   German   *Strassburg,* 1541

Title [Tabulæ decem; Fig. 22A]: There is no title. The first sheet begins: Kurtze Vorred zü dem/güthertzigen Leser./Durch Magistrum Gualtherum H. Ryff,/Argentinum Medicum.

Imprint: Zů Strassburg, bey Balthassar Beck,/M. D. xli.

Contents: The ten sheets, printed on one side only, of unwatermarked paper, measure 29 by 38 cm. The printed matter on each folio is paired so that the sheet when folded in the middle would bring the illustrations and textual matter face to face, making thus ten folded gatherings of 29 by 19 cm. which might be bound, as had once been done to my set of the German plates; these were subsequently restored to their original open form by Mr. Maltby, the Oxford binder.

Thus restored, the ten opened sheets are seen to bear signatures A–E, a–e; the verso of all opened sheets is of course blank.

Left	*Right*
Fol. A Ryff's foreword.	Seated male showing viscera after Phryesen, with lettering.
Fol. B Seated female showing viscera, after Vesalius.	Superficial anatomy male: front.
Fol. C Superficial anat. male back and right side.	Vena cava system with liver on seated figure. Lettering from Vesalius not explained.
Fol. D Arterial system on seated figure after Vesalius' Tab. 3, lettering unexplained.	Front view of skeleton from Vesalius' Tab. 4 via Wechel(?) of Paris with lettering unexplained.
Fol. E Side view of skeleton after Vesalius' Tab. 4, lettering unexplained.	Rear view of same from Tab. 6 without colophon. Vesalius' lettering unexplained.
Fol. a Dryander's open mouth and tongue.	Dryander's craniometric shaved head.
Fol. b Dryander's cranium, scalp reflected.	Dryander's cranium with skull cap removed.
Fol. c Dryander: dura reflected.	Dryander: ventricles opened.
Fol. d Dryander's cerebellum from above: optic chiasm.	Dryander. Cerebellum incised: carotids and rete mirabile.
Fol. e Base of skull from above after Dryander?	Base of skull from below and lower jaw from behind.

The foreword on the first sheet in the two sets differs considerably. That in the German set intended for the general public indicates the purpose of the plates, *viz.,* to describe the construction of "God's most wonderful creature". That in the Latin (Fig. 22B) set is more formal and may be englished as follows:

"You have here, candid reader, the first and most useful part of medicine, meaning the description of all the parts of the human body, or anatomy, now compressed into a fascicle of plates and brought into the light of day. If you will compare this work with the four books of anatomical institutions by Guenther of Andernach, and frequently consult them, instead of merely looking at the picture ('pro inani pictura'), may I perish if you will not easily perceive and retain in your memory the situation of all bones and their shape, the extension of veins, arteries, and nerves, the joining of the muscles, and all the other single parts of the human body, interior and exterior, in their minutest particles. In the meantime I wish to admonish the youthful student of this one thing, that we have arranged this first yet most difficult part of medicine in the form of tables for visual study, merely with the purpose of making study easier. Therefore, should it appear to anyone that we have carelessly omitted something, or have not expressed it with sufficient diligence, let him admonish us candidly, and not bite (wildly) into us. Some time in the future, when we shall undoubtedly possess more erudition or more leisure, we shall attempt to supply something more instructive. Farewell, and think kindly of our effort." [Followed by mnemonic verses on the various members of the human body.] *Copy used:* H.C., from Rappaport, Rome, in 1927 for 380 lire.

II.—11

WALTER RYFF, Tabulæ decem.   Latin   *Strassburg,* 1541

Head-title [Tabulæ decem; Fig. 22B]: First page: Omnivm hvmani / corporis partivm descriptio sev vt / uocant Anatomia, in qua singula membra ad uiuum, picturæ linea- / mentis q*uam* iustissime sunt expressa, in præsentes Ta- / bulas redacta opera & diligentia. / M. Gvaltheri H. Ryff Argenti- / ni Medici.

Imprint: Argentinæ ex officina libraria Balthassari / Pistoris. M. D. xli. / Cum gratia & priuilegio Reg. Maiestatis.

Contents: Similar to II.10 with the same plates, and with the explanatory matter in Latin.

Copies: J. C. Trent (formerly belonging to the late LeRoy Crummer; see Fig. 22B.)

II.—12

WALTER RYFF, Tabulæ decem.   Latin   *Paris,* 1545

Head-title: First page: Omnium humani corporis par- / tivm descriptio, sev vt vocant anatomia, / In qua singula membra ad viuum, picturæ lineamentis quam iustissime sunt ex- / pressa, in præsentes Tabulas redacta opera & diligentia M. gualtheri h. Ryff Ar- / gentini Medici.

Imprint [on first text page]: Parisiis. / Apud Hiero-nymum Gormontium, via Iacobæa, sub trium Cor-onarum. / 1545.

Collation and contents: As with II.10, 19 woodcuts are mounted on ten folding sheets printed on one side only.

Note: The general arrangement coincides with that of II.10 and II.11 with the title and imprint on the first page of text. The figures, 19 in number, are from identical blocks, except for the two awkward muscle men on *ll.* B and C which are entirely new, and as far as can be gathered they had not been used previ-ously, nor were they employed thereafter. This issue, known to Dr. LeRoy Crummer (90), was stated by him erroneously to be in French. The printer, Jérosme de Gourmont (Gormontius), successor of Gilles de Gourmont, of Rue St. Jacques at the sign of the three silver crowns, flourished at Paris from 1524 to 1554. His shop was close to that of Wechel on Rue St. Jacques. This seems to have been Gour-mont's only excursion into medical printing (*cf.* Renouard, P., *Imprimeurs Parisiens,* Paris, 1898, p. 139).

Copy: The only copy so far traced is in the Library of the College of Physicians, Philadelphia.

There was of course nothing novel in such anatomical broadsides. Their great rarity is due to the fact that if inserted (folded) in printed books, they were likely to be removed or accidentally torn out and lost. They have been dealt with copiously by others more competent, such as the late LeRoy Crummer (90, 91), who made a large collection of them. Examples that I happen at the moment to have at hand chiefly depict the skeleton which always aroused the layman-

Es aller fürtreff=
lich sten/höchsten vnnd adelich=
sten gschöpffs aller Creaturen/von Got
dem Herren/schöpffer aller ding auff er=
den/erschaffen/Das ist/des menschen/
(oder dein selbst) warhafftige beschreibung oder Anatomi/seines
wunderbarlichen vrsprungs/entpfängkniß/schöpffung inn mütter
leib/vnd sorglicher geburt/sampt künstlicher vnd artlicher Contra=
factur/aller eüsserlicher vnd innerlicher glider vnnd glidstuck/auß
welchen der mensch wunderbarlich zůsamen gesetzt ist/mit gnůgsa=
mer/eygentlicher vnd gründtlicher erklärung jetz vilfaltigen nutz=
barkeyt/krefft/würckung/natur vnd vermögen/warzů sy von Got
dem Almechtigen verordnet seind.Die trefflichen vnd vnaußsprech=
lichen wunderwerck Gott des Herren/in disem irrdischen gschöpff
vnd sterblichen Cörper/augenscheinlich zůerkennen vnnd mercken.
Allen denen so die herrlichen vnergründtlichen wunderwerck Got=
tes vnnd würckůng der natur/zů lob vnnd ehr des Schöpffers/nutz
vnd wolfart jres nechsten/betrachten vnd erkündigen wolten/von
vnzälicher vilfaltiger nutzbarkeyt wegen menschlicher blödigkeyt/
auß sunderlichem geneygtem willen/erstmals inn Teütsche
sprach verfasset vnd an tag geben.Vormals weder
gesehen noch gelesen worden.

Durch M. Gualtherum Hermenium Ryff/
Argentinum/Medicum.

Kumpt her/vnd schawet die werck des Herren/dann der Herr ist
wunderbar/vnd seine werck vnergründtlich.

M. D. XLI.

Mit Künigklicher Maie.Freiheyt.

FIGURE TWENTY-ONE

Title-page of Ryff's *Anatomi*, 1541.

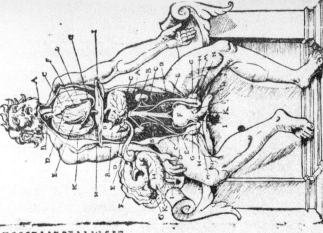

FIGURE TWENTY-TWO

The first plate of Ryff's *Tabulæ decem*, 1541: above, German edition; right, Latin edition.

reader's interest. They are: (1) the large, twice-folded plate (42 by 29.5 cm.) "*Anatomia ossium*," showing what is known as the Hela skeleton which occurs along with other early anatomical illustrations in the *Antropologium* of Magnus Hundt (Leipzig, 1500); (2) the two folded plates, both dated 1517, in Phrye-sen's *Spiegel der Artzny* (Strassburg, 1518): A, *Ein Contrafact Anatomy der inneren glyderen des menschen* (34.5 by 27 cm., twice folded); and B, a skeleton on one side of a twice-folded sheet (37 by 27 cm.) with text on one half of the verso; (3) the same are described in Gersdorff's *Feldtbüch der Wundtartzney*, Strassburg, 1517, but they are lacking in my copy; they occur, however, in my copy of a later edition of the *Feldtbüch* published in 1530. The skeletal figure is undoubted-ly the basis of the Berengario skeletons (Fig. 11) and those of Balamio (Fig. 12) mentioned earlier. The history of these important fugitive sheets is discussed at length by Mortimer Frank in his translation of Choulant (80).

So, while there was nothing unusual in the issuance by Ryff or his printer Beck of these ten "fugitive leaves," the fact that the three skeletal figures may have originated elsewhere than Strassburg must be borne in mind when we come later on to discuss the Paris plagiarist. Ryff also issued in 1541 from Beck's press a squat quarto volume with a formidable title beginning *Rechter und nutzlicher gebrauch*, etc., which deals chiefly with pharmaceutical matters most of which had been impudently stolen from the *De sanandis totius humani corporis malis* of Leonard Fuchs (148). It is of present interest only in that a copy happens to be bound with the rare 1542 first edition of Ryff's *Kleyner Chirurgi* which contains two newly cut engravings of the vascular plates of the *Tabulæ sex* already used in the 1541 plagiaries (Figs. 19C and 20C). The figures are here no longer seated on a bench but are in a squatting posture.

II.—13

WALTER RYFF, Kleyner Chirurgi — Strassburg, 1542

Title: Die kleyner Chirurgi / D. Gualtheri H. Ryff. / Das ist, der grund vnnd kern gemeyner eynleyt-/tung der gantzen wundartzney . . . M. D. XLII.

Colophon: Getruckt zů Strassburg bey / Balthassar Beck.

Collation: 4°. Gothic type. A-Z⁴, a-z⁴, AA-GG⁴; [4], 198, [10] *ll.*

Contents: A1*a* title (*cf.* Fig. 23); A1*b* blank; A2-3 foreword; A4*a* Vesalian plate, verso blank; B1*a*-EE2*b* text, leaves numbered i to cxcviii; EE3*a*-GG3*b register* (subject index); GG4 blank. The second Vesalian plate occurs on G1*b*. The first plate (A4*a*) is repeated on H2*b*.

Copies: ICJ; Cushing.

Copy used: H.C., bought from H. P. Kraus, Vienna, Jan. 1937, for $140. Bound with the 1541 Ryff on pharmacy, in half pigskin on boards. Contemporary *ex libris*.

II.—14

WALTER RYFF, Kleiner Chirurgi   *Strassburg,* 1551

Title: Die kleiner Chirurgi / D. Gualtheri H. Ryff. / Das ist, der grund vnd kern gemeyner eyn- / leyttung der gantzen wundartznei, . . . M. D. LI.

Colophon: Getruckt zů Strassburg durch / Balthassar Becken / Erben.

Collation: as in II.12.

Contents: as in II.12, though type entirely reset.

Copies: DSG; Cushing.

Copy used: H.C., bought from E. P. Goldschmidt, 1929, for £42. Bound in contemporary stamped pig-skin, measuring 18.9 by 14.5 cm.

Ryff meanwhile is a difficult person to circumvent, and before abandoning his "Ten Tables" at this juncture, it should be pointed out that the nineteen wood-blocks found their way to Paris where Ryff made arrangements with Chrestien Wechel to issue them in book form, this time with an expanded text (now referred to as the "Anatomica"). Editions appeared in 1543 and 1545, in both French and Latin, and all are apparently of the greatest rarity. A copy of the 1543 Latin edition has been found in the New York Academy of Medicine, and the French edition of the same year is registered at the British Museum. The 1545 Latin edition had long been in my possession (see II.17), and in 1930 I obtained from Lier (who offered it as a *unicum*) a copy of the 1545 French edition with three leaves missing. [The editors are responsible for the descriptions of all but the 1545 Latin edition.]

II.—15

WALTER RYFF, Anatomica.   Latin   *Paris,* 1543

Title: [Device] Anatomica [device] / omnivm hvmani corporis partivm / de- / scriptio, picturæ lineamentis singula mem- / bra ad viuum exprimens in / tabulas redacta, / operâ & diligentiâ M. Gualteri / H. Ryff. Argentini medici. / Quibus præmissi sunt / phlebotomiæ canones aliqvot ma- / xime consider- / andi in missione sanguinis vigilantissimè collecti / & in lucem æditi operâ eiusdem. / [Printer's device] / Parisiis / Apud Christianum Wechelum sub scuto Basiliensi in vico Iacobæo: / & sub Pegaso in vico Bellouacensi. Anno / M. D. XLIII.

Collation: Fol. A-C⁶, D⁴; 43 pp.

Contents: A1*a* title; A1*b* letter to reader; A2*a*-4*a* directions for bleeding; A4*b*-D4*a* same series of 19 plates, with text on verso facing figures on recto pages except in case of B2*b* and B3*a* where surface anatomy figures face each other. The three Wechel

(?) skeletal plates from the *Tabulæ sex* occur on pp. 39, 41 and 43 (*i.e.,* D2*a,* D3*a* and D4*a*). D4*b* printer's device.

Copy used: NNNAM, measuring 28.7 by 20.7 cm., in modern paper binding, from the E. C. Streeter Collection.

II.—16

WALTER RYFF, Anatomica.   French   *Paris,* 1543

Title: Description anatomique de toutes les parties du corps humain exprimant au vif tous les membres, rédigée en tables . . . Devant laquelle sont premises aulcunes reigles de phlebotomie lesquelles fault observer en tirāt du sang, *etc.* Paris, Chrestien Wechel, 1543.

Note: The above title has been taken from the entry in the *British Museum Catalogue,* and the volume has not been seen. A note under the Latin edition of 1543 states the same illustrations are used in both editions.

II.—17

WALTER RYFF, Anatomica.   Latin   *Paris,* 1545

Title (Fig. 24): Anatomica / omnium humani corporis / partivm descriptio, pictvræ line⁃ / amentis singula membra ad viuum exprimens, in tabulas redacta, ope⁃ / ra & diligentia M. Gualtheri H. Ryff. Argētini Medici. Qui⁃ bus præ⁃ / missi sunt phlebotomiæ canones aliquot maximè considerandi / in missione sanguinis, vigilantissimè collecti & / in lucem editi operâ eius⁃ dem. / [Printer's device] / Parisiis, / Apud Christianum wechelum sub scuto Basili⁃ / ensi in vico Iacobæo: & sub Pegaso in / vico Bellouacensi. Anno / M. D. XLV.

Collation: as in II.15.
Contents: as in II.15.
Watermarks: open cross.

Copy used: H.C., bought from J. L. Syme, Paris, 1909; measures 28 by 19.5 cm., untrimmed. Prove⁃ nance: inscribed F. R. Noëus, Paris, 1552.

II.—18

WALTER RYFF, Anatomica.   French.   *Paris,* 1545

Title (Fig. 24): Description Anatomique / de tovtes les parties dv corps / hu⁃ main, exprimant au vif tous les membres: redigée / en tables par maistre Gualther H. Ryff. / Medecin de Strasbourg. / Devant laqvelle sont premises / aucunes reigles de Phlebotomie, lesquelles fault obseruer / en tirant du sang. Le tout diligemment / colligé par le mesme. / [Printer's device] / On les vend à Paris, en la maison de Chrestien wechel, / demeurant en la rue sainct Iacques, à l'escu de / Basle: & en la rue sainct Iehan de Beau⁃ / uais, au Cheual volant. L'an / M. D. XLV.

Collation: Fol. in sixes. A⁃C⁶, D⁴; 22 *ll.* paginated to 43; 2 inserted plates.
Contents: A1a title; A1b letter to reader; A2a⁃4a (pp. 3⁃7) directions for bleeding; A4b text descrip⁃ tive of A5a (p. 9, male plate); A5b description of plate on A6a (p. 11, female plate); A6b⁃B1a (pp. 14⁃15) *"L'exposition sur la suivante paincture des veines de tout le corps humain"*; B1b⁃2a (pp. 14⁃15) *"La grande artere appellee aorta … (ainsi qu'on peult voire)"*; B2b⁃3a (pp. 16⁃17) front and side views of male figure show⁃ ing surface muscles; B3b⁃D1a (pp. 18⁃37) ten plates of skull and brain (on right side of page) with de⁃ scriptive text (on left side); D1b⁃4a (pp. 38⁃43) descriptive text (left) and three skeletal figures (right);

D4*b* printer's device. Venous and arterial plates, printed on one side only, were intended to be inserted.

Note: The illustrations are from identical blocks as used for the preceding, *i.e.,* II.15, 16 and 17.

Copies: Only copy known that of author, purchased in 1930 from Lier (lacks pp. 17-18, 23-24, and inserted arterial plate).

Nor does this serve to shake off Ryff entirely, since other books, some with Vesalian interest, continued to appear under his name. We shall shortly hear disparaging things of a certain Christian Egenolph of Marburg who printed Dryander's early books from which Ryff had pirated and at the same time improved Dryander's set of cuts showing the anatomy of the head. The printer Egenolph ere long moved to Frankfurt which promised to become a great book mart, and it was from his press there that Ryff issued in 1545 his *Grosz Chirurgei* with its remarkable "bloody" title-page appropriately printed in red and black.

While this volume has countless illustrations taken from Gersdorff and Phryesen, it is without Vesalian associations. Yet when Ryff came in 1551 to issue again at Beck's Strassburg press what he called *Die Kleyner Chirurgi,* he once more fell back upon the arterial and venous plates of the *Tabulæ sex,* using the same blocks as in the 1542 edition (Figs. 19C and 20C).

(4) *The Marburg and Frankfurt slave* (Dryander). John Dryander, or Eichmann, was unmistakably the other "slave of the sordid printer at Marburg and Frankfurt," meaning of course Christian Egenolph who in 1541 and 1542 had printed for him two books containing, among other woodcuts, some evidently taken from the *Tabulæ sex.* Dryander, the professor of mathematics and medicine at Marburg, was, as a matter of fact, one of the first anatomists after Berengarius to make drawings of his own dissections, and his pre-Vesalian woodcuts of the brain and its envelopes are, for the period, truly remarkable. His *Anatomia capitis humani* (Fig. 25), a rare quarto of fourteen leaves* in which the eleven serially numbered cuts (bearing the initials or monogram of an unidentified engraver) first appeared, was printed in Marburg by Eucharius Cervicornus in September 1536 when Vesalius was presumably still in Paris.

In the very year 1527 when Rome was being sacked by the mercenaries of Charles V, Philip, the Landgrave of Hesse, founded the first Protestant University at Marburg and it was through his intelligent support of the existing sciences that a law was passed ere long permitting public anatomies to be performed, the first of which was held in June 1535 and the second in March 1536 by the Professor of Medicine (Dryander) who had been requested by the Rector to publish cuts of the drawings which had then been made.

* Copies cited of both books are those in the Surgeon-General's Library. Dr. Cushing had forgotten that he also possessed a copy of the 1537 edition (Fig. 26).—Ed.

Die kleyner Chirurgi

W. Gualtheri H. Ryff.

Das ist / der grund vnnd kern gemeyner eynleytung der gantzen wundartzney / alle zůfäll vnd gebꝛechen menschlichs Cöꝛpers / als verwundung vñ verletzung / Apostem / betilé / gschwell / offne eyngebꝛochne veraltete vnd newe böse schäden / vnd dergleichen böser zůfäl / so die handtwürckung erfoꝛdern / künstlich vnd artlich zůheilen vnd Curieren / auß rechtem grundt der leib vnd wundartzney / durch heymliche griff / verboꝛgne vnd bewerte stuck biß auff dise zeyt in Teütscher sprach nit gelesen woꝛden / für die jungen angonden wundärtzt / in kürtze begriffen / vnd in sechs fürnäme theyl vnderscheyden.

Sampt gwisser vnbetrüglicher pꝛob / besichtigung vnnd Cur der aussetzigen oder veldtsiechen.

Auch wie man alle salben / pflaster vnd öl / künstlichen vnd artlichen bereytten soll / so von den erfarnesten berümptsten meystern gebꝛaucht / auch in rechtgeschaffnen Apotecken bereyt werden.

Mit Künigklicher Maiestat freyheyt.

M. D. XLII.

FIGURE TWENTY-THREE

Title-page of Ryff's *Die kleyner Chirurgi*, 1542, containing the venous and arterial plates shown in Figs. 19C and 20C.

ANATOMICA
omnium humani corporis
PARTIVM DESCRIPTIO, PICTVRAE LINE-
amentis singula membra ad viuum exprimens, in tabulas redacta, operâ & diligentiâ M. Gualtheri H. Ryff. Argëtini Medici. Quibus prae-
missi sunt phlebotomiae canones aliquot maximè considerandi
in missione sanguinis, vigilantissimè collecti &
in lucem editi operâ eiusdem.

naueigens Rassuis voeus
Aienue, rue, use.

PARISIIS,
Apud Christianum wechelum sub scuto Basiliensi in vico Iacobaeo: & sub Pegaso in
vico Bellouacensi. Anno
M. D. XLV.

Description Anatomique
DE TOVTES LES PARTIES DV CORPS
humain, exprimant au vif tous les membres: redigée
en tables par maistre Gualther H. Ryff.
Medecin de Strasbourg.

DEVANT LAQVELLE SONT PREMISES
aucunes reigles de Phlebotomie, lesquelles fault obseruer
en tirant du sang. Le tout diligemment
collige par le mesme.

On les vend à Paris, en la maison de Chrestien wechel,
demeurant en la rue sainct Iacques, à l'escu de
Basle: & en la rue sainct Iehan de Beauuais, au Cheual volant. L'an
M. D. XLV.

FIGURE TWENTY-FOUR

Title-pages of the Latin and French editions of Ryff's *Anatomica* (1545). Similar issues also appeared both
in Latin and French from Wechel's press at Paris in 1543. All four editions contain the skeletal plates
shown below in Fig. 35 issued from the same woodcut blocks.

ANATOMIA

CAPITIS HVMANI, IN MAR-
PVRGENSI ACADEMIA
SVPERIORI ANNO,
PVBLICE EX-
HIBITA,
PER
Iohannem Dryandrum medicum.

INEVITABILE VATVM.

Omnia recens nata, Marpurgi ex officina Eucharij Ceruicorni
Agrippinatis, Anno 1 5 3 6 mense Septemb.

FIGURE TWENTY-FIVE

Title-page of Dryander's *Anatomia capitis humani*, 1536, containing eleven
woodcuts of the brain and its envelopes.

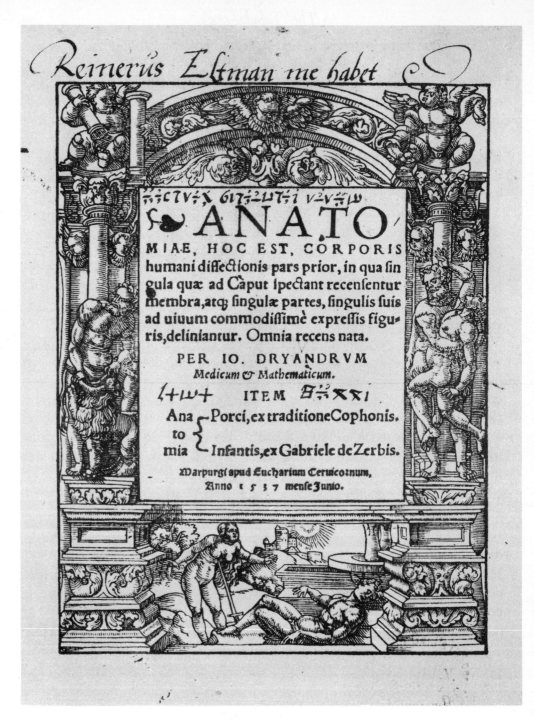

FIGURE TWENTY-SIX

Title-page of Dryander's *Anatomia* published in June 1537, a quarto of 36 leaves with brain plates repeated.

There was nothing to which Vesalius could object in all this. Dryander had obviously forestalled him by illustrating, however inadequately, a treatise on the brain with which he soon was to deal far better himself. Nor could he complain of Dryander's second book, *Anatomiæ, hoc est, corporis humani dissectionis pars prior,* also a small quarto of only 36 leaves, which in June 1537 (Fig. 26) came from the same press with a few additional illustrations of the thorax and viscera, some few (*e.g.,* the excellent antero‑lateral and postero‑lateral views of the skull) being dated 1536 by the engraver. This was only a portion of a general anatomy he vainly hoped some day to complete.

In both of these books Dryander had gone needlessly afield, as Edouard Turner points out, to borrow from Berengarius (1523) in the first and from Magnus Hundt (1500) for the crude plate of the ventricles in the second. But when four years later (1541) in his illustrated Anatomy of Mundinus (Fig. 27) not only were Dryander's own early drawings of the brain pilfered (which Ryff [*cf.* II.9] had pirated and then elaborated upon for his own anatomy in that same year of 1541), but figures were lifted directly from the *Tabulæ sex,* this to Vesalius was quite a different matter. These figures included those of the spleen as well as of the male and female organs of generation, all of which were taken from plate I of the *Tabulæ sex,* while in plates 4 and 6 are shown, atrociously copied, the front and rear views of the skeleton whose raised fingers flippantly twiddle what seems to be a cautery iron (Fig. 28).

In the dedicatory epistle to a friend in Frankfurt, Dryander gives an un‑ friendly dig at Vesalius' insistence on a polished Latin style, but otherwise makes no mention of him:

"If there are today such as think that nothing should be used in schools unless it caresses the reader with picturesque and enticing language, they are welcome, as far as I am concerned, to admire and esteem the elegantly latinized books on dissection of Alexander Benedictus, and the most eloquent commentaries of Johann von Andernach, Andreas a Lacuna, Vesalius, and others; they cannot deny, however, that the present work has its own virtues, nor are we so much possessed by hatred of rough expression that we would repudiate a work for that reason alone, even though it contains matter which has been correctly set forth."

II.—19

DRYANDER, Anatomia Mundini   *Marburg,* 1541

Title: [Device] Anatomia / Mvndini, ad vetvstis‑ / simorvm, ervndemqve [*sic*] ali‑ / quot manu scriptorum, codicum fidem / collata, iustoque suo ordini restituta./Per Ioannem Dryandrum/Medicum professo-/rem Marpur-/ gensem./Adiectæ sunt, quarumcunque partium corpo-/ris, ad uiuum ex-/ pressæ figuræ. Adsunt & scholia non indocta, quæ prolixorum com-/ mentariorum uice esse possunt./[Printer's device]/Marpvrgi, in officina/ Christiani Egenolphi.

Colophon: [Printer's device] M. D. XLI.

Collation: 4°. A-S⁴; [4], 68 *ll.*

Contents: A1a title (Fig. 27); A1b blank; A2a-3b preface to Glauberger dated Marburg Academy, August 1540; A4a index; A4b torso skeleton labelled "Inevitabile fatum"; B1a-S3b (*ll.* 1-67) text; S4 ?blank. The text contains 46 large and small woodcuts of anatomical figures, many of them from

the 1536 *Anatomia capitis,* 16 of the head and brain. It contains six plates from Berengarius and two from Vesalius' *Tabulæ sex.*

Copies: Waller; DSG; IEN-M; MiU (Crummer); NBMS; Cushing; CaMM-Os; Clendening.

Copy used: H.C., lacks S4; measures 18.4 by 14.4 cm.; title damaged. From Weiss & Co., Munich, 1926, RM. 275.

These same Vesalian cuts were again used under the date of *March 1542* in the following volume from the press of Egenolph, now moved to Frankfurt:

II.—20

DRYANDER, Artzenei Spiegel   *Frankfurt, 1542*

Title: Der gantzen Artzenei ge-/meyner Inhalt, Wes einem Artzt, bede in/der Theoric vnd Practic züsteht. Mit anzeyge be-/werter Artzneienn, zü allen leiblichen Gebrechenn,/durch naturliche mittel, Hiebei beneben des men-/ schen cörpers/Anatomei, warhafft Contrafeyt, vnd beschriben. Allen Artz-/ten, vnd eim ieden zu sein selbs, vnnd seins nehsten noturfft dienlich, wol zu/haben vnd zuwissen. Newlich in Truck verordnet durch/D. Ioan. Dryandrum Medicum, Ordinarium/zu Marpurgi./ . . . Cum gratia & priuilegio Imperiali./Zu Franckfurt am Meyn, Bei/Christian Egenolph.

Colophon: Getruck zü Franckfurt am Meyn, bey Christian Egenolff,/Anno M. D. XLII, Mense Martio.

Collation: Sm. fol. *³, A-R⁶, S-T⁴; [3], 110 *ll.*

Contents: *1a title-page (see Fig. 30); *1b blank; *2a foreword; *2b register with woodcut skull dated 1536; *3a-b register continued (table of contents); A1a to the reader; A1b-2b introductory; A3a-4a regimen of pregnancy (*Rosengarten*); A4b-6b muscle figures with text after Berengarius; B1a combined vascular figure (from Estienne plate not published until 1545); B1b explanation of figure; B2a rear view of circulation, also lifted from Estienne, 1545; B3a-6b figures from author's *Anatomia,* 1537; C5a, C6a, C6b figures modified from leaf one of *Tabulæ sex;* D2a-b skeletal figures from *Tabulæ sex;* D3a-

T4a miscellaneous regimen, etc.; colophon at bottom of T4a; T4b Egenolph's device.

Note: The book contains all the plates from the *Anat. Mundini* (cf. II.19) with numerous small woodcuts of landscapes, scenes and a great variety of objects after the clever manner of Egenolph's wood engraver (presumably Hans Brosamer), many of which had already appeared and were subsequently to reappear in other publications from his press. The following errors occur in pagination: 93 for 63, 97 for 67, 8B for 82, 85 for 95, 97 unnumbered.

Copies: Waller; DSG; MH; NNNAM; Cushing.

Copy used: H.C. (imperfect), measuring 26.5 by 18.7 cm.; bought of Ackermann, Munich, 1926, for RM. 30.

Of the two plates in this volume which are entirely new, one is highly inter-esting because it fuses into a single diagram (Fig. 29A) the two vascular plates from the *Tabulæ sex* which, as we have seen, Ryff had previously superimposed on the human figure. In this new schema which is truly Galenic, the arterial and venous systems are quite separate. It is noteworthy that Dryander has clearly shown the azygos to which much attention had been recently (1539) paid in the Venesection Epistle of Vesalius (*cf.* IV.1). This figure has evidently been pilfered from Estienne in whose publications the downward pointing finger indicates the frame in which the legend (Latin or French) is printed (*cf.* Fig. 29B).

This 1542 edition must have been a profitable venture for both Dryander and his printer, who could have had no great difficulty in persuading the author to expand the text and to add further illustrations collected from various sources. The volume published in 1547 under a slightly altered title is to all intents and purposes but an enlarged second edition of *Die gantze Artzenei* which has expanded from 110 to 153 numbered leaves, crowded with an uncountable number of illustrations (200 and more, often repeated) but with only a slight change in the wordy title which now emphasizes *Artzenei Spiegel*:

II.—21

DRYANDER, Artzenei Spiegel   *Frankfurt, 1547*

Title (Fig. 30): Artzenei Spiegel Ge-/meyner Inhalt derselbigen,/Wes bede einem Leib/vnnd Wundtartzt, in der Theoric, Practic, vnnd/Chirurgei züsteht./Hie beuor durch D. Ioan. Dryandrum,/.../Zü Franckfurt am Meyn, Bei/Christian Egenolph.

Colophon: [Printer's device] Getruckt zu Franck-fort am Meyn bei Christian Egenolff/Im Jar M. D. XLvij.

Collation: Fol. *⁴, A-Z⁶, a-b⁶, c³; [4], 153 *ll.*

Contents: *1a title; *1b blank; *2a-b foreword; *3a-4b register; A1a-M4b First part (*Theoretica*); M5a-X6b Another part (*Practica*); X6b-c3a Third part (*Chirurgia*); c3b colophon. The figures from the *Tabulæ sex* occur on sigs. D3-6.

Note: These editions can be distinguished from one another by the tooth-pulling woodcut. In the 1542 edition, it occurs on *l.* 85a; in the 1547, on 101a; in 1557, still on 101a, a new cut of a mandible has been substituted with various extraction accessories. Errors in numbering leaves are: 102 for 112, 126 for 128, 141 for 140.

Copies: DSG; MiU (Crummer); NNNAM; PPCP; Cushing.

Copy used: H.C., measuring 29.5 by 20 cm. Bound with Phryesen's *Spiegel der Artzney*, Strassburg, 1546. No provenance.

II.—22

DRYANDER, Artzenei Spiegel　　　　　　　　　*Frankfurt, 1557*

Title (Fig. 30): Artzenei Spiegel Ge-/meyner Innhalt derselbigen, Wes beide, einem/Leib vnd Wundartzet, in der Theoric, Practic, vnnd Chi-/rurgei zusteht. Hieuor durch D. Ioan. Dryandrvm,/.../[woodcut device] Cum/Gratia & Priuilegio Imperiali./Zu Franckfort am Meyn, bei Christian Egenolffs Erben.

Colophon: Getruckt zu Franckfort am Meyn bei Christian/Egenolffs erben Im Jar M.D.LVII.

Collation: as in II.21.

Contents: identical with II.21.

Note: This is a page-by-page reprint of II.21 with type entirely reset. Even the errors in pagination persist, with one more added (106 for 109).

Copies: DSG; MBM; Cushing.

Copy used: H.C., bought from Taeuber and Weil, Munich, in 1929, for RM. 675. Bound in old vellum; measures 29.5 by 19.5 cm. Contains the woodcut *Ex libris* of the Nürnberg patrician family of Palmer. A second copy, imperfect (lacking title-page and leaf 29) and much cut down (27 by 17.7 cm.) had been bought in 1910 from J. Halle for RM. 30.

(5) *The pirates of Paris.* It would have made this story simpler could we have left Dryander completely out of the picture, for he never escaped from the clutches of Egenolph, now at Frankfurt, and we may safely leave him there. When compared with the treatment he had received at the hands of the unconscionable Ryff, Vesalius had no grounds for bitterness toward him; and it was Ryff who had turned to his own use Dryander's brain plates. To be sure, Dryander himself was no tyro at this illegal form of sport in which Ryff and his friend Beck, now become a doctor of medicine, held the inter-city championship for Brussels, Marburg and Frankfurt.

From what has gone before, it will already have become apparent that Ryff by 1541, or possibly Beck, had made contact with the printer Chrestien Wechel at Paris, who presumably loaned him the three wood-blocks, cut by someone unknown, roughly to imitate Calcar's rendering of the three skeletal figures in the *Tabulæ sex.* Not only were these blocks used for Ryff's Ten Tables in 1541 (II.10 and 11) but they appeared again in 1543 and 1545, showing no sign of over-use in Ryff's *Anatomica* (*cf.* II.15-18), published in Paris by Wechel himself. Who could have been this baffling person at Paris who successfully copied the three first plates (presumably meaning the skeletal figures which may very well have been cut first) but omitted the others because they were more difficult to engrave? There would seem to be three possibilities, *viz.,* Charles Estienne, Jean Tagault and Loys Vassé. For and against each of them there is something to say.

ANATOMIA
MVNDINI, AD VETVSTIS.
SIMORVM, ERVNDEMQVE ALI.
quot manu scriptorum, codicum sidem
collata, iustoq; suo ordini restituta.
Per Ioannem Dryandrum
Medicum professo.
rem Marpur.
gensem.

Adiectæ sunt, quarumcunq; partium corporis, ad uiuum expressæ figuræ.

Adsunt & scholia non indocta, quæ prolixorum commentariorum uice esse possunt.

MARPVRGI, IN OFFICINA
Christiani Egenolphi.

FIGURE TWENTY-SEVEN

Title-page of Dryander's illustrated anatomy of Mondino in which he used his own brain woodcuts, as
well as visceral cuts from the *Tabulæ sex*.

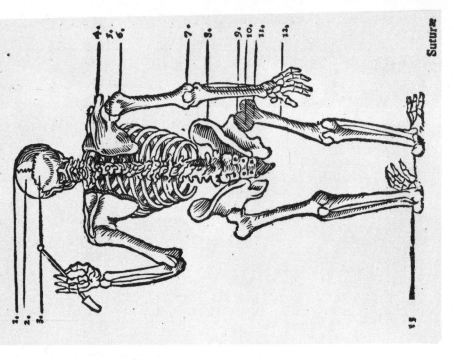

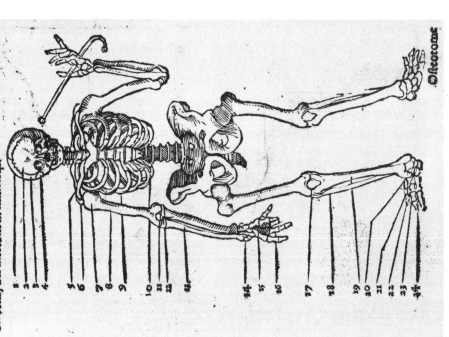

FIGURE TWENTY-EIGHT

The skeletal figures from Dryander's Mondino, 1541, copied from plates IV and VI of the *Tabulæ sex*.

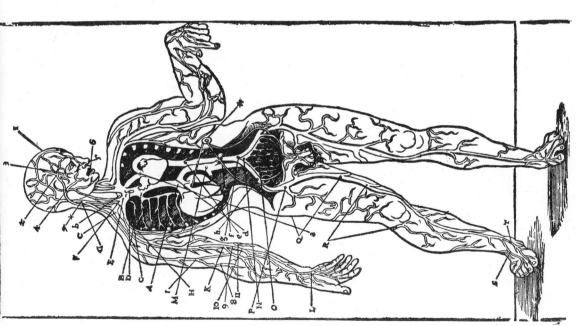

FIGURE TWENTY-NINE

A, Dryander's (1542) fused diagram of the two vascular plates of the *Tabulæ sex*; B, Estienne's (1546) diagram of the vascular system from *La dissection des parties du corps humain*.

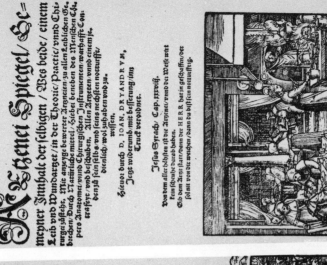

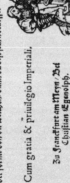

FIGURE THIRTY

Title-pages of the three editions of Dryander's *Artzenei Spiegel*: left, 1542; middle, 1547; right, 1557.

(i) *Was Charles Estienne the Paris offender?* In one of his letters Vesalius spoke slightingly of those Parisian anatomists and printers who in one combination or another bore the name Stephanus; and one need not be surprised, for there was not only this Charles Estienne (Stephanus) but his friend Estienne (Stephanus) Rivière, who was surgeon, artist and engraver all in one. *Charles Estienne* (Carolus Stephanus) was a member of the famous family of Paris printers which for three generations had rivaled the Venetian house of Aldus. After serving as foreman of the press for some time, he relinquished his interests in favour of his brother Robert, turned to medicine and received his M.D. from Paris in 1542, five years after Vesalius got his bonnet at Padua.* In collabora- tion with his talented friend and co-worker, Rivière, he had evidently been engaged for several years in a project to issue in three books an illustrated anatomy; indeed, some of the woodcuts bear dates ranging from 1530 to 1533, the initials S.R. appearing on what may have been among the first to be engraved. The other plates are either unsigned or bear the monogram of François Jollat, a celebrated contemporary Parisian engraver. Some of the engravings suggest the handiwork of Geofroy Tory who designed his printer's device for Colines. In consideration of the time in which they were made, it is natural that the anatomy, at least of the earlier plates, should be largely pre-Vesalian and the woodcuts, after a French Renaissance fashion, are more decorative than prac- tical from the standpoint of illustrative anatomy, due to the small size of the anatomical inserts.

* Although the *Paraphrasis* was a dissertation published at Louvain, there is no certain evidence that Vesalius actually received a Louvain degree. Dr. Max H. Fisch of the Army Medical Library who has recently looked into the question writes: "A Louvain degree might be inferred from the fact that the Louvain edition of the *Paraphrasis* bears the phrase 'medicinæ candidato' and that this is omitted in the Basel edition; but this need not mean that he was a candidate for a degree at Louvain; and even if it did, it would not be conclusive evidence that he got it. The *Paraphrasis* was probably well along and perhaps finished at Paris, and may have been intended as his thesis for the doctorate there; but after the interruption of his studies at Paris, I think he would scarcely have been interested in a degree at Louvain, and was probably already set on Padua at the time he prepared the *Paraphrasis* for publication. Roth says nothing about a Louvain degree, and Wauters [422, p. 22] says: 'Mais ce ne fut pas dans sa patrie qu'il conquit le grade de docteur, quoique Molanus le cite parmi les maîtres sortis de l'Université de Louvain. Les pièces produites par le docteur Roth (pp. 425-428) lèvent tout doute à cet égard. Ce fut à Padoue . . .' The best authority (apart from Vesalius' own writings) on the relations of Vesalius (and also of his ancestors) with Louvain is Jan vander Moelen (Johannes Molanus, 1533-1585): *Historiæ Lovaniensium libri XIV,* written about 1582 but first printed by P.F.X. de Ram in 1861 (in the *Collection de Chroniques belges*) in two large quarto volumes, pp. xcix, 1371. It was not used by Roth, but is frequently cited and referred to (as above) by Wauters. Vander Moelen was professor and rector of the University of Louvain, and used its archives. In his brief account of Andreas Vesalius on pp. 572-573 of volume 1, he says nothing of a Louvain degree or *licentiatus,* though he places Vesalius first under the head, 'Scriptores aliquot medici studii Lovaniensis;' but de Ram's index commits this howler: 'Vésale (André), docteur en médecine, 1564, 573.'"

The date (1545) of Estienne and Rivière's first edition (Fig. 31) would seemingly preclude the possibility that Vesalius had either the author or his printer Wechel in mind, were it not that Estienne in his preface states that some of his woodcuts had already been plagiarized. Parts of this preface, addressed to his students of anatomy, are of sufficient interest to render in English:

"He who describes the history of the parts of the human body renders a service not at all inferior to that of a person who publicly records the vestiges of past events . . . It is incumbent upon us, having undertaken this task of composing . . . a history of the human body in three books to make it so that we should aim principally at brevity in describing things which we have observed . . .

"We have described the single parts of the body as they lay before (our) eyes. But it is not verbal description alone, but rather visual representation of (even) the minutest things which promotes such knowledge as will be of use to you in the future. In bringing this about, we have been aided principally by Rivière the surgeon, whose labour was most assiduously and frequently contributed both in drawing what was necessary, such as bones, ligaments, nerves, arteries, veins, muscles, etc., and in picturing the methods of dissection, in which subject he has had much experience. You will see these dissections, described by us in the lettering engraved within the pictures, throughout the book.

"Some of all this was ready in the year 1539, and was already in print up to the middle of the third book, when because of a controversy brewing, it became necessary to suppress the whole work . . . *But the typographers could not, long enough, diligently guard the portion of the work already in type . . . and some of it was secretly carried away . . . to Germany, where copies of it, more especially of the pictures of nerves, veins, and arteries, were later procured there by our Paris friends who apprised us of the theft thus committed, to which however we paid no attention.*

"It is our business to write for anyone's benefit about particular matters pertaining to general knowledge, whether desired by our (friends) or by other persons; what becomes of it afterwards, the students (themselves) shall see. For insofar as it concerns original authorship and arrangement of this work, or even what some of you may object to as heaviness of style in description, we have little to fear from the thieving of those people . . . We were satisfied if in our mediocrity we succeeded in showing the form, position, connection and function of the (various) parts (of the body).

"Even if this work should not entirely please you (since it cannot satisfy every-

De dissectione partium corporis

humani libri tres, à Carolo Stephano, doctore Me=
dico, editi. Vnà cum figuris, & incisionum decla=
rationibus, à Stephano Riuerio Chirurgo cōpositis.

Cum priuilegio.

PARISIIS.
Apud Simonem Colinæum.
1545.

La dissection des parties du corps

humain diuisee en trois liures, faictz par Charles Estienne
docteur en Medecine: auec les figures & declaratiō des in=
cisions, composees par Estienne de la Riuiere Chirurgien.

Imprime a Paris, chez Simon de Colines.
1546.
Auec priuilege du Roy.

FIGURE THIRTY-ONE

Title-pages of the Latin and French editions of Charles Estienne's
De dissectione of 1545 and 1546 respectively.

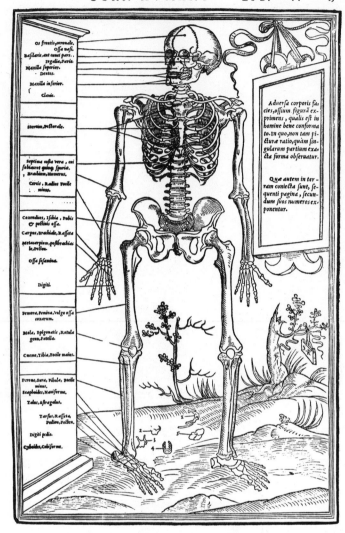

FIGURE THIRTY-TWO

Rivière's skeletal figure in Estienne's *De dissectione* (1545). Note that it is signed "S.R."

LES
FIGVRES ET POR-
TRAICTS DES PARTIES DV
corps humain.

A PARIS,
Par Iaques Keruer, rue S. Iaques, au deux cochetz.
1557.

LES
FIGVRES ET POR-
TRAICTS DES PARTIES DV
corps humain.

A PARIS.
Par Iaques Keruer, rue S. Iaques, à la Licorne.
1575.

FIGURE THIRTY-THREE
Title-pages of the two Kerver editions (1557 and 1575) of the Estienne plates.

FIGURE THIRTY-FOUR

Two of the figures in the Kerver collection which had not been used in the Estienne *De dissectione*.

one in an equal measure), perchance there shall be found something among so many trifles which may further a little your studies; you will then compare it with the other authors who wrote diligently on this subject, in the meantime lending the pictures a new soul by dissecting a human cadaver, or one of another species . . ."

Thus, as can be learned from the lines I have taken the liberty of italicizing, sometime after 1539 the materials so far prepared by Estienne and his collaborator Rivière got into the hands of those pirateprinters Balthasar Beck and Egenolph; and as one of the woodcuts which Egenolph first used in 1542 for Dryander's *Artzenei Spiegel* had obviously been built up for Estienne sometime after 1538 by combining the venous and arterial plates of the *Tabulæ sex* (*cf.* Fig. 29), it may in all likelihood, along with prints of Rivière's first crude renderings of the 1538 Calcar skeletons, have come to the attention of Vesalius before September of 1542.

Two editions of Estienne and Rivière's combined treatise on dissection of the human body finally appeared, the first in 1545 in Latin—the second in 1546 in French, almost the last volume to bear the imprint of Simon de Colines (Fig. 31). How he got into the picture is easily told, for he was the third printerhusband of Guyone, widow of Henri, the founder of the Estienne Press, whose management Colines had taken over, and it was perhaps natural that he should have offered to print his stepson's book whose publication, according to Renouard (326), had been delayed by the privilege granted to Vesalius. That Charles Estienne did not entrust the task to his brother Robert, who had done much fine printing, was probably due to the fact that he had drifted into printing less pretentious books.

II.—23

ESTIENNE, De dissectione.   Latin   *Paris*, 1545

Title (Fig. 31A): De dissectione partium corporis / humani libri tres, à Carolo Stephano, doctore Me / dico, editi. Vnà cum figuris, & incisionum decla / rationibus, à Stephano Riuerio Chirurgo cōpositis. / [Simon de Colines device] / Cum priuilegio. / Parisiis. / Apud Simonem Colinæum. / 1545.

Collation: Fol. *,**⁶, A-Z⁸, AA⁶; [12] *ll.,* 379 pp., wrongly numbered 375.

Contents: *1a title; *1b blank; *2 preface; *3a**6a alphabetical subject index and errata; **6b blank; A1aL1b (pp. 1158) Book I; L2aR2b (pp. 159256) Book II; R3aAA6a (pp. 257375) Book III;

AA6b blank; 62 fullpage woodcuts, one signed S.R., 5 with Lorraine cross of Geofroy Tory; 6 signed by Jollat in various ways;* legends in frames on 47 of the 62 plates.

Note: Watermark small gothic P; 45 lines to page, every five numbered; handsome initial letters of two sizes, manner of Geofroy Tory. The plate chiefly discussed appears on page 134. Cæsarean section is described on p. 261. The pagination is erratic: p. 39 for 37, 97-98 omitted, 102-103 repeated, etc.

Copies: Waller; DSG; DLC; CaMM-Os; MH-M, PPCP, NNNAM, CSt-L, NBMS; NNC-M; MdBJ-M; MiU (Crummer, Pilcher); J. C. Trent; Cushing; Clendening; MBM.

Copy used: H.C. Bought at the Van den Corput sale, item 41, for Fl. 28. Formerly in library of Dr. A. M. Ledeboer. Measures 38.3 by 24 cm.

* For a discussion of these engravers, see G. B. Ives' translation of August Bernard's *Geofroy Tory, painter and engraver,* Riverside Press, 1909 [pp. 223-226].

II.—24

ESTIENNE, De dissectione.   French   *Paris,* 1546

Title (Fig. 31B): La dissection des parties du corps/humain diuisee en trois liures, faictz par Charles Estienne/docteur en Medecine: auec les figures & declaratiō des in-/cisions, composees par Estienne de la Riuiere Chir-urgien./[Printer's device]/Imprime a Paris, chez Simon de Colines./ 1546./Auec priuilege du Roy.

Collation: a⁸, A-Z⁸, AA-BB⁸, CC⁴; [8] *ll.,* 405 pp. + 1 blank; 45 lines to page, every 5 lines numbered. Watermark same as in II.23.

Contents: a1a title; a1b blank; a2 to reader; a3a-8b subject index; A1a-L3a First book; L3b-S3b Second book; S4a-CC3a Third book; CC3b errata; CC4 blank.

Copies: DSG; MH; NNNAM; ICU; NNC-M; MBM; NN; CU-M; Fulton. A copy from the library of Diane de Poitiers, elaborately bound for her with her customary symbols, was sold (item 324) at the Samuel P. Avery Sale, Nov. 10, 1919, for $2250.

Copy used: H.C., measuring 36.5 by 24 cm.; bought from Menno Hertzberger, Amsterdam, for fl. 200, in 1924.

It is difficult precisely to enumerate the number of full-page engravings in these two Colines impressions (Fig. 32). They have been variously counted from 60 to 65 due to the fact that two are repeated once and two others twice. My own estimate is that there are 56 different full-page plates in the 1545 and 58 in the 1546 edition, which is of bibliographical interest only in connection with the Kerver-Jollat collections to follow. Both of Colines' editions, as a matter of fact, were over-illustrated through inclusion of pairs of plates of earlier and later periods. For example, toward the end of *Livre I* in the 1546 French edition (pp. 151-153), there occur three écorché figures, front, right side, and back without letters or pointers, the two latter having been engraved in 1532 and signed by Jollat. At the beginning of *Livre II* are two other very similar figures dated 1530 and 1531, also by Jollat, to show the surface anatomy, these figures having letters and pointers.

Since the influence of the *Fabrica* is clearly apparent in many of the small insets, they must have been engraved after 1543 and as Vesalius' privilege did not expire until 1545-46, Estienne's further delay in publication of his illustrated anatomy, so long prepared for, may thus be accounted for.*

Jacques Kerver's reprints of Estienne's plates. How or when Jacques Kerver, a printer of less consequence than his better known father Thielman, came into the possession of the Estienne-Rivière wood-blocks is not apparent. He had been printing inconspicuously in Paris for some time and may have overlapped the later years of Simon de Colines, who ceased work soon after the publication of the Estienne volumes. So far as is known, they had had no business connection and it may be assumed that Kerver bought the blocks from Colines' successors, either directly or indirectly through some intermediary.

It is stated by Renouard (326) that Kerver published two editions of the collected prints (1537 and 1575), but there is every reason to believe that a 1537 edition is a myth and was a misprint for 1557. Copies of both a 1557 and a 1575 edition are known (Fig. 33), and from these volumes it is possible to learn what plates were discarded by Estienne (Fig. 34) and what ones were selected to illustrate the text of Colines' two editions.

Two new and highly creditable but different renderings of both front (Fig. 32) and back views of the skeleton are found in each of the Colines editions; crude representations of a lateral view, both right and left, are obviously influenced by Calcar. These latter plates were omitted from the Latin edition of 1545 but were used in the French edition a year later. Though the skeletal front view of one pair used in both editions has a placard bearing the initials S.R. (Stephanus Riverius?), it is not dated (Fig. 32) nor are any of the others. The right lateral view of the skeleton both in Kerver's set and of course in the 1546 French edition has been signed by Jollat with a date that appears to be 1532, *i.e.,* six years before the six Vesalian tables were printed. Hence, if the date is dependable, the drawing could scarcely be a Vesalian plagiary. Indeed, a good case might be made in the reverse direction, *viz.,* that they had actually influenced Calcar. A collection of anatomical pictures as distinct from the text they were intended to illustrate has always had its appeal to the lay public, and Kerver,

* Conversely it may be argued that this inset-sequence dates before 1539. By autumn of that year Estienne's *De dissectione* was three-quarters printed. No alteration of the illustrations could have been effected while the injunction brought by Rivière against Estienne was in force. It became necessary to suppress the whole work, while the co-authors carried their differences through all the lower courts, up to Parliament. It seems little likely that, after bitterly contending for six years, these two weary and impoverished litigants should come to a last-minute agreement to reprint, at very great cost, the entire series of 'inset' quaternions, involving the closest kind of collaboration once again, and the loss of any possible profit. Vesalius and Estienne were fellow-students in anatomy under Sylvius in Paris in the year 1535, and it was in that year also that Estienne conceived the idea of his manual (Guinterius, *Inst. Anat.,* Paris, 1536). The delay in publication is better explained as due to the protracted legal proceedings (1539-1545)—E.C.S.

once Estienne's wood-blocks were in his hands, must have looked upon their re-issuance as a good business venture. This was fortunate from our present standpoint as he included among the prints those discarded as well as those that Estienne had chosen for reproduction by Colines. Since the gatherings are rare and have never been accurately described, it is possible that all issues under each date (1557 and 1575) may not have contained the same number of plates and that the gatherings for the two years may have differed slightly as they do in the writer's copies. In my 1557 gathering are 61 full-page plates; in the 1575 gathering there are 59 full-page plates and two pages with eight smaller figures showing the dissection of spinal cord and eye. Framed legends often differ from those used in the Colines Latin and French issues. Kerver makes no reference anywhere to Estienne or Rivière, or to the source of the plates.

II.—25

KERVER, Estienne woodcuts   *Paris,* 1557

Title (Fig. 33): Les / figvres et por- / traicts des parties dv / corps humain. / [Printer's device] / A Paris / Par Iaques Keruer, rue S. Iaques, au deux cochetz. / 1557.

Collation: Fol. [*]¹, A⁷, B-D⁶, E⁷; 33 unnumbered *ll.* Legends in French, marginal or mostly in frames on plates.

Contents: [N.B. Page numbers in square brackets refer to L. 1545 edition, F. 1546 edition.]

[*]1a title; [*]1b blank

A1a to the reader

A1b Zodiac plate with cross of Lorraine, dated [Jollat(?)] 1533; [not used L. or F.]

A2a front view skeleton (Type I), no lettering, "S.R. plate" [L.13; F.10]

A2b left lat. view of skeleton, with Jollat's sign [not used L.; F.11]

A3a rear view skeleton, no lettering [L.15; F.12]

A3b right lat. view skeleton, signed Jollat 1532 [not used L.; F.15]

A4a peripheral nerves ant. view [L.59; F.54]

A4b peripheral nerves, post. view with legend in frame [L.63; F.59]

A5a front view skeleton (Type 2) with lettering [L.43, 102, 308 with different framed legends; F.37, 96, 336, ditto]

A5b écorché front view with lettering [L.103, 309; F.97, 337]

A6a planet plate front view, with cross of Lorraine and Jollat's sign, dated 1533 [not in L. or F.] (See Fig. 34)

A6b planet plate rear view, with cross of Lorraine and Jollat's sign, dated 1533 [not in L. or F.]

A7a rear view skeleton (Type 2) with lettering [L.44, 115, 324; F.38, 113, 352]

A7b écorché, rear view, with lettering [L.116, 325; F.114 (for 113), 353]

B1a combined vascular plate with lettering [L.134; F.135]

B1b rear view superficial veins [L.135; F.136]

B2a écorché front view without lettering [L.149; F.151]

B2b écorché side view (signed Jollat 1532), no lettering [L.150; F.152]

B3a écorché back view (Jollat 1532), no lettering [L.151; F.153]

B3b écorché (Type 2) front view (Jollat 1530) [L.154; F.160]

B4a écorché (Type 2) back view (Jollat 1531) [L.155; F.161]

B4b écorché (Type 2) semi-lateral [L.161; F.168]

B5a panniculus abdom. [L.163; F.171]

B5b abdominal muscles [L.165; F.174]

B6a deep abdominal muscles [L.166; F.175]

B6b diaphragm; peritoneum [L.168; F.177]

C1a omentum *in situ* [L.170; F.179]

C1b intestines *in situ* showing appendix [L.172; F.181]

C2a stomach and duodenum *in situ* [L.175; F.185]
C2b liver and portal circulation [L.180; F.191]
C3a vena cava, kidneys, etc. [L.189; F.202]
C3b vena cava, etc. (Type 2) [L.190; F.203]
C4a hemorrhoidal veins; rectum (Jollat) [L.196; F.210]
C4b subcut. thoracic; breast [L.202; F.216]
C5a thoracic; pectoral muscles; ribs [L.205; F.219]
C5b thorax; removal sternum [L.208; F.223]
C6a thoracic organs *in situ* [L.210; F.225]
C6b heart; sup. cava; aorta [L.213; F.228]
D1a cardiac ventricles [L.218; F.235]
D1b aorta; recurrent laryngeal nerve [L.221; F.238]
D2a œsophagus, aorta, phrenic nerve [L.224; F.241]
D2b neck; hyoid; tongue [L.228; F.246]
D3a mouth, tongue, larynx [L.229; F.247]
D3b tongue, tonsils, palate [L.230; F.248]
D4a muscles of scalp; pericranium (Jollat) [L.236; F.255]

D4b removal skull cap; dura [L.237; F.256]
D5a cerebral convolutions; falx [L.239; F.258]
D5b ventric. cavities; cerebellum [L.241; F.261]
D6a fornix; pineal gland; iter [L.242; F.262]
D6b optic chiasm, cranial nerves, etc. [L.246; F.266]
E1a removal basilar dura; spinal cord [L.250; F.271]
E1b cranial fossæ from above [L.253; F.275]
E2a-6b Ten plates in the gravid-uterus series follow and are used in both Latin and French editions though in somewhat different order.
E7a printer's device; E7b blank.

Watermarks: Crown and shield, bearing initials NB.

Copy used: H.C., bought through A. C. Klebs from E. P. Goldschmidt, London, January 1927, for £60. Measures 32.8 by 23 cm.

II.—26

KERVER, Estienne woodcuts   *Paris,* 1575

Title (Fig. 33): Les / figvres et por- / traicts des parties dv / corps humain. / [Printer's device] / A Paris. / Par Iaques Keruer, rue S. Iaques, à la Li- corne. / [rule] / 1575.

Collation: Fol. A⁸, B-D⁶, E⁸; [34] *ll.*

Contents: A1a title-page; A1b blank; A2a to the reader; A2b Zodiac plate. From A2b to E6b same series of plates in same order as in II.25 except that the planetary leaf comes earlier. E7 with eight small figures and legends of nervous system and eye, not in

II.25; E8a printer's device; E8b blank. No water- marks (Fig. 34).

Copies: London (BM); Cushing.

Copy used: H.C., bought through Dr. Klebs from E. P. Goldschmidt, May 1924, for £60. Measures 30 by 23 cm.

This matter of the various Stephani of Paris may have been unduly drawn out. Even so, much has been omitted that is highly interesting from an engraver's standpoint, such as the peculiar manner in which small wood-blocks carrying the anatomical details have been used as insets in the larger blocks.

(ii) *Was Chrestien Wechel the Paris offender?* Wechel may be introduced as having been a successful Huguenot printer in Paris for some twenty years before his death in 1554. The greater part of Henri Estienne's types supposedly had come into the possession of Wechel and his printer-son André, who after the St. Bartholomew massacre seems to have found Frankfurt a more healthy place for the exercise of his Protestant beliefs.

It will be recalled (*cf.* page 23) that in 1541 Balthasar Beck had printed for Ryff, the Strassburg plagiarist, ten folio leaves carrying side by side in pairs twice that number of anatomical figures, three of them having been ugly copies of Calcar's skeletal plates (*cf.* Fig. 10). There was nothing particularly unusual in this act for ten other figures had been pilfered from Dryander and re-engraved. However, in 1543 Wechel had printed (*cf.* II.16) the same set of plates for Ryff's *Anatomica* with descriptive text in French. What is more, in that same year (1543) Wechel also printed for Jean Tagault a surgical treatise patterned after Guy de Chauliac in which the identical wood-blocks of the Calcar skeletons used by Beck in 1541 were again utilized (Fig. 35) though on this occasion by themselves. To this treatise which, curiously enough, is not cited either by Choulant or by Garrison, we may now turn. The author, as dean of the Paris Faculty from 1534 to 1537, must have been known to Vesalius, but so far as observed he nowhere makes mention of him.

Wechel's first edition of Tagault's book, a handsomely printed folio, was so favourably received it was frequently reprinted. All copies that I have seen have the three skeletal plates in the same position before Liber VI, accompanied by the text and distich from the *Tabulæ sex* of 1538 (Fig. 35). The woodcuts, however, had been reduced from a height of 21 centimetres to just half that size and in the process were so vastly improved they came into popular use for over a century. They are found, for example, in Gesner's *Chirurgia* (Zurich, 1555); in Pierre Franco's *Traité des Hernies* (Lyon, 1561); in della Croce's *Cirugia* (Venice, 1583); and they were re-engraved with the addition of a third figure for Borgarutius who used them in 1568 and 1569 in his apocryphal Vesalian surgery—the *Chirurgia magna* (see appendix to Chapter X, p. 217).*

Since the privilege of the 1543 edition of Tagault is dated July 1542, Vesalius could scarcely have seen the book before his letter to Oporinus was written. This, however, does not preclude the possibility that Wechel had previously printed and circularized the three plates copied from the *Tabulæ sex* which appear to have been added to the volume as an afterthought when Jacob Holler's contribution to the volume of a sixth book was about to be printed. Indeed, the embarrassing question is raised whether these three wood-blocks originated in Strassburg and were loaned to Wechel or were engraved in Paris and loaned to Balthasar Beck.

* Attention may be drawn to the fact that the skeleton's right hand is raised in all three figures of the *Tabulæ sex*. In Ryff's plagiary of 1541 the figures were reversed with the left hand raised, the same cuts having been used by Tagault in 1543. In the half-size reproductions used after 1544 the position shifts from right to left several times as the blocks were re-engraved, ending with Borgarutius in 1568 with the left hand raised. In the last printed edition of 1645 the blocks were again re-engraved with the left hand raised.

II.—27

TAGAULT, De chirurgica institutione   *Paris,* 1543

Title (Fig. 36): Ioannis Tagavl⁄/tii Ambiani Vimaci, Parisien⁄/sis medici, de chirvrgica / institutione libri quinque. / His accessit sextus liber de materia chirurgica, authore / Iacobo Hollerio Stempano, medico Parisiensi. / [Print⁄er's device] / Parisiis. / Apud Christianum wechelum, sub scuto Basiliensi, / in vico Iacobæo: & sub Pegaso, in vico / Bellouacensi. M.D.XLIII. / Cum Priuilegio.

Collation: Fol. in Italic. Aβγδ⁶, a⁄z⁶, A⁄F⁶, G1⁄3 [G4⁄5 inserted], G4⁄6, H⁄L⁶, M⁸; [24] *ll.,* 421 pp., 1 blank *l.*

Contents: A1*a* title; A1*b* privilege dated July 12, 1542; A2⁄4 to reader; A5*a*⁄6*b* preface; β1*a*⁄γ3*a* index; γ3*b*⁄δ2*b* compendium; δ3*a* blank; δ3*b* cata⁄logue of the books; δ4*a*⁄6*b* divisions of Book I; pp. 1⁄120 Book I; pp. 121⁄251 Book II, with 2 pp. [143⁄144] wound⁄man and battle⁄field scene from Gersdorff (1517) and 4 pp. [153⁄156] instruments from Gersdorff; pp. 253⁄317 Book III; pp. 318⁄341 Book IV with illustration of Galen's Glossocomium on p. 342; pp. 343⁄353 Book V. Between p. 354 which is blank and p. 355, two leaves containing the three Ryff skeletal plates printed on paper differ⁄ent from the rest of the book are inserted. (They carry the redundant page numbers 354 and 355 [sigs. G4⁄5]; back of last inserted leaf blank.) pp. 355⁄421

Book VI; M7*b* blank; M8*a* errata; M8*b* printer's device.

Note: Watermarks of two sorts (Fig. 37): (1) open palm of hand with wrist in cuff; and (2) small shield with initials P.M. The paper of the two sheets bear⁄ing the figures from the *Tabulæ sex* is evidently from the same paper maker but of another time since the open palm filigrane is quite different in pattern. Errors in numbering pages are: 46 for 47, 64 for 76, 69 for 81, 132 for 131, 955 for 159, 327 for 325, 358 for 356, 399 for 400.

Copies: DSG, NNNAM; ICJ; IEN⁄M; MiU (Crummer); Cushing; Trent.

Copy used: H.C., measuring 27.5 by 19.5 cm., in contemporary leather binding repaired. Purchased from R. Lier, 1926, Cat. VIII, Part IV, No. 394, for Swiss frs. 70. From Bibliotheca Dr. J. Flandrin of Grenoble.

There is no reference to the added leaves in the text and what is perhaps even more telling, they are printed as stated on paper whose "open palm" watermark differs from those in the rest of the book, and the chain⁄lines are closer. If these two leaves, therefore, had been struck off and distributed prior to July 1542* and thus have become known to Vesalius, the question would be answered. Interestingly enough, Tagault's book was dedicated to Francis I, the born rival of the Emperor Charles V to whom the *Fabrica* was dedicated that very same year. That would have been provocation enough even had the Calcar skeletons with the Vesalian lettering not been so abominably copied and in places mis⁄represented, more particularly in the omission of the first rib and in the Dry⁄ander⁄like sternum.

Tagault's *De chirurgica institutione* was a book of great popularity, having not less than 22 separate editions between 1543 and 1645. It would serve no

---

* Possibly along with the fused blood⁄vessel plate which first appeared in Dryander's 1542 issue.

useful purpose to describe the editions in detail; they may be listed briefly as follows (editions marked with an asterisk have not yet been located):

II.28   V. Valgrisii, *Venice*, 8°, 1544.
  Copies: Cushing; DSG; NNC-M; MdBJ-W.

II.29   G. Roville, *Lyon*, 8°, 1547.
  Copies: Cushing.

II.30   V. Valgrisii, *Venice*, 8°, 1549.
  Copies: Cushing: van Wagenen; DSG; CaTAM; MiU (Pilcher).

II.31   G. Roville, *Lyon*, 8°, 1549.
  Copies: Cushing; NjP; CaMM-Os; DSG; NNC-M; MiU (Crummer).

II.32   Italian. *Venice*, 1550.
  Copies: MiU (Crummer); PPCP.

II.33   A. & J. Gessner, *Zurich*, fol., 1555 [*in:* Gesner, *Chirurgia*].
  Copies: Cushing; CaMM-Os; PPCP; DSG; NNNAM; NNC-M; IEN-M.

*II.34   Dutch. *Antwerp*, 1557.

II.35   Dutch. [A. Birckman], *Antwerp*, fol., [1559].
  Copies: DSG.

II.36   G. Roville, *Lyon*, 8°, 1560.
  Copies: DSG.

II.37   G. Roville, *Lyon*, 8°, 1567.
  Copies: Cushing; DSG; NBMS; MiU (Crummer).

II.38   Italian. G. Angelieri, *Venice* 8°, 1570.
  Copies: Cushing; PPCP.

II.39   German. G. Raban & S. Feyrabend, *Frankfurt*, fol., 1574.
  Copies: MiU (Crummer).

II.40   French. B. Honorat, *Lyon*, 8°, 1580.
  Copies: DSG; NNNAM.

II.41   French. E. Michel, *Lyon*, 8°, 1580.
  Copies: Cushing.

II.42   Italian. L. Spineda, *Venice*, 8°, 1607.
  Copies: DSG.

II.43   N. Hoffmann, *Frankfurt*, fol., 1610 [*in:* Uffenbach, *Thesaurus chirurgiæ*].
  Copies: DSG; PPCP; CStL; ICJ; MiU (Pilcher); NBMS.

*II.44   French. *Paris*, 1618.

*II.45   Dutch. *Dordrecht*, 1621.

II.46   French. A. de Sommaville, *Paris*, 8°, 1629.
  Copies: DSG.

*II.47   French. *Paris*, 1645.

II.48   French. D. Loudet, *Rouen*, 8°, 1645.
  Copies: Cushing; NNNAM; MBM.

(iii) *Was Loys Vassé* (Lodoicus Vassæus Catalaunensis) *the Paris offender?* He must not be confused with others of similar name, for there were seven of them all told, as was first pointed out (1882) in one of Edouard Turner's illuminating essays (403)—all of them contemporary physicians and all more or less distinguished. Even Turner had never seen a copy of the 1540 *Tabulæ quatuor* of this particular Loys Vassé (or Vasse) of Châlons-sur-Marne; and there was nothing about it to have caused Vesalius to take umbrage had a copy fallen into his hands. They must have been acquainted in Paris when both were pupils of the great Sylvius but their ways inevitably parted for Loys Vassé was as conservative a Galenist as his master, and equally opposed to those whose interpretations were more liberal and who chose to illustrate their texts with woodcuts.

Doubtless under the influence of Sylvius, whom he praises in his dedication, Vassé eschewed such devices as quite unnecessary for anatomical teaching and no illustrations appear in his brief though admittedly popular compendium of

A Os coronale, quod & os frõ
tis appellatur. B Clauicula,
& offa furcule. C ἀκρώμ-
ον, proceffus fuperior omopla
te. D Caput brachij, feu
pars humeri fuperior. E Os
pectoris, quod ςέρνον Greci vo
cant, conftãs offibus 7. excipi-
tibus 7. veras coftas, quæ fugi-
ores funt & perfectæ: inferiores
verò, quæ numero funt quinq;,
nothæ, imperfectæ & mendofæ
dicantur. F Chartilago ofi-
nifterni adherefcens, ab enis
fimilitudine dicta Grecis ξιφο
2xỏ, h.c eft, enfiformis, vulgus
malum punicum feu granatum
appellat. G Brachium, feu
humerus & os adiunorij Guia
doni, ornū offium (femore ex-
cepto) maximum.
H Collum brachij. I Humeri orbita tro-
chleis familis. K Os inferi' & lõgius cubiti,
quod Latinis vlna, & nomine totius cubitus di
citur, C uidoni & vulgo focile maius, Grecis
πῆχυς: minimo occurrit digito, eíq; rectum, ut
fuperius obliquum. L C s fupius cubiti, (latius fumpto nomine) quod Latinis radius, & fo
cile mini' Guidoni, Grecis verò κερκίς vocatur.
occurrit pollici. N κερκίς Greci, Latinè
brachiale, & raíceta Arabicè. Conftat oibus 8.
duris & exiguis, fios cū cū ad pollicem punet,
non numerauerit. O μετακάρπιον, μ ᵽ podi-
brachiale, & pecten, conftat tantū offibus 4.
Galeno, ã fefe diftant i us, palmam inter digitos ad carpum explentibus P Offa digitio-
rum, quæ numero funt 1;. reρετ tria fingulis.
Q Patella & rotula genu, græcè nonnullis μῶ
λμ imola, aliis επιγουνατις, quafi fupra genu, os
chardiagnofum nulli alteri confcrtum.
R Os bafilfæ vulgo, Latinis ta us, ἀςράγαλον,
λος grecis. S Os ςκαφοειδεί, hoc eft,
nauiforme, fua cauitate nu ui fimile, unde nomē
fumpfit, circunambit caput aftragali.
T Offa tarfi, & raíceta 4. carroreíiodent.
V Offa pedinis, feu predij ac plantæ 5. figura
tereti & obloga metacarpio refpõdent.
X Offa digitorum pedis, quæ numero funt
14. In fingulis digitis præter pollicem terna,

G iiii

A Offa ςτέφματος, id eft, fin
cipitis 2. vulgo parietalia appellatur.
B Offa λ,θοειδῆ,id eft, lapi-
dofa vel petrofa, 2.
C Os frontis 1.quod & co-
ronale vocant.
D Os occipitis 1. denfiffi-
mum & firmiffimum.
E ζύγωμα, velos ζυγώδη
.iugale, & Paris vulgo fuperi-
orem maxillã capiti coniungit.
F Os ςφ ωνοειδές, cuneifor-
me, bafilare, aliquando à multiplici forma πολύμορφον, co-
latorij, cauilla.
G Maxilla inferior: hæc in
maximis oris hiationibus inter
dum à fua fede diftorquetur.
H Proceffus duo maxillæ
inferioris.
K δλεφαργοέ, feu cubiti tu-
ber, fuperior vlnæ, pceffus grã-
dior Hipp.ώγκρᾳω nominauit.
L Offa validiffima quæ offi
facro commituntur, Arabicè
gaf herua dicta.
M Os ilium, & ancha, pars
fuperior offis coxæ.
N ἰςχίον, feu os ifchij, quod
recipit finuo fuo caput. Pais coxæ dicta.
O Os pubis et pectinis, pars
& anterior offis coxæ ad pu-
denda.
Q Os manus tibiæ, quod &
tibia nonṅie totius appellatur,
& crus. V lnæ feu cubito refpõ-
det, μεῖζων Grçcis nominatur.
R ρεξόin feu fibula, & os
furæ.os minus tibiæ radio cubiti, quod focile minus appel-
lan, confimile.
S Malleolus externus, ima
pars fibulæ.
T Malleolus internus, pars
infima cruris feu tibiæ.
V Os calcis, feu calcaneus,
Grçci πῆσωο offis pedis maxie
mum,

G v

FIGURE THIRTY-FIVE

The Ryff skeletons used by Beck in Ryff's *Anatomi* (1541), and again by Wechel in Ryff's *Anatomia* (1543, 1545, both French and Latin texts). Wechel used them once again in Tagault's *De chirurgia institutione* (1543) from which the above photographs were taken.

IOANNIS TAGAVL-

TII AMBIANI VIMACI, PARISIEN-
SIS MEDICI, DE CHIRVRGICA
inſtitutione libri quinque.

His acceſſit ſextus liber de materia chirurgica, authore
Iacobo Hollerio Stempano, medico Pariſienſi.

PARISIIS.
Apud Chriſtianum wechelum, ſub ſcuto Baſilienſi,
in vico Iacobæo: & ſub Pegaſo, in vico
Bellouacenſi.   M. D. XLIII.

Cum Priuilegio.

FIGURE THIRTY-SIX
Title-page of Tagault's *De chirurgica institutione*, 1543.

FIGURE THIRTY-SEVEN

Watermarks in paper used for first edition of Tagault's *De chirurgica institutione*, 1543.

FIGURE THIRTY-EIGHT

Title-page of the earliest illustrated edition of Vassé (1553).

Galenic anatomy, which during the next two decades went through at least eleven editions and was translated into both French and Italian. Meanwhile, the ponderous and fully illustrated *Fabrica* and its *Epitome* by Vesalius, printed at Basel only three years later than the compendium by Vassé, were scarcely if at all used in the schools. Not until 1553 did the *Tabulæ quatuor* carry illustrations (Fig. 38), for by this time Vassé had possibly seen the light, and in his dedication there is less said than previously in praise of Sylvius even though there continues to be complete silence regarding Vesalius. Though the *Fabrica* had been in print for ten years, the four pictures that were selected, two of them skeletons, bear only the slightest trace of Vesalian influence (Fig. 39).

It may indeed be significant that the artist, whoever he may have been, sedulously avoids any imitation of Calcar. The two skeletons with their peculiar misfit of radius and ulna are more suggestive of the pre-Vesalian Cratander skeletons (*cf.* Figs. 11 and 12) than of those in the *Tabulæ sex*, though a combination of the two can easily be read into them even to the lettering (Fig. 39). The more difficult skeletal view from the side was not attempted and the two visceral mannikins derived from Ryff by way of Berengario, Gersdorff and Laurentius Phryesen, show interestingly enough the asymmetrical insertion of the spermatic veins discovered by Vesalius during their student days and also for the first time the duodenum in its proper relations to the stomach. The female organs of generation in the fourth plate obviously have their basis in the *Tabulæ sex* but that was hardly a theft worth quibbling over.

In my Vesalian collection there is a copy of the first French translation by Canappe of the *Tabulæ quatuor* published at Lyon in 1542 by Dolet, the martyr printer (Fig. 40); also a copy of the 1553 Latin issue with the imprint of Gaultherot on the title-page and of Michael Fezandat in the colophon, with the four added leaves bearing illustrations to which there is no reference in the text.

With this possessive background I had expected to deal more thoroughly herein with the bibliography of Vassæus, but the recent appearance of the admirable paper by Crummer and Saunders (95) fully covering the subject makes this unnecessary. After all, it may have been stretching matters to have included Loys Vassé in this present study on the slim assumption that he or his three interlocking publishers and printers (Fezandat, Gaultherot and Foucher) might have represented the Paris culprit to whom Vesalius alluded.

❧ CHAPTER III ❧

GUENTHER'S 'INSTITUTIONES ANATOMICÆ'

AFTER THE TEDIOUS task of attempting to identify the plagiarists of the *Tabulæ sex* mentioned in Vesalius' letter to Oporinus, we must return to Venice. Here Vesalius had been far from idle, and it is interesting, after what has been said concerning conservative and also the liberal Galenists, to find Vesalius getting out a personal edition of Guenther's *Institutiones Anatomicæ*. Of all the many commentaries on Galen's innumerable works that followed rapidly on the heels of one another during the late Renaissance, few proved more popular than Guenther's manual of four books which had been specifically prepared for medical students. In the first edition (Fig. 41), handsomely printed at Basel by Balthasar Lasius and Thomas Platter in August 1536* while Vesalius was still his pupil in Paris, Guinterius—a Galenist to the core—pays his young prosector a great compliment in the following passage [pp. 46-47] concerning the vasa seminaria:†

"(Serving as) seminal vessels are also two veins, and as many arteries, one on each side, extensions of the great vein and the great artery (respectively), carrying blood downwards through the groins to the testicles; they vary from one another in respect of their origin. The vein at the right side takes its beginning not from the side of the vena cava, but centrally from that (portion of it) which in this region extends into the kidneys. The one inserted in the testicle on the left side proceeds from that (portion of the vena cava) which goes to the kidneys, to which is sometimes attached a small offshoot from the vena cava; it continues in union with it. These seminal veins are attached, in a downward direction, to the back, by delicate membranes; in the region of the groins you will find attached to them arteries which are directed quite differently from the veins issuing from the vena cava; I found this fact in no work of previous anatomists, nor do I believe that anyone of them had noticed it.

"It was only recently found with the help of Andreas Vesalius, son of the Emperor's pharmacist—a young man, by Jove ['*me hercules*'], of great promise, possessing a singular knowledge of medicine, erudite in both languages [Latin

---

* De Feyfer cites a Paris edition in the same year which does not contain the Valla addition. This edition I have never seen—H.C.

† This is the first published reference to Vesalius; at the time he was 21 years of age.—Ed.

and Greek] and most skilled in dissecting bodies—after extensive research in the parts (of the human body). These (arteries) are very difficult to notice, because they are of a pale whitish colour like the adjoining parts (muscles). Anatomists neglected to trace their origin, being content with the axiom, that there are few, if any, veins going down in the lower regions aside from the (vein) accompanying the artery."

This novel observation indicates, as well as anything could, the perspicacity of Guenther's pupil and one need not be surprised to find that it had been illustrated on the first plate of the *Tabulæ sex*, which in all probability was drawn by Vesalius himself rather than by Calcar; I can well remember, as a first-year medical student in 1891, that the asymmetrical insertion of the two seminal veins was a favourite catch question for quiz masters of anatomy.

What may have led Vesalius to edit a new edition of Guenther's anatomical compendium and to have it printed by D. Bernardinus only a month after the six *Tabulæ anatomicæ* had come from the press is not apparent (Fig. 42A). In his long prefatory letter addressed to Armenterianus, rector as well as professor of medicine at Louvain and dated from Padua on May 5, 1538, Vesalius, while praising the book as a student's compendium, states that owing to the printer's carelessness it contained many errors which deserved correction. For this undertaking he felt qualified inasmuch as he had been demonstrator of anatomy in three leading universities.

Since Guenther's long paragraph, quoted above, was reprinted unchanged, that citation at least could not be regarded as erroneous. What is more, Vesalius was probably not unmindful of the fact that his two anatomical sketches printed just a month before on the margin of the first leaf of his *Tabulæ sex* had served to show what his minor anatomical description, unknown to Galen, had amounted to, much better (by Hercules!) than did Guenther's textual description. Vesalius' prefatory letter follows:

> *To the illustrious Joannes Armenterianus, most expert*
> *Professor of Medicine at Louvain, Andreas*
> *Vesalius of Brussels sends greetings:*

"I think, most erudite Sir, that those do rightly who faithfully contract into compendia those matters in the (various) disciplines (of knowledge) which have been handed down in a detailed and prolix form. This (procedure) is not devoid of utility in other branches of medicine, but in Anatomy, I believe, it is both exceedingly useful and necessary, since this (discipline) has been handed down and perfected by Galen in nearly forty books [a phrase quickly picked up by de Necker, as we have seen]. Inasmuch as I perceived that because of the difficulty and prolixity of the matter, very few peruse it sedulously, I began to consider what path might lead to this easily accessible field; none seemed better to me than that which Johannes Guinterius had smoothed and laid out for this purpose—a man blessed with many gifts of mind, to whom not only students but nearly all professors of medicine owe a great deal, inasmuch as he has helped the cause of medicine more than anyone else. He possesses not only an admirable facility ['*promptitudinem*'] of translating ['*vertendi*'—perhaps meant here in the sense of 'paraphrasing'], but in an equal measure a singular variety of words. However, even his work, due to the excessive haste demanded by the printers and their negligence, is not free from errors; I therefore thought that I would be undertaking a work greatly desired by all students, if I should through my diligence cause the (fruit of the) vigils of this man of great merit in studies to appear (again) in a corrected and authoritative form. Many begged me to do this. I trust to the liberality of the author who, I think, will not be offended by this, since I have received the major part of my studies from him—a teacher both most liberal and most learned. In what measure I have excelled here, I shall not say; I have desired to perform a service for the benefit of many—and those who will read this with (fair) judgment and candid spirit will, I think, agree with me (in that respect). Of my experience in dissection I shall say nothing, because there are many witnesses to testify to what I have done in this field, for I have conducted anatomical (courses) in the three most celebrated of European universities which I have visited for the purpose of (advanced) study. For the rest, whatever labour we have performed in this matter ought (rightly) to be offered to you, for you are a consummate philosopher as well as an accomplished physician, and were, because of your singular knowledge of anatomy, praised by all as a master (at a time when) I performed dissections at Louvain under your guidance.

"I shall say nothing here of your rare industry, your mastery of letters, or your other mental gifts, by which you have earned the honour of being repeatedly clothed with the dignity of rector; for many years you have presided over and have directed your college in such a way as to cause the university to flourish not only in philosophical and philological studies, but in all others as well. Accept, therefore, this our effort as a token of our friendship, until such time as we shall undertake to treat of this matter afresh. Show me (I pray) the same liberality

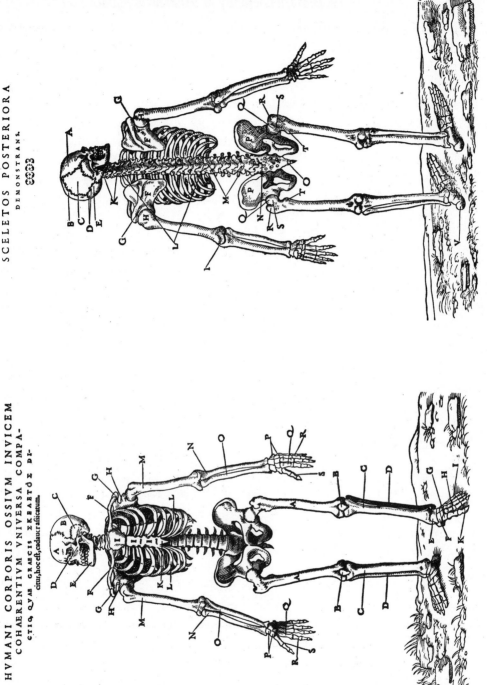

FIGURE THIRTY-NINE

The two Vassé skeletons (1553).

ules Anato‗
‗ICQVES DV
corps humain uniuersel:
soit de lhomme, ou
de la femme.

*

Premierement composées en Latin, par
maistre Loys Vassée. Et depuis tra
duictes en Francoys, par mai‗
stre Iehan Canappe.

ADAMVSSIM DOLO,

SCABRA, ET IMPOLITA   ATQVE PERPOLIO.

A LYON.
Chés Estienne Dolet.
1542.
Auec priuileige pour dix ans.

70

Tables Anato‗
MICQVES DV
corps humain uniuersel.

TABLE SECONDE.

Du Thorax.

Gal. 6. & 7.
le usu part.

THORAX c'est tout
ce, qui est circonscript,
c'est a dire comprins par
les costes, d'une part, ɛ̃
d'aultre: comme ung parc
bien fort, enuironnant le
cœur, ɛ̃ le poulmõ: pour
tutele, ɛ̃ desence. Que
nature à faict non pas du
tout osseux, comme est le crane: ne du tout charneux,
comme l'epigastre: mais par une cõmutation d'ordre,
elle y a mys des os, ɛ̃ des muscles, l'ung apres l'aultre.
Le thorax à troys parties.

1 La fin superieure par deuant, ce sont les cla‗
uicules, en Grec cleis, en Latin claues, ou claui‗
culæ. Et sont ainsi appellées, pource qu'elles
conferment les wmoplates auec sternon, qui est
l'os

FIGURE FORTY
The Canappe translation of Vassé with a page illustrating his Galenic leanings.

INSTITV
TIONVM ANATO
MICARVM SECVNDVM GALE
ni sententiam ad candidatos Medici=
nae Libri Quatuor, per Ioannem
Guinterium Anderna=
cum Medicum.

BASILEAE,
M. D. XXXVI.

vide editori Veneti en calti, ee em xiiisi
ạ Andrea Vuesalia

FIGURE FORTY-ONE

Title-page of the first edition of Guenther's *Institutiones anatomicæ*. It is dated August 1536, the reference
to Vesalius occurring on p. 46.

INSTITVTIONVM
ANATOMICARVM
SECVNDVM GALENI
sententiã ad candidatos Me
dicinę Libri Quatuor,
per Ioânem Guin
terium Ander
nacum Me
dicum.
AB ANDREA VVESALIO
Bruxellensi, auctiores & emendatiores redditi.

VENETIIS.

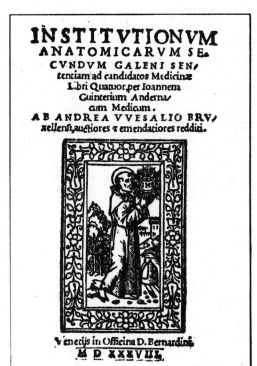

INSTITVTIONVM
ANATOMICARVM SE-
CVNDVM GALENI SEN-
tentiam ad candidatos Medicinæ
Libri Quatuor, per Ioannem
Guinterium Anderna-
cum Medicum.
AB ANDREA VVESALIO BRV-
xellensi, auctiores ꝛ emendatiores redditi.

Venetijs in Officina D. Bernardini
M D. XXXVIII.

FIGURE FORTY-TWO

Title-pages of the two 16mo editions of Guenther's *Institutiones anatomicæ* edited by Vesalius: below, the first
edition of 1538; above, the Sessa edition, probably of 1540.

with which you enveloped all students of ancient medicine, and commend me to Leonardus Vuillemars, most excellent professor of medicine and happy imitator of Galen, and to Marcus Florenas, that most promising youth, our mutual friend.

"May you live and prosper for a long time, a principal ornament of the University ('*gymnasium*') of Louvain. Padua, the third day before the nones of May (May 5th), in the year of the world's redemption 1538."

[The editions of Guenther's 'Institutes' so far traced are listed below. Those marked with an asterisk follow the text which was edited by Vesalius in 1538, and these are described in detail, whether Vesalius is mentioned on the title or not. The Basel edition of 1539 has textual and other changes from the edition of 1536, but since those were evidently made by Guenther himself, and not by Vesalius, the book is not described.—Ed.]

   1. B. Lasius and T. Platter, *Basel*, 8°, August 1536, ed. princeps (Fig. 41.)

   2. ————, *Paris*, 1536 (cited by de Feyfer and Roth; no copy traced).

*3. D. Bernardinus, *Venice*, 16°, May 5, 1538 (Fig. 42A).

   4. R. Winter, *Basel*, 4°, June 1539.

*5. [Sessa], *Venice*, 16°, [? 1540] (Fig. 42B).

   6. S. Gryphius, *Lyon*, 8°, January 1541.

*7. J. Fabrianus, *Padua*, 8°, 1550.

   8. ————, *Padua*, 8°, 1558 ("ab And. Vesalio auctiores redditi." Roth and de Feyfer; no copy traced).

*9. ———— [*Wittenberg*], 8°, 1585 (Fig. 43A).

*10. S. Selfisch, *Wittenberg*, 8°, 1613 (Fig. 43B).

  11. ————, *Wittenberg*, 8°, 1616 (a copy offered for sale but not seen).

III.—1

GUENTHER, Institutiones anatomicæ   *Venice*, 1538

Title (Fig. 42A): Institvtionvm / Anatomicarvm se-/ cvndvm Galeni sen-/ tentiam ad candidatos Medicinæ / Libri Quatuor, per Ioannem / Guinter-/ ium Anderna-/ cum Medicum. / Ab Andrea VVesalio Brv-/ xellensi, auctiores & emendatiores redditi. / [Printer's device] / Venetijs in Officina D. Bernardini / [rule] / M D XXXVIII.

Collation: 16°. ✚⁸, ✚✚⁸, A-O⁸; [16], 112 *ll.*
Contents: ✚1*a* title; ✚1*b* blank; ✚2*a*-4*a* dedication to Armenterianus; ✚4*b* blank; ✚5*a*-✚✚4*a* index; ✚✚4*b* errata; ✚✚5-8 blank; A1*a*-5*a* Guenther's preface to Nicolaus Quelain; A5*b* the typographer to the reader, plus "furniture" (see note); A6*a* beginning of Book I; F2*a* beginning of Book II; I7*b* beginning of Book III; L5*b* beginning of Book IV; O1*a*

beginning of Georgii Vallæ / Placentini de hv- / mani corporis partibus, opu / sculum sane elegans & perutile. Text ends on O8*b*.

Note: Bernardinus was a patrician, scholar and ex- cellent printer but his compositor's devil showed a fit of carelessness at the bottom of A5*b*. The meaningless eleven lines were evidently used as "furniture" to fill the blank space in the locked form, and Bernardinus' devil subsequently forgot and inked them.

The *Typographus lectori* which occurs in the middle of the page warns the reader that the letter *B* in the margins (*e.g.*, leaf 6*b*, 10*a*, etc.) indicates a "barbaric" (*i.e.*, Arabic) word.

Copies: CaMM-Os [given Osler on his 70th birth- day by H.C.]; NIC; Cushing; Waller; Louvain.

Copy used: Cushing; bought from Leo S. Olschki, Florence, Oct. 30, 1915 for $50. Bound in original limp vellum with two other 16mo tracts by same printer, both in 1538: (1) *Anathomia Mundini* of Berengarius; (2) Galen's *De ossibus,* the Balamio translation without the skeletal figures; measures 10.6 by 7.5 cm.

Whether Guenther's 'Institutes' were always bound with Mundinus and Galen, as in my copy, or whether they were sold separately has not been ascer- tained; but in the assemblage of the new text, sandwiched for comparison between the old traditional anatomy of Mundinus and Galen's *De ossibus* of Balamio (see above, Fig. 12), the purposeful hand of Vesalius may perhaps be seen. Although he had taken many liberties with the Guenther text, he appears not to have tampered with the Balamio translation.

This tiny book must have found its way promptly into the hands and pockets of the flock of student-onlookers who were crowding in to see the demonstra- tions of the young Paduan appointee, and its rarity suggests that the copies became worn out with use. Roth speaks of it with enthusiasm as follows: "Anyone who peruses this insignificant-looking little pocket edition may well be surprised at two things: first at the modesty, indeed the anxiety of Vesalius who fears to offend his earlier teacher with his corrections . . .; and secondly, at the old arrangement of Mundinus after Vesalius had just published the syste- matic representation in the six *Tabulæ anatomicæ.* This is explainable on the basis of his having published the Institutes only as a makeshift for the students."

Very soon, possibly in the same year, though commonly ascribed to 1540, another Venice edition in the same small format was issued by the printer Sessa. This is also a 16mo in eights with 16 preliminary and 101 numbered leaves including, as usual, the opusculum of Valla at the end. The most noticeable difference between these two pocket editions lies in the fact that while the cat- and-mouse press of Sessa (Fig. 42B) might pounce upon the book and reprint it, its limitations are evident from the absence of any font of Greek type.

III.—2

GUENTHER, Institutiones anatomicæ   *Venice* [? 1540]

Title (Fig. 42B): Institvtionvm / anatomicarvm / secvndvm Galeni / sententiā ad candidatos Me / dicin*æ* Libri Quatuor, / per Ioānem Guin / terium Ander /

nacum Me / dicum. / Ab Andrea VVesalio / Bruxellensi, auctiores & emen⁄ / datiores redditi. [Cat⁄and⁄mouse device of the printer Sessa] Venetiis.

Collation: 16°. *⁸, **⁸, A⁄N⁸; [16], 101, [3] *ll.*

Contents: *1a title; *1b blank; *2a⁄3a dedication to Armenterianus; *3b blank; *4a⁄**5a index; **5b⁄ 8b blank; A1a⁄4a Guenther's preface, ending with the '*Typographus lectori*'; A4b beginning of Book I; E3a beginning of Book II; H4b beginning of Book III; K1a beginning of Book IV; M3a⁄N5a Valla's *opusculum*; N5b⁄8b blank.

Note: The Balamio translation of Galen's *De ossibus*

is omitted from this edition.

Copies: MBM; Cushing [2].

Copies used: H.C.: (1) bought of Charles Singer, London, 1926, for £25, measuring 10 by 6.5 cm., bound with *Anatomia Mundini*, also Sessa press with⁄ out printer's name or date; (2) bought of Hertz⁄ berger, Amsterdam, July 1937, for $150, size 10.4 by 7.5 cm.; last three blanks missing.

III.—3

GUENTHER, Institutiones anatomicæ   *Padua,* 1550

Title: [Ornament] Insti⁄ [ornament] / tvtionvm / anatomicarvm / secvndvm Galeni sen⁄ / tentiam ad candidatos Medicinæ Libri / Quatuor, per Ioannem Guinte⁄ / rium Andernacum Me / dicam. / [Printer's device] / Patavii / Iaco⁄ bus Fabrianus Excudebat / M D L.

Collation: 8°. [a]⁄b⁴, A⁄T⁴; [8], 76 *ll.* (an octavo gathered in fours).

Contents: [a]1a title; [a]1b blank; [a]2a⁄b4a tabula alphabetica; b4b blank; A1a⁄T4a text; T4b blank.

Note: The text is copied exactly from the Vesalius 1538 (1st) edition, correcting the errors that had been listed therein. The '*Tabula alphabetica*' is, however, greatly curtailed from the '*Index rerum*' of the first edition. It is interesting that in both editions, with and without Vesalius' name on the title⁄page,

Guenther's complimentary reference to him was allowed to stand unchanged (*l.* 20a).

Copies: NNC⁄M; MdBJ⁄W.

Copy used: Welch Medical Library, formerly in the library of Dr. Howard A. Kelly. It measures 15.6 by 9.8 cm. and is curious in having been gathered in duplicate foldings throughout (*i.e.,* each page is duplicated), probably the result of its having been an octavo gathered in fours; there are thus two complete copies bound in one.—Ed.

From this point the bibliography of Vesalius' edition of Guenther's *Institu⁄ tiones anatomicæ* becomes confused. Of de Feyfer's eight cited issues, No. 7, the undated Venice issue, is doubtless the Sessa volume described above. His No. 2, the June 1539 Basel edition from the press of Robert Winter of which I have the Broeckx copy, is a handsome new edition with many changes (including the title) from Guenther's first edition of 1536. The name of Vesalius does not appear on the title⁄page, although both he and Servetus are mentioned in the preface. This preface to the Basel edition of 1539, addressed to Jacobus Ebulinus may be rendered as follows:

"While demonstrating anatomy at Paris, I was urged to write down the pertinent information in a brief and easy manner. There are no such modern handbooks, while Galen is much too voluminous. Anatomy was of old re⁄

garded as well worth studying, as witness Alexander the Great, and Marcus Aurelius. A builder cannot restore a collapsed house without knowing the construction of its parts—neither can a physician heal a human body unless he knows its make-up. Yet nowadays many physicians who claim to emulate Hippocrates, Galen, or Avicenna know nothing of anatomy. Even worse, in France and Germany nowadays louts and hags pose as practitioners of the art of medicine. The fault lies with the magistrates who do not discriminate between learned and trained doctors and charlatans. [Follows a description of the contents of this work, then a passage (a5a) mentioning Vesalius, as follows:]

"Now as for myself, I have revised, augmented and perfected this treatise, which was composed several years ago, in the light of many dissections performed since, and a careful inspection of the parts (of the body). In this task, not an easy one, I have had the help, first, of Andreas Vesalius, a youth—by Jove—most diligent in anatomy, and a professor of pure medicine for whom one ought to be grateful; only recently, in his edition at Venice of this my treatise, he furnished an excellent piece of work. My second assistant was Michael Villanovanus ... [There follows the cryptic challenge: should anyone value the work because of its Galenic basis, let him know that the work is mine; should anyone despise the work because it is my handiwork, let him know that the work is Galen's.] Dated at Metz, in the month of January."

From a bibliographical standpoint, therefore, this is not a Vesalian item since it does not contain his text. The 1550 Padua octavo (III.3), and probably also the Padua 1558 octavo, follow the Vesalian text, but they do not always carry Vesalius' name on the title-page. This leaves the Wittenberg editions of 1585 and 1613 which may now be described. A Wittenberg 1616 octavo is cited by Eloy and a copy has been offered for sale, but it has not been seen.

III.—4

GUENTHER, Institutiones anatomicæ   [*Wittenberg*] 1585

Title (Fig. 43): Institvtionvm / anatomica- / rvm secvndvm / Galeni sententiam ad / candidatos Medicinæ Libri Quatuor, / per Ioannem Gvinterium An- / der- / nacum Medicum. / Ab Andrea VVesalio / Bruxellensi, auctiores & / emendatiores redditi. [human skull] Anno M D XXCV.

Collation: 8°. A-I⁸, K⁴; [3] *ll.,* 143 pp., 1 *l.*

Contents: A1a title; A1b blank; A2-3 Vesalius' preface dated May 5, 1538; A4a-7a Guenther's preface; A7b beginning of Book I; D5a beginning of Book II; F7b beginning of Book III; G7b beginning of Book IV; I4a beginning of Valla's *Opusculum*; K3a *Finis*; K3b and K4 blank.

Note: There are the following errors in signatures and

'INSTITUTIONUM
ANATOMICARUM,
SECUNDUM GALENI
SENTENTIAM, AD CANDIDA-
tos Medicinæ, Libri Quatuor, per JOHAN-
NEM GVINTERIUM Anderna-
cum medicum, editi.
Ab
ANDREA VESALIO
Bruxellensi auctiores facti,
Quartùm nunc emendatiores re-
cogniti.

WITTEBERGÆ,
Impensis Samuelis Selfischii, Bibliopolæ
M. DC. XIII.

INSTITVTIONVM
ANATOMICA-
RVM SECVNDVM
GALENI SENTENTIAM AD
candidatos Medicinæ Libri Quatuor,
per Ioannem Gvinterium Ander-
nacum Medicum.
Ab Andrea Wesalio
Bruxellensi, auctiores &
emendatiores redditi.

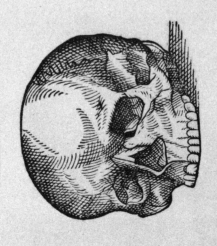

Anno cIↃ IↃ xxcv.

FIGURE FORTY-THREE

Title-pages of two later editions of the Vesalian rendering of Guenther's Institutes: left, 1585, probably published at Wittenberg; right, Wittenberg, 1613.

FIGURE FORTY-FOUR

Title-page of A, Brissot's tract on venesection, 1525, and B, the first
edition of Vesalius' Venesection Epistle, 1539.

pagination: 2I for I2, 0I for 10, 37 for 73, 85 for 86, 86 for 87, 89 for 90.

Copies: Waller; Cushing; DSG; NBMS.

Copies used: H.C.; (i) measures 16 by 9.5 cm.; bought of Leo Olschki, Florence, in 1916 for Swiss frs. 193; previously bound with other anatomical tracts, two of which bore the imprint of the heirs of Joannes Crato, Wittenberg; (ii) also in contemporary binding with 3 other tracts, one the *Historia humani corporis* of Salomon Alberti (2), printed at Wittenberg by Crato, 1585; measures 15.5 by 9.5 cm.

III.—5

GUENTHER, Institutiones anatomicæ   *Wittenberg,* 1613

Title (Fig. 43): Institutionum / Anatomicarum, Secundum Galeni / Sententiam, ad candida- / tos Medicinæ, Libri Quatuor, per Johan- / nem Guinterium Anderna- / cum medicum, editi, / Ab / Andrea Vesalio / Bruxel- / lensi auctiores facti, / Quartùm nunc emendatiores re- / cogniti. / [Printer's device] / Wittebergæ, / Impensis Samuelis Selfischii, Bibliopolæ / M. DC. XIII.

Collation: 8°. A-M⁸; [8] *ll.*, 176 pp. (wrongly numbered 175).

Contents: A1a title; A1b blank; A2a-3b Vesalius' preface dated May 5, 1538; A4a-8b Guenther's preface; B1a beginning of Book I; F1b beginning of Book II; H8a beginning of Book III; K4b beginning of Book IV; M1b beginning of Valla's *Opusculum*; M8b Finis.

Note: This edition, surprisingly enough, is apparently the first and only one to be illustrated, the 30 small anatomical woodcuts being after Vesalius. The paper is greatly foxed; faint indications of watermarks occur on several pages. There are innumerable errors in pagination.

Copies: London (BM); Cushing.

Copy used: H.C.; bought from Taeuber and Weil, Munich, in 1928 for RM. 175; measures 15.3 by 9 cm.

III.—6

GUENTHER, Institutiones anatomicæ   *Wittenberg,* 1616

Note: Cited by Eloy; and a copy was offered for sale by Herissant.—Ed.

CHAPTER IV

THE VENESECTION EPISTLE

IN HIS PREFATORY note to Narcissus Parthenopeus in the *Tabulæ sex*, Vesalius had referred to the existing tempest of discussion concerning vene-section, and what prompted him to write the epistle under consideration was a request from his correspondent for further information concerning the printed marginal notes on the vena cava table of the *Tabulæ sex* (see Figs. 18 and 29) which concerned the azygos vein and its relation to the question of blood-letting in cases of pleurisy. His correspondent, Nicolaus Florenas, was not the only one thus to have his curiosity aroused, for in the Marciana copy of the *Tabulæ sex* (*cf.* II.1A) a contemporary reader has scribbled some notes at this very place where the azygos vessels are mentioned. The written notes have been expunged from the New York Academy facsimile (*cf.* II.4[A]) of the Marciana set, but they still show faintly on the left side of the vena cava leaf in the facsimile of Holl and Sudhoff (*cf.* II.3 [A]) despite its considerable reduction in size.

Even in this day of frequent controversies, it is difficult fully to appreciate the bitterness of the schism which had a far-reaching effect on conventional Galen-ism—namely, where to bleed. The Arabs on purely conjectural grounds had taught that bleeding should be "revulsive" and blood withdrawn from a vein as far away as possible from the seat of trouble. Others claimed that it should be "derivative" and therefore a vein near by should be opened. This was a question of vital importance at that very time when fevers were rife and there had been a spread from Venice of epidemic pneumonia for which blood-letting was the traditional treatment.

Pierre Brissot (54), a scholarly French physician who practised in Portugal after holding a professorial chair in the Paris Faculty, proclaimed in 1515 (not published until 1525; see below, Fig. 44A) that the Arabic doctrine was opposed to the views of Hippocrates and that blood should be taken from the *same* side for the purpose of removing the stagnant blood from the affected part in order that good blood could flow in to take its place. For this therapeutic heresy Brissot was finally banished by an act of the Paris Faculty, but the polemic he had started continued for years with ever increasing fury—even reaching the Vatican and the Emperor's Court. The presses had been kept busy printing innumerable tracts, *De curatione per sanguinis missionem,* either for or against the Arabians, and in the exchange of heated dissertations Leonard Fuchs, Hieremias Thriverus (J. Drivere), Andreas Turinus, Leonardus Botallus, Matthæus Curtius, Thaddæus Dunus and many others participated. In the midst of all this tempest in a bleeding bowl, it so happened that a kinsman of the Emperor died of the prevalent pleuropneumonia and the rumour spread that he had been bled in the orthodox "derivative" Arabian manner. And so it came about that Vesalius was asked to give an opinion on the matter by no less a person than Nicolaus Florenas, the friend and patron of his undergraduate days—then professor of medicine at Louvain, but now principal physician at the Emperor's Court.

In order to orient ourselves, no less than Vesalius, on this matter, it will be necessary to retrace our steps and consult the first (1536) edition of Guenther's Institutes (see Fig. 41) in which this statement [p. 80] is made:

"The following are the minor extensions coming from it [*i.e.,* the vena cava] as it passes upward. First, before it reaches the heart, there is a solitary vein, called (in Greek) *azygos*; in some creatures it ascends to the fifth vertebra of the spine on the left side of the chest; in others it ascends a little above the right auricle of the heart; in others, including humans (it extends to) where the vena cava touches the auricle, although nowadays we find it, in both men and dogs, a little above the auricle. It then proceeds downwards along the spine, distributing itself on both sides of eight inferior ribs up to the diaphragm and the enclosing membrane."

This paragraph in the Venice edition edited by Vesalius (1538: III.1) is altered to read (f. 53*b*):

"Having passed a little way beyond the heart, the vena cava gives rise to a large vein, lacking a companion and therefore called *azygos*. This having ascended over the fifth spinal vertebra turns downward and provides nourishment for eight, sometimes nine or ten inferior ribs of the chest, by distributing a vein for each rib on either side. So far we have never found it originating below the heart, only rarely from the region of the right auricle; but only, as in dogs and monkeys, a little above the auricle."

This statement by Vesalius led to modification in Guenther's second edition (Basel, 1539, p. 58) and was apparently accepted *in toto* for in his third (Lyon, 1541, p. 61) edition it is repeated with only slight difference in wording. When in 1538 the vena cava drawing for the *Tabulæ sex* was made, and by Vesalius himself, the stump of the partly concealed azygos was marked B (Fig. 18) and the legend on the left reads "*Ad octo inferiores costas, Græcis* ἄζυγος *hoc est paris expers dicta. Considera ex dextra parte venæ cauæ hanc produci.*" On the right side of the page this brief note is expanded to read:

"B. This unpaired vein, which is said to nourish the lower eight ribs, was never seen by us to extend below the right auricle of the heart—indeed in dogs and monkeys it is found a little above the auricle. Hence, in pleural pain tending downwards, venesection rather than purgatives should be resorted to; and considering Hippocrates' opinion, I think Galen's commentary on Hippocrates' 'Regimen in acute diseases' has spoken obscurely about this vein. Moreover, it would perhaps be reasonable to assume from the origin of this vein that the inner vein of the right elbow should always be opened in pleural pain under the fourth or third rib spreading downwards ... Often pain affects the middle of the thorax from which it would follow that it is still the right vein which should be opened. I wish anatomists would consider this more carefully with a view to investigation (*speculatio*)."

With this understanding of Vesalius' relation to the subject, it is not surprising that his patron and friend, Nicolaus Florenas, should have written requesting him to develop still further the views on bleeding expressed in his note B (Fig. 18). The Epistle (Fig. 44B) was dated January 1, 1539, from Padua, where for the past year he must have been hard at work, not only teaching but pushing along his great project, his brief allusion to which, relative to Calcar, has previously been noted (see Introduction, p. xxxiii). For our present purposes a few extracts from Vesalius' intimate, affectionate and highly interesting reply to this request must suffice. After expressing his reluctance to enter into the fray he says:

"For you know with what open variance, with what excited feelings and with what array of argument all the most learned authorities combat one another with regard to the particular vein to be opened in pleurisy—to such a degree that few doctors of any reputation can be found who have not undertaken to publish upon that subject some sample or other of their erudition, arousing against themselves very fierce rebukes from their opponents and very serious storms of ill-will. But let me pass over for the moment those argumentative persons who reject everything new, and, being eager to defend the heresy they have once imbibed, attack with the severest insults and abuse those who think a vein should be opened on the same side as that affected.

"I imagine that what I wrote some time ago about the Louvain doctors has not yet dropped out of your recollection. Among them was one, remarkably learned in his own opinion and self-satisfied because of his private wealth, who in a crowded assemblage was not ashamed to call Manardus, Fuchs, Curtius and Brissot the Luthers of Medicine . . . Of course this reverend gentleman thought that those who were reclaiming Hippocrates' ancient system of healing . . . ought to be thus derided . . . while he, wise to himself alone . . . accuses them of heresy."

He then goes on to explain the difference between "revulsive" and "derivative" bleeding, using of course highly scholastic speculations built up on want of knowledge that the blood actually went round in a circle, and only made possible on the Galenic theory that the venous blood had its independent ebb and flow from the liver.* Indeed, it came to be disputed whether revulsion and derivation might not sometimes be practised together by cutting the same vein: "For we see some leaders of this second party so enmeshed in their reasonings that they do not fear to make three venesections in pleurisy; cutting a vein first in the foot on the same side; secondly in the opposite elbow, and only then in the elbow on the affected side." Then after a long and detailed description of the vein "that has been frequently called in Latin the *vena coniuge carens* (lacking a consort) and *sine pari* (without a fellow), and in Greek *azygos*, deservedly so named as it has no corresponding vein on the opposite side," he goes on to say: "Let me now add what induced Galen to discuss the *vena sine pari* in man more obscurely (and inconsistently with his own statement in the same passage) than in the case of the other veins of the body, and why he treats elsewhere, almost as a side issue, the veins omitted in his regular discussion of the veins—if it may be permitted to express any doubt of his oracular pronouncements." To make the matter more clear before the eyes, he gives a drawing, doubtless his own, which he thus describes:

"In this exact though rather clumsy representation (Fig. 45A), the letter *A* will indicate the axillary vein of the right arm, carried down to the elbow and there cut off; *B*, the left axillary; *C*, the great bifurcation [junction of the in-nominates] in the *glandium* or *jugulum*; *D* and *E*, the two veins creeping under the breast bone to the anterior parts of the chest; *F*, the veinlet nourishing the

* Vesalius used the word "capillares" in the modern sense; the idea thus antedates the microscope and the discovery of the circulation. On p. 60, line 16, of the Venesection Epistle, 1539, one reads: "*eos ramos in minores ac in capillares venas . . .*" even hair-like veins! First use in English (N.E.D.), *Phil. Trans.*, 1667, II, 511: "The capillary's of the arteries and veins".—W.W.F.

three uppermost ribs on the right side; *G*, the vein supplying the three upper-most left ribs; *H*, the trunk of the vena cava, cut off just where it meets the right auricle of the heart and enters the right cardiac sinus; *I*, the unpaired vein, branching off the cava; *K*, *K*, etc., *L*, *L*, etc., the nine branches supplying the nine lower ribs on the right and left, respectively; *M*, the terminal portion of the vein in question, which passes through the same inferior foramen of the dia-phragm as the artery, and continues as far as the lumbar vertebræ.

"Now then, if *F* is affected, I shall lance *A*: . . . and for that reason I shall suitably accomplish both revulsion and derivation at the same time . . . With equal reason if *G* is affected with phlegmon, I shall have recourse to *B*, following the same course as in my lancing of *A* when *F* is affected. The procedure in the case of the pectoral veins is also the same, for if *D* is affected, *A* is opened; but if *E* is involved in the inflammation, *B* is lanced. And I agree with you up to this point; in fact, further; if *I* be affected, I shall open vein *A*. So if any of the intercostal parts indicated by *K* begin to be affected by inflammation, I say *A* is to be lanced . . .

"But let me tell you in what I differ from you; if any one of the veins indi-cated by *L*, that is, of the ten lower intercostal regions, be involved in phlegmon, will you not forget your principles, confirmed by Achillean reasoning, and cut vein *B*, that is, the left axillary? . . . In my judgment, if you put your mind on this, you will have to lance not *B* but *A*; for the blood driven into *L* can be drained off nowhere except at *I* . . . But if *I* is affected, *A* is opened . . . Further-more, the nearness of *L* and *B*, which is a quality especially regarded in deriva-tion, is not so great as in the case of *L* and *A*. In fact, we see that *I* is nearer *A* than *B* is; so *L* also is necessarily nearer *A* than *B*.

"Accordingly it follows from these statements that whether it seems best to practise revulsion and derivation at the same time on the arm, or, in the case of persons of slight strength we desire revulsion alone, and then, after some interval of time, derivation—the axillary of the right elbow will always be the vein to open [*etc. etc.*].

"To make the situation clearer, let us imagine a young man, whose body is plethoric, and strength unimpaired, attacked by inflammation of the right pleura; any of those physicians will at once prescribe blood-letting from the left axillary. But on the next day, or when he thinks the fluxion has ceased, he will cut the right jecorary (cephalic) vein. Accordingly, supposing there is inflam-mation in some of the *F* veins; first they will open *B*, as a vein farther away than *A*; then, when proposing to practise derivation, they will cut *A*, as if they were lancing a nearer vein. In the same way if *G* is affected, they will lance *A* first. In fact, if any of the veins of the nine lower left ribs be seized by inflammation (*i.e., L*), they will open *A* immediately, then *B*, disgracefully oblivious of their own principles; since in accordance with their own views, they should at the start cut a vein at some distance, *i.e., B*, but not *A* which is a nearer vein . . .

"Accordingly, on these principles, if distance or nearness were the sole consideration of our discussion of cutting the elbow vein in cases of pleurisy, I should not consider it of the slightest importance whether I lanced a vein in one or the other elbow, no matter what part of the chest the inflammation attacked. Don't they then seem to you to be having a fine wrangle and to be barking like dogs at each other, while they reject that noble principle of Hippocrates regarding the alignment and continuity of the fibres? In fact, it has gone so far that in a public edict to those practising medicine in Spain, venesection on the same side as that affected has been forbidden; for after long discussion held at Salamanca regarding this point, those who yielded complained to the most illustrious Spanish senate (as you call it) that venesection on the same side causes not less harm to the human body than the Lutheran heresies to the human soul."

And after mentioning pressure that had been brought to bear on the Emperor to take sides in the matter, he goes on to say:

"But he will never grant them this, nor will he allow it by his dictum, because he will of course not have forgotten the sad demise, laid deep to heart, of the Prince of Piedmont, in whose case the Court whispers rather guardedly that the doctors killed him by lancing the elbow vein on the opposite side; for they say that the doctors, desiring to practise revulsion, and letting a moderate amount of blood, so as to have blood left for derivation, changed his simple pleurisy (as they call it) to double; never considering that by this kind of incision more harm was done a prince worthy of longer life than if they had inspired in him what they themselves call heresy; since the persuasive efforts of any priest or monk might perhaps have been able to heal this latter, while their other error not even the whole divine Asclepiad choir could heal . . .

"In support of these views of mine regarding the vein to be lanced in pleurisy, views never previously advanced by anyone, I should endeavour to bring in the oracular utterance of Hippocrates, in the second book on 'Regimen in acute diseases,' if the authority of Galen did not manifestly contradict me, and I am almost as afraid to argue about his authority as I would be tacitly to doubt the immortality of the soul in our holy religion [*etc. etc.*]."

And this is followed by a long discussion in answer to the second query of Flo-renas as to where and how one should draw blood from the hæmorrhoidal vessels.

The three editions of the Venesection Epistle may now be described. The first edition is well known, the second exceedingly rare, and the third a recent reprint with Dutch translation by M. A. van Andel. Other editions at Venice in 1541 and Basel in 1542 are mentioned in several of the older bibliographies, but no copies have been traced and they are probably "ghosts."*

IV.—1

VENESECTION EPISTLE *Basel,* 1539

Title (Fig. 44B): Andreæ / VVesalii Brvxellensis, / Scholæ Medicorvm Pata-vinæ / professoris publici, Epistola, docens uenam / axillarem dextri cubiti in dolore laterali secan- / dam: & melancholicum succum ex uenæ / portæ ramis ad sedem pertinen- / tibus, purgari. / Basileæ.

Colophon: Basileæ, / in officina Roberti / VVinter, Mense / Aprili. Anno [rule] M. D. XXXIX.

Collation: Sm. 4°. A-G⁴, H⁶; 66 pp., [1] *l.*

Contents: A1a title; A1b Latin couplets *ad Candi-dum Lectorem;* A2a-H5b text of epistle to Florenas, ending on p. 66: *"Patauij, ex ædibus filiorum Illus-trissimi Comitis Gabrielis ab Ortemburg. Calend. Ianu-arij. Anno salutis M.D. XXXIX . . . Finis";* H6a colophon; H6b printer's device.

Illustration: F1a, p. 41 (see Fig. 45A).

Copies: London (BM); Waller; Cushing; CaMM-Os [21 by 14 cm.]; PPCP; NNNAM; Trent; DSG; NIC; MiU (Pilcher).

Copy used: Cushing (lacking H6); bought in the Van den Corput sale (No. 43), Amsterdam, January 1911, for fl. 150. Formerly from the sale (1877) of the Bib. Broeckx with his characteristic binding. Pencilled notes by both previous owners: *"Ouvrage très rare de Vesale. Il n'existe de cette édition qu'un autre exemplaire à l'Universite de Liège."* Size: 19.5 by 13.5 cm.; considerably cut, to judge from contemporary marginal notes.

IV.—2

VENESECTION EPISTLE [*Venice*] 1544

Title (Fig. 46): Andreæ VVe- / salii Brvxellensis, / scholæ medicorvm / Pata-uinæ professoris publici, / Epistola, Docens / venam axillarem dextri cubiti in do- / lore laterali secandam: & melancholi- / cum succum ex venæ portæ ra- / mis ad sedem pertinen- / tibus, purgari. [Printer's device] Apvd Com- invm de Tridino / Montisferrati, Anno / M.D. XXXXIIII.

Collation: Sm. 8°. A-D⁸; 64 pp.

Contents: A1a title; A1b Latin couplets; A2a-D8b text of epistle to Florenas, the last page ending as does p. 66 in IV.1. Illustration on C5a (p. 41) same as in IV.1, reduced in size. No colophon.

Copies: Louvain; Cushing.

Copy used: Cushing; measures 14.2 by 9.5 cm. Bought from Ludwig Rosenthal, Munich, Feb. 1906, for M. 50.

* Dr. J. B. de C. M. Saunders of San Francisco plans to bring out an English translation with critical commentary in the near future. Dr. Cushing had had the full text translated in 1908 by Professor C. U. Clark; the bound manuscript of this translation in the Cushing Collection has been used freely in com-piling this chapter.—Ed.

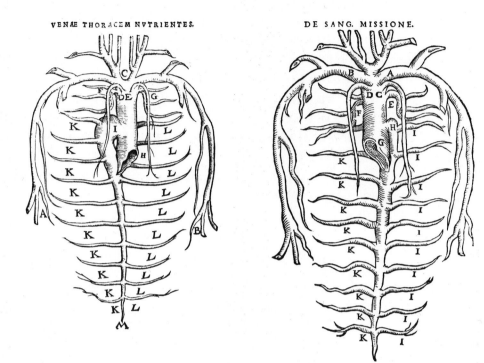

VENAE THORACEM NVTRIENTES.

DE SANG. MISSIONE.

FIGURE FORTY-FIVE

The venesection plate showing the azygos veins. A (left), Vesalius' diagram from IV.1 of 1539, p. 41.
B (right), Fuchs's diagram with plate reversed, from *Libellus de curatione per sanguinis missionem*, 1546.

ANDREAE VVE-
SALII BRVXELLENSIS,
SCHOLAE MEDICORVM
Patauinę profeſſoris publici,
EPISTOLA, DOCENS
venam axillarem dextri cubiti in dolore laterali ſecandam:& melancholicum ſuccum ex venæ portæ ramis ad ſedem pertinei-
tibus, purgari.

IN LABORE

APVD COMINVM DE TRIDINO
MONTISFERRATI, ANNO
M. D. XXXXIIII.

FIGURE FORTY-SIX

Title-page of the rare second edition of Vesalius' Venesection Epistle, 1544.

VENESECTION EPISTLE   *Amsterdam,* 1930

Title in elaborate woodcut border: Opuscula selecta / Neerlandicorum / de arte
medica / Fasciculus Octavus / quem / Curatores Miscellaneorum / quæ voc⁄
antur / Nederlandsch Tijdschrift / voor Geneeskunde / collegerunt et edide⁄
runt / Amstelodami / Sumptibus Societatis. / MCMXXX [in shield] Ve⁄
salius / Lommius / Forestus.

Sub-title: Drie grepen uit de / 16ᵉ eeuwsche genee⁄
skunde [rule] Vesalius—Lommius—Forestus [rule]
Three specimens of the / medicine of the 16th cen⁄
tury.

Half-title (p. xi): Andreas Vesalius / epistola docens
venam axil⁄ / larem dextri cubiti in dolore / laterali
secandam [rule] (Brief leerende dat de oksel⁄ / ader
van den rechter elleboog / moet worden geopend bij
zijdewee) / [rule] / Latijnsche text van 1539, met /
Nederlandsche vertaling. / Voorzien van een voor⁄
rede / door / Dr. M. A. van Andel.

Collation: 8°. lxvii, 314 pp.

Contents: p. i half title of *Opuscula*; p. ii blank; p. iii
title of *Opuscula*; p. iv blank; p. v sub-title of vol⁄
ume; pp. vi⁄ix preface to volume in Dutch and
English by G. van Rijnberk; p. x blank; Plate I *a*
title-page of *Fabrica* (1555), *b* plate from *Epistola
docens*; p. xi half-title for *Epistola docens*; pp. xii⁄xxxi
Dr. van Andel's preface to *Epistola docens* in Dutch
and English on facing pages; pp. 1⁄75 text of the
Venesection Epistle in Latin and Dutch on facing
pages.

Copy used: H.C.; from J.F.F., August 25, 1939.

Should anyone have gained the impression that Vesalius was a clever but
bumptious young man who had small respect for his medical predecessors, it
will be banished by a careful perusal of this extraordinary letter which deserved
a better fate than the neglect meted out to it. One wishes that he could have
written a series of such letters to Florenas on the live medical topics of the day;
for as a contemporary document, it is of no less moment than the China⁄root
Epistle composed seven years later in which with some bitterness he offers an
apologia for his frustrated career. The controversy over *when, how* and *where* to let
blood was an extraordinary one, the absurdity of which could not be realized
until the publication nearly a century later of Harvey's *De motu cordis.* Even so,
its shadow long lay, possibly still lies, over some of us who use leeches, cupping
whether dry or wet, poulticing, blistering, scarification, cauterization, counter⁄
irritants and *Stauungsmethoden,* all of which are but forms of revulsion under other
names. From polemics—such, for example, as the current row over compulsory
versus voluntary health insurance—the profession may never expect to be wholly
free, and bibliographers of the subject a few centuries hence will doubtless
wonder why it caused such a tumultuous hue and cry—though to be sure less
blood is being spilled than there would have been in the sixteenth century.

That the scholarly Brissot as early as 1515 should have begun quoting the opinions of Hippocrates as opposed to the Arabic doctrines may be taken as a straw to indicate the oft-repeated "back-to-the-fathers-of-medicine" movement. Yet another eleven years must elapse before the first Greek edition of the Hippo- cratic texts was published by Aldus and his writings made available to those who could either read them in the original or put them into Latin for the benefit of those less fortunate. And so from Greek to Latin to what was even a more important step—their translation into the vernacular for those, like Ambroise Paré, able to read them only in the vulgar tongue. Thus Etienne Dolet in 1542 printed at Lyon Jean Canappe's translation into French of Galen's tract on the letting of blood.

While venesection was of course a clinical subject, Vesalius nevertheless handled it with moderation and his anatomical approach put the matter on an entirely new basis. In spite of this, he was attacked by those even of his own kind and as late as 1564, the very year of his mysterious death, Eustachius came back at him with a stinging criticism of his views. There were many factors—this schism over venesection among them—which led to the break-up of traditional Galenism and loosened its restraining hand on medical progress. Then there were other contemporary matters of concern on which Galen's writings could not be consulted for they had been unknown to him, such as the cure of wounds made by firearms and the treatment of syphilis which had become widespread. What is more, the seed of pathological anatomy which was to have far-reaching effects on medical thought, had but shortly before been planted by a Florentine surgeon, Antonio Benivieni (1507)—a seed slowly to mature and blossom later on in Morgagni's garden (1761).

Though Brissot has been held responsible for starting the controversy, it was not until three years after his death in 1522 that his published opinion on the subject was printed, first by Simon de Colines at Paris in 1525(54) with three successive Basel reprints in 1528, 1529 and 1530, during the height of the polemic. A copy of Colines' edition (which had originally been bound with four other tracts on the same subject) fell into my hands a few years ago. On the title-page (see Fig. 44A) has been written in Latin in the contemporary hand of the previous generous owner, *Sum Bernardi Cronenburgii et amicorum:* "The same subject was treated by Manardus of Ferrara, in the fifth epistle of the twelfth book and in the first of the fourteenth book; similarly after him, by Fuchs in his work against Brachelius, and by certain other very learned men. It was herein, how- ever, that he most likely obtained this doctrine from its very originator." All five tracts were fully annotated in the same hand and after the last of them, by

Thriverus (Drivere), Cronenburg had written: *Hæc epistola placeat cui velit, mihi non placet:* Anyone who will may like this letter; I don't.

Here we might well enough dismiss the subject were it not for one thing which concerns the Fuchs in Cronenburg's note. This was of course Leonard Fuchs whose great Botany was just then being prepared for Isingrin's press at Basel even as the *Fabrica* of Vesalius was being got ready for Oporinus. I had long ago observed, in the edition by Fuchs of Galen's *Libellus de curatione per sanguinis missionem* printed at Lyon by Frellon in 1546, that the azygos plate used by Vesalius had been reproduced with the azygos on the left instead of the right side (*cf.* Fig. 45A & B). This I had always taken to be an accidental reversal for which the engraver was responsible; but whether accidental or purposeful, Fuchs was aware of the reversal and had modified his description accordingly so that the veins are described as though observed from behind whereas in Vesalius' plate they are seen from in front. What is more, in reversing the plate Fuchs reversed the lettering only in part, which leads to some confusion. What his purpose may have been is not clear to me. The reversed plate was used also in a later (Lyon 1550) edition of Fuchs's tract.

Nor can the subject quite be dropped without some reference to the reactions of Bartholomæus Eustachius, that gifted but unlucky contemporary of Vesalius who in his comparable position at Rome lost no opportunity to criticise his more fortunate Paduan rival who, from birth through maturity to death, always managed to keep a decade ahead of him. Eustachius' only publication during his life was a volume of six separate tracts called *Opuscula anatomica*, which was printed at Venice by Vincent Lucchino in 1563. This was only a year before the death of Vesalius, so it is quite probable that he never even saw the book in which the next to the last treatise is entitled: *De vena, quæ ἄζυγος Græcis dicitur, et de alia, quæ in flexu brachij communem profundam producit.* This article amounts to a sharp counter-criticism of Vesalius' corrections of Galen so far as they concerned the unpaired vein and the branches of the deep axillary vein as they appear at the flexure of the elbow. The article is made up of a series of twenty-two *syngrammata,* in other words, that number of Vesalian statements or propositions quoted chapter and verse, each of which is repudiated or criticised in subsequent *antigrammata* by Eustachius. The volume contains eight of his engraved plates—the first to be published. The engravings cover a variety of subjects, most of them having to do with the anatomy of the kidneys. In one plate, however, there are three representations of the azygos vein in which anomalies occur; in another there are four representations of the venous system of the right upper arm showing the great variation of the vessels at the flexor surface of the elbow where one is advised to bleed.

On the heels of the Venesection controversy, Vesalius took time off to study and edit several tracts of Galen for his friend, Lucantonio Giunta, the printer. To these we may now turn.

❧ CHAPTER V ❧

CONTRIBUTIONS TO THE 'OPERA GALENI'

I
N THE LETTER addressed to Florenas under the date of January 1, 1539, so freely drawn upon in the preceding chapter, Vesalius states that he had just paid a visit to Bologna, partly to discuss the venesection controversy with Curtius, and partly to give himself what was evidently a much needed vacation. He had concluded the letter (see Introduction, above) with the remark that could he only secure the continued services of an artist like Calcar, he hoped to make progress with the illustrations for his contemplated work on human anatomy. That by itself would supposedly be enough to occupy his time and energies, yet he must soon have begun work on his three contributions to a new Latin edition of Galen—a project of the Giunta press.

As we have seen, he had already called attention to certain flaws in Galen's anatomical descriptions and had even ventured to suggest that in some instances they applied to animals rather than to human beings. That so young a man should dare to criticise or have the presumption to correct Galen may not have been altogether wise even though it exhibited a spirit of independence; but it was something more than that. He had hit upon a method of solving the apparent contradictions between Galen's statements and the things he had seen with his own eyes in the human body. In short, when he came to check the latter on dogs which were always available, he soon found that Galen's statements often applied only to canine anatomy. Consequently he must have been no less gratified than other scholars to learn that Lucantonio Giunta, founder of the Venetian dynasty of printers, was planning to publish a new and complete Latin edition of Galen's works in order that physicians, few of whom could read Greek, might have access to precise translations made from the extant codices and thus avoid further dependence on distorted fragments transmitted through Arabic sources.

This formidable undertaking was organized on a scale unprecedented. The celebrated Joannes Baptista Montanus of Verona was engaged as the editor-in-chief and to him the proper arrangement of the books was entrusted. No expense was spared to seek out and identify the oldest Greek manuscripts and to have them translated by carefully selected scholars who gladly gave their aid without compensation. Vesalius who had probably learned more Greek than anatomy

63

from long sitting at the feet of Guenther von Andernach was among the chosen participants. The final revision of the proof was to be made by the learned Augustinus Gadaldinus, who from strain and excitement soon suffered a nervous breakdown. What is more, the elder Giunta himself did not long survive the early stages of the work so that the imprint in all volumes at the time of publication was changed to that of his heirs who with loyalty had seen the project through to its fulfillment.*

The Montanus preface consists of fourteen numbered leaves, the first of which has a title-page suitable for the whole undertaking (*cf.* Fig. 47). This is followed: (i) by an explanatory note addressed to medical students by Gad-aldinus concerning the contributors; (ii) the undated preface by Montanus addressed to the spirit of Lucantonio Giunta; (iii) the two privileges from the Pope and the Doge of Venice dated 1540; (iv) a condensed index of the several divisions [*classes*] into which the writings were grouped; and finally (v) an errata leaf. The thing that chiefly concerns us is what Gadaldinus (rather than Montanus) has to say of Vesalius' reluctant participation in the undertaking, for when it was proposed that he re-edit the large fragment *De anatomicis admini-strationibus* previously translated by Guenther, he demurred, fearing to offend his former teacher and only after long urging did he finally submit.

"It was he," says Gadaldinus, "who contributed the books on the dissection of veins, arteries and nerves, with corrections in many places. Persuaded finally by the entreaties and arguments of ourselves and others, to the effect that he would be doing great harm should he let the fear of giving offence to his teacher Andernach—a fear which obsessed him—deprive others of so much that was useful, he also improved the books on dissection to such an extent as almost to make them new."†

It may be recalled that John Caius was in Padua at this very time engaged in translating some Greek codices for his own purposes, quite apart from the

---

* Some twenty years ago it was disconcerting for a collector who already had more books than shelf-room to have seven folio volumes of the 1541 Giunta (Venice) *Opera Galeni* weighing over forty pounds dumped at his door for the sake of the three brief Vesalian articles hidden somewhere in one of them. The volumes contain no note of the source, time of purchase or price, and I am free to confess that they had never before been opened and examined, having remained tied up in red tape (to keep the much worn vellum covers from warping) and set aside in two huge bundles awaiting this day which might never have come. The formidable bulk of these volumes quelled any enthusiasm for acquiring, when occasion arose, a set of the Froben (Basel) *Opera* published in 1542 which, as cited by de Feyfer, also contained a reprinting of Vesalius' three contributions.

† One of the corrections had to do with the number of muscles of the arm and hand which Calcar, we may assume, was at the very moment illustrating in his portrait sketch and to which Vesalius particularly refers in the text of the *Fabrica* (p. 309, Lib. II, Chap. 43).

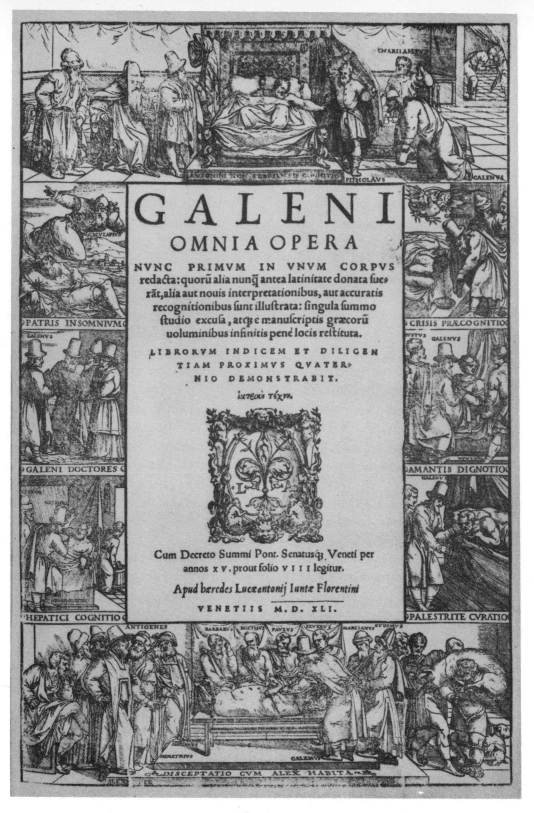

FIGURE FORTY-SEVEN

Title-page of first volume of the Giunta Galen of 1541.

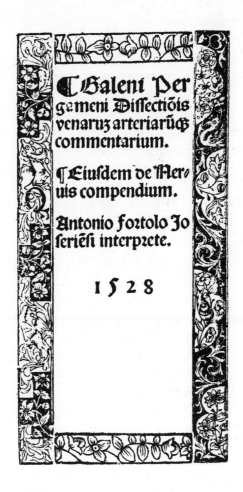

¶ Galeni Per
gameni Dissectiōis
venaruz arteriarūcᶻ
commentarium.

¶ Eiusdem de Ner-
uis compendium.

Antonio Fortolo Jo
seriēsi interpᵣete.

1528

FIGURE FORTY-EIGHT

Title-page of Antonio Fortolo's commentaries on Galen's *Dissectio venarum arteriarumque* and *De nervis compendium*, 1528.

Giunta project which he somehow escaped, even though he had studied under J. B. Montanus; and as already mentioned (p. xxxiv), he had lived for a period of eight months in the same house with Vesalius. In his 1544 Basel edition of Galen's *Libri aliquot Græci* (159), Caius says: "Some Greek notes, and those were few, from an old Greek codex in the possession of the Giuntas, forwarded through Augustinus Gadaldinus, were sent to Vesalius in order that he might correct from them the Latin of Galen's anatomical books; but since these notes were of little use to either Vesalius or myself, being mostly wrong, they caused us to enquire more diligently for other manuscripts . . ." And so Caius, before his return to England in 1544, spent the next three or four years scouring the Continent in search of early Greek manuscripts; all of which temporarily removes him from the present story.

After this digression let us return to, and get behind us, the citation of what proves to be the earliest Giunta edition of the *Opera Galeni* in whose second volume* the three articles by Vesalius appear. The title-page (Fig. 47) and preliminary leaves from the general volume may be cited first. This will be followed by a description of the second volume (*Prima classis*) neglecting the other six. It may not be amiss at the outset, however, to show the title-page of the small tract, printed somewhere in France in 1528, which contains the two articles translated by Antonio Fortolo which Vesalius was called upon to revise (Fig. 48). A description of the first Giunta Galen follows.

V.—1

GALEN'S *OPERA OMNIA* *Venice,* 1541-42

Title of Vol. I (Fig. 47): Galeni / omnia opera / nvnc primvm in vnvm corpvs / redacta: quoru*m* alia nunq*uam* antea latinitate donata fue- / rāt, alia aut nouis interpretationibus, aut accuratis / recognitionibus sunt illustrata: singula summo / studio excusa, atq*ue* manuscriptis Græcorum / uoluminibus infinitis pene locis restituta. / . . . [Printer's device] / Cum Decreto Summi Pont. Senatusq*ue* Veneti per / annos x v. prout folio viii legitur. / Apud hæredes Lucæantonij Iuntæ Florentini / [half rule] / Venetiis M.D. XLI.

Title of Vol. II (*Prima classis*): [Ornament] Galeni [ornament] / Prima classis hvmani / corporis originē, formationem, dissectionem, / temperaturam, facul- tates, facultatumq*ue* / cum actiones omnes, tum instru- / menta & loca

---

* In the later editions of the Giunta Galen, the general volume with the Montanus-Gadaldinus prefatory material is clearly marked as Volume I. In the first and second (1550) editions, the volumes must have appeared in irregular sequence for the volume numbers are not indicated except now and again arbitrarily by a binder. In Dr. Cushing's copy the explanatory first volume is marked by a previous owner as Vol. VI.—Ed.

singula / complectitur. / . . . / Apud hæredes Lucæantonij Iuntæ Florentini / [half rule] / Venetiis M.D.XLI.

Collation: Fol. (in eights). Rom. type. a-m⁸,n-o⁶, p-z⁸, aa-ss⁸, tt¹⁰+² (last 2, blanks, not called for in Register); [2] *ll.*, 3-334 *ll.* Folio measures 35 by 22.6 cm.

Contents: a1a title; a1b table of contents of *Prima classis* covering 28 separate works. Each work begins with an ornamental woodcut illustrating scenes or objects from natural history and also with a decorative woodcut initial.

The three Vesalian items are the 8th, the 9th and the 11th. They have the following titles:

(1) *Galeni de nervorum dissectione liber ab Antonio Fortolo Ioseriensi latinitate donatus, et ab Andrea Vuesalio Bruxellensi aliquot in locis recognitus,* g1b-g2b (*ll.* 49b-50b);

(2) *Galeni de venarum arteriarumque dissectione liber ab Antonio Fortolo Ioseriensi latinitate donatus, et ab Andrea Vuesalio Bruxellensi plerisque in locis recognitus,* g2b-g7a (*ll.* 50b-55a);

(3) *Galeni de anatomicis administrationibus libri novem ab Ioanne Andernaco latinitate donati, et nuper ab Andrea Vuesalio Bruxellensi correcti, ac pene alij facti,* h2b-o1b (*ll.* 58b-103b). A footnote concluding the section points out that: "The remainder of the 9th book, and books 10-15 are missing also in the Greek codices."

Note: The title is framed in an elaborate woodcut border surrounded by eight scenes from the life of Galen: (1) [at top] Galen doffing his hat, in demonstration of the perfect bedside manner, informs Antoninus, who is throwing off the bedclothes, that he has no fever; (2) [reading clockwise] G. prog-nosticating a crisis; (3) G. diagnosing love sickness; (4) G. letting blood from the right elbow; (5) [at bottom] G. demonstrating recurrent laryngeal nerve; (6) G. palpating the liver; (7) G. and his teachers; (8) Æsculapius inspiring G.'s father in a dream to send his son into the study of medicine.

The same woodblock frame was used ten times in the seven volumes, and it finally became cracked and was repaired at the upper left corner. In the 1542 index volume, the letterpress of the title-page is printed in red and black types, the only one of the ten framed title-pages thus treated.

It will be observed that a privilege for fifteen years had been secured by Giunta's heirs both from the Pope and the Venetian Senate. A satisfactory licensure was a matter over which the Roman Curia and the Council of Ten of the Republic were long at odds to the great embarrassment of the Venetian printers who doubtless had helped to spread the Lutheran heresies. It accounts in large measure for the loss of prestige suffered by Venice as a typographical centre—one of the factors which must have influenced Vesalius in his choice at this very time of Basel as the best place to have his *Fabrica* printed.

Copies: DSG; PU; Cushing.

Copy used: H.C.; bought *ca.* 1916. On pasted flylea of Vol. 1, "Prezzo dell'opera F[lorin]. 35". There is no provenance to the set, but it has been thoroughly read and there are marginal notes in a contemporary hand on almost every page.

It was a great compliment for the young Vesalius to have been asked by Montanus to serve with humanistic scholars of high repute like Thomas Linacre, Niccolò Leoniceno, Guenther von Andernach and Jacobus Sylvius, to mention but a few of those sufficiently familiar with Greek to be entrusted with the responsible task of turning Galen's original texts into readable Latin. It was the more so perhaps for the very reason that he had ventured to question Galen's infallibility, in which most of the other editors still implicitly believed.

The *De administrationibus* is unquestionably the most important of the three contributions re-edited by Vesalius. And since the first of the nine books is given over largely to the muscles of the arm which move the digits, one naturally looks to see what may have been his special contribution to the text. Unfortunately, in the absence of marginal notes in the eleven solid pages of unparagraphed type, this is difficult to determine.* To be sure, in the fourth Giunta edition of 1565 the text of the nine books has been divided into chapters and numerous marginal notes have been added, like that on leaf 64 verso, which says: "*Ita castigauit Vesalius & fidel'r.*" (Thus Vesalius corrected and justly.) Special interest attaches to this first book of the *De administrationibus* for the reason that Vesalius may have been correcting Guenther's text (under the difficulties mentioned by John Caius) some time in the year 1540 when he was engaged in writing his own Liber II on the muscles for which the dissection of the forearm included by Calcar (*cf.* Frontispiece) in his portrait sketch had been freshly made.

News of the Giuntas' gargantuan project must have spread rapidly by word of mouth and probably the publication needed no other form of advertising, but whether each *Classis* was sold separately as issued volume by volume, or the completed work by subscription does not seem to be known. How many copies were printed, what was their market price, and who manufactured the sturdy, unwatermarked paper on which the printing was done, are all questions for which there are no definite answers. The great demand for the book despite its size is shown by the fact that repeated Giunta editions were called for and presses both at Basel and Lyon began soon to reprint it, de Feyfer cautiously citing only the first (1541) Giunta and the first (1542) Froben editions. The editions of Galen so far traced containing some of the Vesalian renderings are as follows:

1.	Venice, Giunta,	1541/42	8.	Venice, Giunta,	1600
2.	"	"	1550	9.	"	"	1609
3.	"	"	1556	10.	"	"	1625
4.	"	"	1565	11.	Basel, Froben,	1542
5.	"	"	1576	12.	"	"	1549
6.	"	"	1586	13.	"	"	1562
7.	"	"	1597	14.	Lyon, Frellon,	1548/1551

Roth in his incomparable biography devotes a special section (Appendix IX, p. 458 *et seq.*) to an analysis of all the successive issues and it will save labour, both mental and muscular, to repeat what he admits are only fragmentary observations of his own:

"There are [he says] at least three (varieties of) editions to be differentiated ... the printings of Venice, Basel, and Lyon.

* This had been left unfinished by Dr. Cushing.—Ed.

"(1) The Giunta editions appeared at Venice in 1541, 1550, 1556, 1565, 1576, 1586 (1597), 1600, 1609, 1625 (*cf.* Choulant: *Bücherkunde*, 1841 [79]).

"(2) There are three Basel printings done by Froben and Episcopius, the so-called Frobenianæ. Frobeniana I (1542) is a repetition of Juntina I of 1541; Frobeniana II (1549) was edited by Janus Cornarius on the basis of the Juntina I; Frobeniana III (1562), with preface and introduction by Conrad Gesner, is a repetition of the Juntina III of 1556.

"(3a) Lyon, G. Roville (Conrad Gesner speaks of an edition in 16mo, 1547 *ff.*; I know of a few printings in 8vo).

"(3b) Lyon, J. Frellon, 1550, folio (Choulant, *Bücherkunde*, p. 114, says this edition is a repetition of the Frobeniana II). [It is in four volumes and was edited by Conrad Gesner. It does not contain the *De administrationibus Libri IX* and has no apparent association with Vesalius. Copy in Army Medical Library.—H.C.]

"The Juntina I, 1541, contains [as cited under V.1] the following:

"(i) *Galen's book on the dissection of the nerves,* translated into Latin by Antonius Fortolus, revised in some places by Andreas Vesalius, of Brussels.

"The same occurs in the edition Frobeniana I, Basel, 1542. It reproduces all marginal notes by Vesalius, but omits the marks (asterisk, two and three dots) which are found in the Juntina. All the marks refer to doubtful passages.

"The same in the edition Frobeniana II, Basel, 1549, omitting the words 'Revised . . . by Andreas Vesalius of Brussels.'

"In the Juntina II, 1550—so I deduce from the two 8vo [16mo in eights] editions of Lyon, G. Roville, 1550 and 1551—the fragment edited by Vesalius has been completed and bears from now on only the name of Gadaldinus.

"Accordingly, in the Juntina III, 1556, the title reads: 'Galen's book on the dissection of the nerves, for students, (now) complete; translated by Augustinus Gadaldinus, of Modena. In the printed Greek editions this book is found in a corrupt and mutilated state.'

"So also in the Juntina IV, 1565, and the Juntina V, 1576.

"(ii) *Galen's book on the dissection of veins and arteries,* translated into Latin by Antonius Fortolus Joseriensis, and revised in many places by Andreas Vesalius, of Brussels.

"The same in the edition Frobeniana I, Basel, 1542.

"The same in the edition Frobeniana II, Basel, 1549, but omitting the words 'Revised . . . by Andreas Vesalius.' (In the table of contents, I, 195, there remains: 'Corrected in many places by Vesalius').

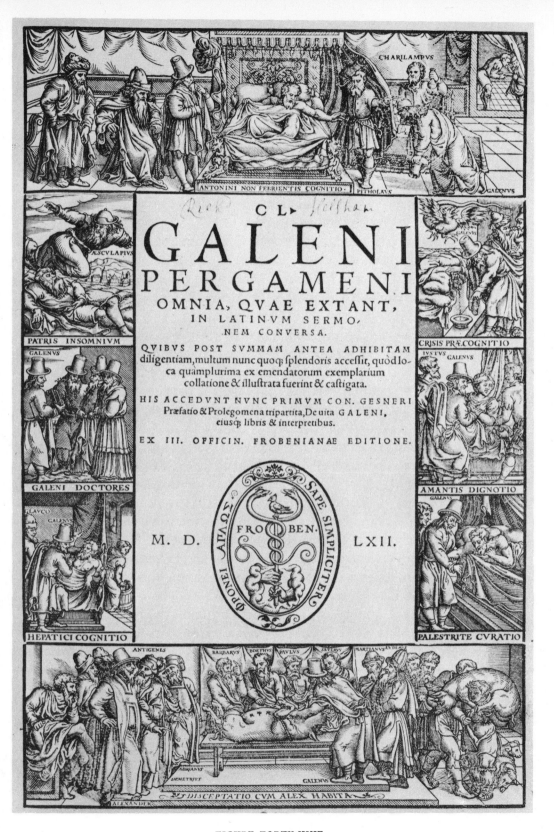

FIGURE FORTY-NINE

Newly engraved frame of title-page for the Froben edition of 1562.

"In the Lyon printing of Galen's *De ossibus ad tyrones* (including the newly found and the old anatomical writings), printed by Roville, 1551, small 8vo, the same additional statement is also missing, at head of the book *On the dissection of veins and arteries*. (It is not, however, a mere reprint from Frobeniana II, 1549, since two marginal notes of Vesalius are reproduced by a paraphrase of their meaning, whereas J. Cornarius omits Vesalius' notes.)

"Juntina III, 1556, has: 'Galen's book on the dissection of arteries and veins, translated into Latin by Antonius Fortolus Joseriensis. Revised,—after the revision by Andreas Vesalius, of Brussels,—in many places, with the help of a very old Greek codex.'

"Similarly Juntina IV, 1565, and Juntina V, 1576, both with Vesalius' marginal notes.

"(iii) *Galen's nine books on anatomical administrations,* translated into Latin by Johann von Andernach [Guenther], and now corrected, and nearly remade, by Andreas Vesalius, of Brussels.

"The same in the edition Frobeniana I, Basel, 1542.

"The same in the edition Frobeniana II, Basel, 1549, with the omission of the words 'And now corrected . . . by Andreas Vesalius.'

"About the edition of Lyon I can supply no information, nor about the edition Juntina II, 1550. [The 1550 Giunta edition is the same as that of 1556.—Ed.]

"In Juntina III, 1556: 'Galen's nine books on anatomical administrations, translated into Latin by Johann von Andernach [Guenther]. Corrected in many places—after the most diligent corrections of Andreas Vesalius, of Brussels, and others.'

"Similarly in the Juntina IV, 1565, and the Juntina V, 1576. Both with Vesalius' marginal notes (Juntina VII, 1600, seems also to contain Vesalius' revision; *cf.* Galen, ed. Kuhn, I, 1821, p. LXXXIV).

"With regard to Frobeniana II, 1549, it shows the meanness of the Galenist Janus Cornarius* in erasing Vesalius' name throughout, except once in the table of contents, where it remained only through Cornarius' oversight. The only two passages from the text which I was able to compare, namely, that on the hyoid bone (in Cornarius' Anatomical administrations, book IV, chapter 14; *cf.* above, p. 67) and the final remark, show that Cornarius followed not the text of Guenther, but that of Vesalius."

* Waller's copy of Cornarius which once belonged to Vesalius, indicates that this slight must have reached a vulnerable spot, Cornarius' name having been erased in many places.—H.C.

Roth does not spare "the learned Gadaldinus" who as time passed "cuckoo'd" Vesalius out of his editorial nest. Nor does the two-faced Cornarius, another ardent Galenist, come off much better. Mention has already been made of one of his printed books which appears to have once been in Vesalius' possession and in which he left his disapproving traces. Evidently there was no love lost between them.

The type for each Giunta edition was entirely reset with new ornaments to distinguish the different contributions, new initial letters, etc. I happen to have a copy of what evidently is the second volume of the Giunta set of 1565, with *Quarta hac nostra editione* printed on the title-page within the customary Giunta woodcut border which has, however, now been wholly re-engraved. It begins with the rendering of Trincavelius of Galen's *De elementis* which has been substituted for that by Leonicenus. So it becomes evident that constant changes and improvements from one edition to another must have been made by the Giunta heirs.

For the opportunity to examine the third Frobenian edition of 1561-1562 edited by Conrad Gesner, I am indebted to my colleague, J. F. Fulton. The work was printed at the press of the second Froben (*i.e.,* Hieronymus, the friend of Erasmus), then in partnership with his brother-in-law, Nicolaus Episcopius. The first volume begins with a newly engraved frontispiece copying that in the early Giunta editions, the block if anything being more expertly cut than the original. It appears only this once and, possibly to prevent wear, is not used in the other three volumes (Fig. 49).

The *Opera omnia* title printed within the frame is of course appropriately altered and the Froben device is added. There follows a dedication by Conrad Gesner to Basil Amerbach, grandson of John, who was the first celebrated local printer of the name; this precedes a long *Vita ac doctrina* of Galen. Then come: (1) a bibliography by Gesner of the earlier Galen editions; (2) a *'catalogus primus'* which is a glorified index of the work; and (3) a *'catalogus secundus'* containing bio-bibliographical notices of all the original contributors, alphabetically arranged under their Christian names. Under Andreas Vesalius he says in part:

"Andreas Vesalius, of Brussels, published seven books on the fabric of the human body, with excellent figures. In these his most learned and accurate books, he explains innumerable passages from Galen, illustrates and amends them, exposes many of what he considers his [Galen's] errors, some of which he was the first to point out. Withal an incomparable man on account of his outstanding skill in anatomy and his diligence, and who has never been sufficiently praised . . . The same Vesalius [he goes on to say] once emended the Latin translation of Galen's nine books on anatomical administrations, as he did also Antonius Fortolus' translation of the book on the dissection of veins and arteries." Why Vesalius' name had come to be omitted from the book on dissecting the nerves he does not say.

The only considerable emendation to Roth's valuable notes concerns the Lyon issues from the Roville press of which he "knew of a few printings in small 8vo." While these small pocket editions must have been printed in large numbers, despite hard usage they are not uncommon and doubtless more would have been made of them by booksellers and collectors had the name of Vesalius, in association with the three articles in question, been in all instances retained.

The Surgeon General's Catalogue (Series 1) gives a list of 34 separate editions of Galen with Roville's imprint, and in my own collection of some twenty volumes there are at least 31 of the separate Galenic tracts, mostly printed by Roville between 1548 and 1553. Among them the *Liber de nervorum dissectione* and the *Liber dissectionis venarum arteriarumque* are found, as stated by Roth, in the 1551 Roville imprint which may be cited as follows:

V.—2

GALEN, De ossibus *Lyon*, 1551

Title (Fig. 50): Galenvs / de ossibvs / ad tyrones. / * / De {Neruorum, / Musculorum, / Venarum & arteriarum, / Vocalium instrumetorum, / Vuluæ,} / Dissectio / ne libri. / De motu Musculorum libri duo. / Adiecimvs præterea Oribasij de Muscu / lorum dissectione libellum [etc.] / [Printer's device] / Lvgdvni, / Apud Gulielmum Rouillium, sub / scuto Veneto. [rule] 1551.

Colophon: Lvgdvni, / Excvdebat / Philibertvs / Rolletivs. [Device].

Collation: 16°. A-Y⁸; 349 pp., 1 *l.*

Contents: [The formerly Vesalian items are in italics for convenience of identification.] A1a title; A1b letter to the reader; A2a-C3b (pp. 3-38) Liber Galeni de ossibus, ad tyrones medicos; C4a woodcut of skull; C4b-5a pre-Vesalian woodcuts of skeleton front and back view; C5b-D8a (pp. 42-63) *De nervorum dissectione ad tyrones liber integer,* Augustino Gadaldino Mutinensi interprete. Liber hic in Græcis exemplaribus impressis corruptus ac mutilus legitur [Vesalius' marginal notes retained]; D8b-I8b (pp. 64-144) De musculorum dissectione ad tyrones liber, Augustino Gadaldino medico Mutinensi interprete. Liber hic in impressis codicibus Græcis desideratur;

K1a-M6a (pp. 145-187) *Dissectionis venarum arteriarumque liber,* Antonio Fortolo Ioseriensi interprete; M6b-N7a (pp. 188-205) Vocalium instrumentorum dissectio, Augustino Gadaldino medico Mutinensi interprete. Argumentum libri. Fragmentum hoc nuper à nobis compertum & translatum, causam, materiam, instrumenta, locum, & modum vocis declarat; N7b-O7b (pp. 206-222) De dissectione vulvæ liber, Ioanne Bernardo Feliciano interprete; O8a-T7b (pp. 223-302) De motu musculorum libri duo, Nicolao Leoniceno interprete; T8a-Y7a (pp. 303-349) Oribasii de musculorum dissectione ex Galeno, Junio Paulo Crasso Patavino interprete; Y7b colophon; Y8 blank.

Copies: DSG; Cushing.

Copy used: H.C.; bound with Galen, *De curandi*

ratione per sanguinis missionem liber, Lyon, Roville,   Voynich for $15; no date.
1549. Measures 12.4 by 7.7 cm. Bought from W. M.

The fate of Vesalius' third contribution, namely, the emendations to Guenther's *De anatomicis administrationibus libri novem,* which he was so loath to have
printed, is still more obscure. The 1541 Giunta says that the nine books have
been "now corrected and nearly remade by Andreas Vesalius." In the 1562
Froben this is modified to read: "in addition to the most diligent corrections by
Andreas Vesalius and others, emended in many additional places." Some of the
supplementary notes are at this time signed with the initials of Gadaldinus.

When we come to Roville's pocket 16mo of 1551 in which the *De administrationibus* separately appears, there is no trace of Vesalius and the arrangement of
the work has been largely changed, with *Argumentum* and *Annotationes* (often in
Greek) preceding each chapter. The elimination of Vesalius in this instance
cannot, however, be laid at the door of Gadaldinus, for the Latin text and its
arrangement almost certainly must have derived from Vesalius' one-time housemate in Padua, John Caius, whom we left long ago scouring Europe for Greek
manuscripts of Galenic texts.

Soon after leaving Padua, Caius states (159) that he had located a manuscript of the *De anatomicis . . . libri novem* in the Marciana at Venice and on his
return in 1544 to England he had found two more, one of them in Linacre's
possession. From these he seems to have composed a new rendering to which he
must refer when he asserts that some of the notes and amended text had been
added by Roville, the printer at Lyon, to his 1551 edition of the book. For these
reasons the reader may be content with the reproduction of a time-worn title-
page and be spared the detailed citation of a translation from the Greek in which
Vesalius probably had no part whatsoever. The only reason to couple Caius'
name with the publication is his own statement, for it nowhere appears in
Roville's book.

We may now turn to Vesalius' crowning achievement, the *Fabrica.*

❧ CHAPTER VI ❧

THE 'FABRICA' AND ITS SEQUELÆ*

VESALIUS MUST HAVE been fully aware of the growing hostility toward him on the part of the firmly entrenched Galenists whose standard text-books and traditional manner of teaching anatomy he had so openly criticised. For many of his opponents he had, to be sure, a feeling of deep respect which in the case of Guenther amounted to genuine affection, but this did not blind him to the faults of their antiquated system. It remained to be seen whether the trouble-maker would be able to withstand their concerted opposition to any curricular novelties which might undermine the authority they had long enjoyed.

As an expression of this opposition, so Vesalius states in the first book of the *Fabrica* (p. 42), Balamio even went so far as to withhold from him a Greek text of Galen's treatise on the bones which he wished to compare with human osteology. Others might use it, but not he! During his anatomies of 1537 and 1538 he did not dare, as he himself later confessed in the China-root Epistle, to criticise anything in this book, the original text of which he had not yet seen. But he had taken recourse to heads of oxen or sheep to demonstrate Galen's *rete mirabile* which he had been unable to find in man. In fact, he had long laboured under such reverence for Galen that he had felt obliged at times thus to deceive his audience. Once when giving his course of anatomy for Professor Albius at Bologna, he was for comparative purposes articulating the skeletons of a man and an ape. In the ape's skeleton he noted the process described by Galen extending from the vertebra toward the hip, but which he had never seen in a human skeleton. It then dawned on him for the first time that Galen may never have dissected a human body; and the more he had come to consider this possi-

---

* A recent unsigned article in *The Times Literary Supplement* of London (403a) gives an illuminating discussion of the word *Fabrica* as used by Vesalius: "It must not be translated 'fabric,' nor does 'mechanism' quite render it. In classical usage it means 'an artisan's workshop,' where something is going on and, by transference, the art of trade itself. This is reflected in modern German, *Fabrik* (factory), and rather better in French, *fabrique*, which means both the process of making and the place where things are made. In Renaissance Latin the word has kinetic associations. A good—if unliterary—rendering would be 'works' or 'workings.' *De humani corporis fabrica*, 'On Man's bodily works.' It was always 'works' in action, living anatomy, that Vesalius was trying to describe and, as a corollary, he had always in mind the body as a whole—the living body. This vision of the *fabrica*, while it made him both a great anatomist and a great artist, renders his work difficult reading, since to understand it we must rid ourselves of ideas that we now accept automatically. To interpret Vesalius we must think as Renaissance artists and not as modern evolutionists."—Ed.

bility while recently engaged in re-editing Galen's texts for the Giunta press, the more convinced he had become of its truth.

A scholar in his own right, possessed of independent means and with powerful friends at court, it must have been apparent that his insistence on reform, in which members of the younger generation were unquestionably show-ing a sympathetic interest, might be difficult to overcome. He of course might be trapped into making some statements which could be construed as running counter to accepted theological dogmas—such, for example, as the seat of the soul—but again, he was intelligent enough to side-step any such commitments.

The great upheaval of the Reformation was at its height. In 1541 while the Giuntas were calmly printing Galen's *Opera omnia*, the conference at Regensburg was being held which the Emperor attended in person. But it was a vain hope that Catholics and Protestants might show enough tolerance to arrive at a peaceful settlement of such moot questions as infallibility, confession, absolu-tion, the sacraments, transubstantiation, and so on. As is well known, the com-plicated issues of European politics were dragged in and largely because of the intrigues they aroused, the conference proved a failure. Where Vesalius person-ally stood in regard to all this or whether, hard at work on his book at Padua, the controversy passed largely over his head, need not concern us. With his *magnum opus* nearing completion, nothing else for him at the time could have greatly mattered. So when in the late summer of 1542 the work was finally ready for the press,* we can imagine him emerging from his concentrated seclusion to find himself caught in what proved to be the most critical period of those unsettled times.

The Emperor and his traditional enemy Francis I were again at war which promised for the first time to be fought on German rather than Italian soil. The shrewd and calculating pontiff Paul III meanwhile was disturbed, on the one hand by the advance of the Turks, who had already turned the cathedral at Budapest into a mosque and were now threatening Vienna, and on the other by the Emperor's increasing power in Germany and the steady growth of Protes-tantism. He resolved that the only course open for him was to organize an active persecution of heretics through the agency of the Roman Inquisition under the direction of the newly established Society of Jesus of which Ignatius Loyola was the superior officer. As a consequence of this, a panicky migration was taking place from the cities of Northern Italy, particularly from Venice where Protes-

---

* The dedication of the *Fabrica* to Charles V was dated August 1st, 1542; that of the *Epitome* to Prince Philip, his son, on August 13th; and the letter to Oporinus, August 23rd.

tants heretofore had received liberal treatment. Many were arrested, tried, and not a few executed, and those who feared persecution and yet could manage to get away, in the effort to reach relative safety among friends in Germany and Switzerland, soon crowded such of the Alpine passes as were not already closed in consequence of the war.

The book trade meanwhile had been hard hit and the art of printing which had reached its highest point in Venice in the early part of the century under Aldus Manutius was distinctly on the wane. This was due in part to faulty copyright laws, in part to lowered standards. Books had to be licensed and the University Commissioners at Padua were charged to examine them before their submission to the Council of Ten for an *imprimatur*. In these trying circum-stances, how did it happen that Vesalius decided to forward his precious man-uscripts and wood-blocks to Oporinus at Basel rather than to depend on some more easily accessible printers like the Giunta press in Venice; and, having so decided, by what possible route at such a time could the mercantile establish-ment of Danoni at Milan to whom the precious cargo was entrusted get it by pack-train most safely from Venice across the Alps to Basel? One can scarcely imagine Vesalius being willing to let such a caravan out of his sight, for the mis-step of a single donkey on the high passes, known to be in a state of great dis-repair, might thwart all his labour of the preceding three years.

A. THE *FABRICA*

Since the publication by Robert Winter of his graduation thesis in 1537 and the Venesection Epistle two years later, Vesalius had been on friendly terms with the Basel printers whose work was as highly regarded as that of the best typographers of Paris and Lyon. The Frobens were by now engaged in reprinting the Giunta Galen, and Isingrin was issuing for Fuchs, both in Latin and in German, his fully illustrated Herbal, which did for botany what the *Fabrica* was destined soon to do for anatomy. Robert Winter was related to and had originally been in partnership with Oporinus for whom Vesalius appears to have formed a particularly strong attachment; and it was natural that Oporinus should have been favoured by Vesalius over any other Basel printers. What infinite pains he had taken can best be told in his own words at the outset of the letter to his "dearest friend Oporinus" who thought so highly of it he decided to print it for reasons given in the following preliminary note from printer to reader:

"We have received from Andreas Vesalius, [now] in Italy, the [following] letter sent to us, together with the plates prepared for this work *De humani corporis fabrica* and for its *Epitome*. It seems to us that this letter contains many things necessary to admonish the reader at the outset, and of significance also to printers, particularly since they esteem but slightly even decrees of princes and are accustomed to pervert such things as serve to spread literary matters among the public. We have deemed it worth the trouble, therefore, to communicate it to the candid readers precisely as it has been sent to us."

Unfortunately this note by Oporinus was not dated, else we might have known when the consignment reached Basel, but Vesalius' letter of August 24, 1542, begins as follows:

"You will shortly receive . . . together with this letter, the plates engraved for my *De humani corporis fabrica* and for its *Epitome*. I hope they will reach Basel safely and intact; for I have carefully packed them with the help of the engraver and of Nicolaus Stopius, the faithful manager of the firm of Bomberg and a young man well versed in humanities, so that they may nowhere rub against one another or receive any other damage in transit. We have inserted separately and in sequence between the plates, schemata ["exemplar"], together with the letterpress belonging to individual figures, to indicate where each is to go, so that their order and disposition might offer no difficulties to you or to your assistants, and that the figures might not be printed out of sequence. You will quickly see from the directions [?] where the nature of the characters should be changed, since I have separated by means of ruled lines that part of the letterpress which describes the history of the organs in the text divided into chapters, from that which serves as an explanation to the characters engraved on the plates, calling the latter for this reason the Index of the plates and their characters. In the continuous text, uninterrupted by references to figures, please use the types called in printing-offices "superlinear," to indicate the annotations which I have added in the inner margin, not with so much industry as with great labour and tediousness, so that they might serve the reader as a commentary showing on what plate the part discussed may be seen; the annotations on the outer margin, on the other hand, are meant to serve as a summary of the text. From the inner annotations, in order to avoid prolixity, I have omitted the number of the chapter wherever the plate referred to is attached to that chapter; where this is not the case, I have indicated the number of the chapter also. The same applies to the number of the 'book.' You will find it abundantly explained, in the titles of the 'books' or in the indices of the characters, why I have assigned the plates to this or that location. We have engraved on the plates the characters, of the sort always used in printing-offices, to indicate individual parts of each drawing; first we used capital letters, then other Latin letters, then lower-case Greek letters, then some capital [Greek] letters such as are not identical with [capital] Latin characters. Where all these were not sufficient, we have used numbers. Where a character has but one explanation, it stands in the margin all by itself; where it does not have it, it is followed in the margin by a period, so as to make the proper relation clear to the reader. I have already written to you, in greater detail, of my reason for all this, and why I thought that the index of characters [his term for explanation of the plates] should not be confused with the description of the parts; now, however, I exhort you most earnestly that everything should be executed clearly and speedily, and that you should acquit yourself satisfactorily with regard to my efforts and do justice to the expectations of everyone respecting your printing-office, now set up for the first time for the greater convenience of students and under the happy auspices of the Muses. The utmost in care should be applied to the impression of the plates, so that they may be executed not amateurishly ['*vulgariter*'] in the manner of elementary school-books ['*scholastice*'] nor in simple lines; in no place should the precise impression of the plate be neglected, except perhaps where the drawing is complemented by [verbal] description. And though in this regard your judgement is so good that I can expect the best from your industry and assiduity, there is one particular request I must make of you, that in producing this work you imitate as closely as possible every mark which you will find made by the engraver, in following his copy, and revealed on the wood-blocks; and thus no character, no matter how much in shadow, will escape the notice of an observant and careful reader. Let also what I consider most skilful and most pleasant to the eye, the thickness of the lines in some parts, be softened by elegant shading . . . I shall take care to come to you soon and to remain at Basel, if not through the entire printing period, then at least for some time, and I shall bring with me a copy of the decree of the Venetian Senate cautioning everyone not to print any of these plates without my consent. My mother sends you from Brussels an imperial licence, since you usually have one such in all the books which you are the first to print; I have procured it a short while ago, but have not yet succeeded in renewing it so as to make it valid for several years longer. The French royal licence will be obtained for me by the French ambassador in Venice, the Count of Montpellier. I am but little troubled on this account, so long as I do not have to fill a whole page with the transcript of official documents."

Whence he goes on to comment on the plagiarists of his Anatomical Tables, whose publication we have already reviewed in a previous section (Chapter II).

So the caravan preceded him, almost certainly by way of Chiavenna and over the Bernina Alps by the Splügen Pass to Chur, the Walensee, Zurich and Basel—a journey of some three or four weeks even under favourable conditions (202). Basel itself had by no means escaped from religious persecutions. It was while some of the professors were for this reason in exile that Paracelsus had wandered in and, with the backing of Johann Œcolampadius, had been granted permission to lecture. That Oporinus had a sorry time of it acting for two years as his valet ("*famulus*"), correcting his Latin meanwhile (more successfully than his habits) concerns an episode outside the present story. But times had changed for Oporinus, and he was now not only head of a renowned printing house, but until 1540 had held the chair of Greek in the University whose Rector at the time was Albanus Torinus, of whom we shall soon hear something more.

Vesalius apparently did not appear in Basel until early in January 1543, and how he may have passed the intervening time is not apparent. He doubtless paid a visit among others to his brother Francis, a would-be physician, though a successful barrister in Ferrara. There among his brother's University friends, he must have met the genial anatomist, Joannes Baptista Canano, who on his own account was writing an illustrated book on the dissection of the muscles of the human body. Indeed Canano had progressed so far as to print within the year the first fasciculus dealing individually with the muscles of the upper extremity which had been cleverly engraved on copper. If the surmise be correct that Vesalius had the opportunity to spread before him prints from some of Calcar's magnificent woodcuts, the cultivated Canano may then and there have decided quietly to withdraw from such formidable competition; at all events, none of the subsequent fasciculi of his work ever appeared (66a).

Wherever else he may have sojourned during the interval before his appearance at Basel early in the year is of no particular moment; but we may be sure that after his arrival things moved rapidly at the press of Oporinus, for the colophons of both the *Fabrica* and its *Epitome* were dated the month of June. This speed may account for the imperfect pagination which after page 312 drops to 213 and continues a hundred pages short until 391, the following page being properly numbered 492, then proceeds correctly to the end, apart from errors in the last two numbered pages. The consternation of both author and printer when this was discovered can be well imagined. That the pagination as the printing progressed was not constantly checked by the register of the gatherings which was necessarily correct is difficult to understand.

But before we go more deeply into this, let us look at the strikingly engraved frontispiece-title on which Oporinus (*cf.* Fig. 55; also Figs. 51-54), in view of the remarks in Vesalius' letter concerning the general disregard even of royal privileges, had placed the licence where it could not possibly escape notice, whereas in the *Tabulæ sex* it came inconspicuously at the very bottom of the last leaf. Also, lest Calcar be forgotten, attention may be drawn to the figure of the young man in the front row holding an open book on whose covers it takes no great flight of imagination to read the initials S.C. That it is a sketch-book rather than, as has been supposed, a Galenic text in which Vesalius' observations are being checked, seems more likely, since what appears to be the end of a pencil in his right hand projects from behind its upper edge.

VI.A.—1

FABRICA   Ed. princeps.   *Basel,* June 1543

Title (*cf.* Fig. 55): [In upper shield] Andreæ Vesalii / Brvxellensis, Scholæ / medicorum Patauinæ professoris, de / Humani corporis fabrica / Libri septem. [In lower shield] Cvm Cæsareæ / Maiest. Galliarum Regis, ac Senatus Veneti gra-/ tia & priuilegio, ut in diplomatis eorundem continetur. [Below woodcut] Basileæ.

Colophon: Basileæ, ex offici-/ na Ioannis Oporini,/ Anno salutis reparatæ M D XLIII./ Mense Iunio.

Collation: Fol. (Rom. and italic types), chiefly in sixes; *⁶, A-Z⁶, a-l⁶, m⁸ [m⁶ ? cancel], n-z⁶, Aa-Ll⁶, Mm⁸; [6] *ll.*, 663 pp. (wrongly numbered 659), [18] *ll.*

Contents: *1*a* frontispiece-title; **1*b* blank; **2*a-4*b* preface to Charles V dated Padua, August 1, 1542; **5* letter to Oporinus dated Venice, August 24th; **6*a* portrait (sometimes inserted facing **2*a*); **6*b* blank.

LIBER I, A1*a*-O6*b*, 40 chapters (last misnumbered LX) on bones and cartilages with 72 woodcuts, major or minor, including three full-page skeletal cuts: p. 163, front view with spade; p. 164, "contemplative" side view with skull ("Alas, poor Yorick"); p. 165, "lamenting" three-quarters back view.

LIBER II, P1*a*-g4*b*, 62 chapters on ligaments and muscles, 36 woodcuts including 14 full-page muscle figures. That on p. 181 wrongly marked *Prima* for *Quarta.*

LIBER III, g5*a*-m3, 15 chapters on blood-vessels with 22 woodcuts, two full-page, ending with folded leaf m3 and second m3 unpaginated.

LIBER IV, m4*a*-p4, 17 chapters on nerves, with two full-page views of peripheral nerves and 7 minor woodcuts, ending with folded sheet p4 showing cerebral and peripheral nerves.

LIBER V, p6*a*-Aa3*b*, 19 chapters on abdominal organs with 30 minor illustrations.

LIBER VI, Aa4*a*-Ee2*b*, 16 chapters on thoracic organs with 13 minor illustrations.

LIBER VII, Ee3*a*-Kk2*a*, 19 chapters, 18 of which are on brain and special senses, with 21 minor illustrations. The final chapter XIX (with one illustration) deals with vivisection and physiology which 'ends his labour concerning the structure of the human body undertaken in the name of the students.' KK2*b* list of errata (which overlooks the misnumbered Chapter LX for XL at end of Liber I); Kk3*a*-Mm7*b* index followed by register; Mm8*a* colophon of printer; Mm8*b* printer's device.

Note: Pagination of text (often faulty, *cf.* de Feyfer [130, p. 453]) begins on sig. A*a* and continues to sig. m3 which is a folded leaf numbered 313 [for 413] on each side (a second m3 is inserted without pagination); pagination continues from 315 on m4*a* to sig. p4 [and 5?], another folded leaf paginated 353-354; continues from page numbered 355 (sig. p6) to 659 on Kk2*a*; succeeding pp. through Mm8 unnumbered.

Errors of pagination: Minor faults as well as the principal one are as follows: 148 for 140, 150 for 148, 179 for 177, 237 for 235, 462 for 262, 266 for 268, 175 for 273, 287 for 297, 288 for 298, *213 for 313 and continues 100 short with minor errors (as 396 for 388) to 392 when it becomes adjusted to proper 492.* From here page numbers continue serially save for occasional minor errors such as 511 for 513, 658 for 662, and 659 for 663, this (sig. Kk2*a*) being the last numbered page. To check this, the register may be quoted. It calls for 59 gatherings as follows: "All in sixes except m and Mm which are in eights. Moreover in m, which is an eight *because of an inserted additional figure, there is an added half-sheet so that from the images impressed on it portions might be superimposed over that figure.* So also p has become a six because of a figure to be inserted." The oversized figures on both folded plates, m3 and p4, had been prepared for the *Epitome,* as stated on page 338. Hence, with 59 gatherings, 57 in sixes and two in eights, there should be 359 leaves and 718 pages, many of those with pagination between A and Kk2 being erroneously numbered.*

Copies: There are too many to enumerate (we have record of 33 copies in the U.S.A. and many abroad); the number printed therefore must have been large. The presentation copy to Charles V printed on vellum, once in the Library of Louvain, is now beyond recall. I well remember being shown a Vesalius on vellum there and that it had a leaf of superimposed figures. However, after 30-odd years I could not now be certain that it was the *Fabrica,* and I strongly suspect that it was rather a copy of the *Epitome* on vellum with figures of the last two leaves superimposed. The British Museum is reported to have had a copy on vellum, but it cannot be traced and is probably again a mistake for Richard Mead's

* The slight discrepancy in reckoning the numbered pages is accounted for by the fact that although m3 and p4 are counted as two *leaves,* they are also counted as only two *pages* each.

vellum copy of the *Epitome* which was sold May 8, 1775, for £8.12s.6d. to a person named Ball during the prolonged sale of Mead's effects.

Copy used: H.C.; traded with Osler for the MacCallum copy, December, 1903. The half-plate m3 is wanting but supplied in photostat; the copy is otherwise intact. Leaves measure 42.0 by 29.0 cm. Paper rather soft and thin; no watermarks. For several years I have kept measurements of the better known copies and know of only three with larger measurements. Richard Mead's copy purchased by William Hunter, December 5, 1754, for £2.3s.0d. and now in the Hunterian Library at Glasgow, measures 43.2 by 28.5 cm.; Brick Row Book Shop copy in contemporary Flemish binding, 42.5 by 28.5 cm.; Denver Medical Society copy, 43.3 by 29.3 cm.; and finally the so-called "Fugger copy," without provenance, bound probably as issued in original limp vellum, sold November 1933 by Karl and Faber at RM.1250, offered to me by a New York dealer for $800 and now in the library of the late S. W. Lambert of New York, measures 43.4 by 29.2 cm. This, the finest copy I have ever seen, probably represents the outside measurement of a practically untrimmed example.

In the copy in the Surgeon General's Library, there is written on two sides of the fly-leaf preceding the title-page a poem by Melanchthon, evidently in his own handwriting, dated Nuremberg, 1552, a rough translation of which follows: "Not haphazardly did the winged, senselessly rushing atoms produce this form of the World, but a wise and very good mind is its shaper, who kept everything secret in his prudence. Here and there he impressed clear signs upon things so that from them God could be recognized as Creator. He knows the ways of numbers and order, and holds immovable rule for the right and the wrong. Such wisdom did not come of blind atoms, but it is the work of nature endowed with foresight. Thus also the position of Heaven and Earth is everlasting, and that certain forces pull all the stars is indeed a testimony that God is wise and good, that he created and ruled these laws. Thus, you should not think that in the human body the joined parts were created by themselves, accidentally and without art. With purpose he distinguished each for definite uses since God wanted us to be a temple of himself. The Divine Wisdom scattered rays into the brain, and he rules the minds with word and with his light. Also, the heart is the house of justice, and it feels the pains when the ire of the revenging

God punishes the guilty. Cleared by God's breath, it feels joy, and it participates in God's everlasting life. When you look at the body formed for such great uses, you should recognize its Maker and adore God. No blemish should desecrate his very temple lest God's anger cast aside the polluted one."

Variants: These chiefly concern the second m3 half-sheet without pagination which is specifically called for in the register, as italicized in the quotation above. This leaf has on its recto eight anatomical figures which were to be cut out and superimposed on the folded m3 double leaf—a highly unpractical procedure. What is more, the half-sheet in question is so often absent that the late Professor George W. Huntington, who was particularly interested in the history of these superimposed figures such as occur in the Remmelin series and even earlier in pre-Vesalian anatomical broadsides, came to the conclusion (*ca.* 1922) that the following three types should be distinguished: In Type I, the unnumbered leaf m3 is present; in Type II, the eight figures have been cut out and are attached to the veno-arterial figure, permitting dissection by reflecting the figures; in Type III, the unpaginated leaf m3 is absent with no trace of its ever having been present or at least bound with the book.

I have at the moment three copies before me: my own, in which there is no trace of the leaf (Type III); one of Dr. Fulton's, in which the leaf is present (Type I [also present in Flint copy recently acquired by the Cushing Collection.—Ed.]); another Fulton copy, in which some previous owner has evidently attempted to attach the figures to the folding plate with complete destruction of the upper half of the latter (? Type II in the making). Two examples of Type II, however, in which Vesalius' directions have been successfully carried out are known to me. One of them was formerly in the possession of the late Paul B. Hoeber. The other, said to have come from the Lancisi Library, formerly in the possession of the late Horace M. Brown of Milwaukee. Later information indicates that it has m3 intact with figures *not* superimposed. So I incline to the belief that Dr. Huntington's variant classification is unjustified and that the majority of copies will show the unpaginated half-sheet m3 present and intact [as in both Osler's copies.—Ed.].

That Vesalius regarded the method of superimposition highly, though the idea did not originate with him, is shown by its use also in the *Epitome* and by the fact that a corresponding unnumbered page with figures to cut out occurs in the 1555 edition as well. Also after his death the tradition was continued in the 1568, 1604 and 1725 editions.

As a book, the *Fabrica* has probably been more admired and less read than any publication of equal significance in the history of science. That it was an amazing *tour de force* for a young man in his late twenties, however industrious and inspired he may have been, goes without saying. Nor does this detract in the least from the credit due either to his co-worker in the task, the still younger and in his own fashion no less talented Calcar, or to Oporinus the printer. How it came to be overlooked by C. E. Heckethorn (183) in his account of the printers of Basel is unexplainable. Due more to the illustrations than to the text, the book was plundered, as we shall soon see, on all sides; but before coming to that, there is something to be said in Calcar's behalf.

Let us begin with the remarkable frontispiece which doubtless represents the kind of glorified surroundings that in the author's opinion were suitable for a public anatomy. It can at the same time be interpreted as a rebuke to the Galenists who were accustomed to read the ancient texts from a professorial pulpit while barbers did the dissection below. Here the situation is reversed; it is a skeleton that occupies the seat of honour while the professor does the dissection and the disconsolate barbers sit on the floor and swap their unused razors. The tall bearded figure to the right motioning a servant to quiet the dog is perhaps Realdus Columbus, his assistant. The interest and eagerness of the crowd of onlookers is evident. The presumptive self-portrait of Calcar with his sketch-book has already been mentioned. Of this celebrated frontispiece there are extant three much debated preliminary sketches of obscure provenance. Though here greatly reduced in size, they will serve to illustrate what may briefly be said of them. The *first* (Fig. 51), a rough though clever wash and line drawing on a sheet measuring 35.1 by 25.5 centimetres is in the National Museum at Stock-holm. It has a date 1675 and the name "Jean Calkar" written on the lower margin. The architectural features are blocked in more or less as they finally appeared, but the skeleton is wanting and the artist has evidently been having trouble with the position of the right leg of one of the quarrelling barbers at the front of the table.

The *second* (Fig. 52), a somewhat more advanced though architecturally incomplete sketch, is reversed as though being prepared for the engraver. Here the skeleton has been added and an additional row of heads is squeezed in under the edge of the balcony to increase the number of auditors. That the artist was still experimenting with the design is shown by the fact that the standing figure on the left margin has been separately drawn, cut out and pasted on the sheet. The awkward (here left) leg of the barber now lies flat on the floor, a position only possible with a dislocated hip. The sketch is the first leaf of the codex lettered on the spine "Desseins origin. de l'anatom de Vesale" (supposedly of Titian) purchased by William Hunter at the sale of Mead's effects on January 20, 1755, for £27. 16s. 6d. It was once carefully studied by Roth (349), who regarded the sketches as unquestionably the work of Calcar. As pointed out elsewhere (Ch. II), most of the 34 leaves comprising the codex have the same watermark as that of the paper on which the *Tabulæ sex* were printed in 1538.

The *third* and last stage (Fig. 53) is represented by the sepia pen-drawing once in the famous Senngracht collection (dispersed in Holland about 1922); in 1926 the drawing came into the possession of the late Dr. LeRoy Crummer (93). It unfortunately had been mounted, thus precluding an examination of the paper for watermarks. Below the drawing there is written in the same sepia ink: *Joh. Stephanus, inv. 1540 Venetiis*. Having been prepared for the engraver, it is of course reversed, and Dr. Willy Wiegand of the Bremer Press in Munich is convinced that it must be the original, for no one could conceivably make in reverse such a line-for-line drawing from the printed woodcut, nor could one easily imagine any reason for doing so. Obviously some changes were made after

FIGURE FIFTY-ONE

The Stockholm croquis: first stage of the *Fabrica's* engraved title-page.

FIGURE FIFTY-TWO

The Glasgow croquis: second stage of the title-page.

FIGURE FIFTY-THREE

The third stage (Crummer sketch).

FIGURE FIFTY-FOUR

Print (reversed) from the original wood-block.

FIGURE FIFTY-FIVE
Title-page of the *Fabrica*, 1543.

FIGURE FIFTY-SIX

Wording on the tablet from the portrait sketch by Calcar in the *Fabrica*. Left (A), from the 1543 editio princeps; right (B), from the 1725 *Opera omnia*.

this stage, in all probability at Basel and at the suggestion of Oporinus. The scroll or cartouche to carry the title was restored as in the first sketch,* the Greek letter *phi* for Oporinus was added, and a scroll below for the privilege. A reversed print recently struck off by Dr. Wiegand from the original wood-block in its final form, still preserved in the Library of the University of Munich, is shown (Fig. 54) for comparison with the Crummer sketch.

The frontispiece in its preliminary as well as final stage (Fig. 55) shows Vesalius beginning to anatomize the female cadaver before him in the traditional manner of all such procedures by first exposing the abdominal viscera. Methods of preserving the body by arterial injection were of course unknown, indeed could scarcely have been conceived of before the discovery of the circulation, and the early removal of the organs which first undergo putrefaction was obligatory, particularly in a warm country, if one were to proceed with the customary three-day demonstration.

Vesalius, however, was strongly convinced that the study of anatomy should begin with the bones which in the course of a dissection were the last to be reached. Hence it was decided not only that Calcar should place a skeleton in the very centre of his drawing as symbolic of this fact, but should also introduce a naked figure to indicate that the surface landmarks were also of anatomical importance. Thus the method of presenting the subject, quite different from that in the *Fabrica*, and which was to be used in the compendium or epitome, was symbolized, *viz.*, first the nude figure, then that particular view of the skeleton in which practically all the bones appear, then layer by layer the muscles are shown removed. These steps may be followed as one turns the leaves toward the front of the book, once the separate sheets according to directions had come to be bound. To this matter we shall shortly return.

The belief was expressed in 1877 by Edouard Turner (401), who had of course never seen the sketches for the frontispiece just described, that Calcar drew the three skeletal plates of 1538 and also, before he parted from Vesalius, the five muscle plates and two nude figures which appear only in the *Epitome* of 1543. Concerning the many other woodcuts of varying sizes in the *Fabrica* he expresses no opinion but leaves it to be assumed that they were drawn by some other artist, or artists, who may possibly have been selected by Calcar from among the many promising pupils in Titian's school. Turner, to be sure, in

---

* This has a "pasted-on effect" in Crummer's opinion and unquestionably destroyed the perspective for which Calcar had striven, and it is to be noted that Wandelaar omitted it in his engraving for he frontispiece in the 1725 Boerhaave edition (*cf.* VI.D.7).

another of his papers (400) expressed the conviction that the portrait of Vesalius in the Louvre, previously ascribed to Tintoretto, was also the work of Calcar. This opinion was vigorously opposed in 1925 by the iconographer, M. H. Spielmann (371), who insists, as he did in the case of the Droeshout engraving of Shakespeare, that the woodcut portrait in the *Fabrica* (see Frontispiece) is the only contemporary likeness of Vesalius and was the basis of all the count-less portraits of him to be found in art museums and university medical schools the world over. While the much discussed Louvre portrait in oil bears the date 1540 and the sitter's age as 26 which is correct for Vesalius, the woodcut portrait is dated two years later, *i.e.,* 1542, and the sitter's age given as then 28.

All that can be definitely said about this at the present time is that an artist, presumably Calcar, made the portrait sketch of Vesalius when he was writing *Caput* XLIII of *Liber* II and inasmuch as the seven books were completed by August 1st of that year 1542, it seems rather late for him to have been still engaged with the muscles of the upper arm. It was hoped that the obscure wording on the tablet shown in the portrait, to which scant attention has been paid, would provide a definite clue to the mystery. While it does not actually do so, my friend Professor F. T. Lewis of Boston has given me some facts which nevertheless are of considerable typographical significance.

The original wood-block was used three times in 1543, for the *Fabrica* as well as for the two *Epitomes*, and it appears again in the China-root Epistle three years later. Hence, the legend on the tablet is the same in all though it relates only to the *Fabrica* and then incorrectly. It begins (Fig. 56A) with the line *"De musculis digitos moventibus Ca.* [for *caput*] *30."* In the first book, *Liber* I, there are 40 chap-ters (the last mistakenly numbered LX) which deal exclusively with the bones, Chapter 30 being given over to the *Os femoris*. The tablet speaks of the muscles moving the digits which are illustrated in the portrait sketch, and since *Liber* II deals with the muscles, one hopefully consults *Caput* XXX, only to find that it has to do with the muscles moving the skull on the vertebræ. But *Caput* XLIII is entitled *De musculis manus digitos moventibus*, and begins in the precise words of the tablet though in altered sequence, thus: *Ossium quinque digitorum constructionem superiori libro prosequentes, longè[a] aliam articuli,* etc. The raised letter "a" is a signal for a marginal note which refers to *ca. 27 lib. 1.* This chapter of *Liber* I is given over to a description of the bones of the hand to which the muscles in question are attached. The opening paragraph of Chapter 43 in Book II reads in transla-tion: "While explaining in the preceding book the construction of the bones of the fingers, we wrote that there is a different sort of articulation in the first joints (phalangeal) of the five digits and in the second joint of the thumb (pollex) from that in the second and third joints of the four fingers and in the third joint of the thumb."

If, as Spielmann supposes, the purpose of the portrait at the very forefront of his book was to flaunt some error of Galen's in the face of all Europe, what particular error it might have been remains obscure; yet it sufficed to infuriate Sylvius who dwelt upon it in his 28th Calumny (385) as follows: "After completely refuting several calumnies that a certain madman has circulated against the names of Hippocrates and Galen, I explained seven successive lines from Chapter 43 of the calumniator's second book, on parts of the hand that are perfectly apparent to anyone," etc. The question in dispute seems to hinge on whether there are four or five metacarpal (postbrachial) bones. Galen thought there were only four while Celsus and Aristotle recognized five. "So [Vesalius generously admits] whenever Galen's opinion is more correct we adopt it and consequently shall enumerate four metacarpals (postbrachial) bones and 15 phalangeal (digital) bones." By a peculiar irony, modern anatomists agree with Aristotle that the thumb has only two phalanges, so both Galen and Vesalius were misled in this matter according to the present verdict. But the point to emphasize is that neither the dissection, in which a modern anatomist can easily see mistakes, nor the quotation on the tablet can be in any way regarded as a reflection on Galen.*

The frontispiece in my opinion expresses far more graphically what he was really aiming at. Picking flaws in Galen's anatomical descriptions handed down through the ages by devious channels was one thing—a sweeping reform in the methods of teaching anatomy to students by setting one's own and their hands to actual dissection was quite another. All this and much more Vesalius makes clear in his dedicatory preface in which he gives details of his own disappointing experiences as a medical student both in Paris and Louvain.†

"I have done my best [he goes on to say] to this single end, namely, in an equally recondite and laborious matter, to aid as many as possible, and truly and completely to describe the structure of the human body—which is built up, not of some ten or twelve parts (as seems to those who give it a passing glance), but

* In all this search for imaginary criticisms of Galen in the text, it is curious that Vesalius' opponents did not point out the two glaring faults in his own muscle figures where the scaleni muscles run over the clavicle on to the chest (p. 184) and the rectus abdominalis reaches to he clavicular level; the description is evidently drawn from the pig.

† For excellent English translations of the long preface, one made by Benjamin Farrington of Cape Town, the other in Clendening, see VI.A.8 and 11 below (p. 96).

of some thousands of different parts—and to bring to students of medicine a substantial contribution towards the understanding of those books of Galen treating of this branch of learning, which of all his writings most require the assistance of a teacher. Moreover I am aware [first] how little authority my efforts will carry by reason of my youth (I am still in my twenty-eighth year); and [secondly] how little, on account of the frequency with which I draw attention to the falsity of Galen's pronouncements, I shall be sheltered from the attacks of those who have not—as I have done in the schools of Italy—applied themselves earnestly to anatomy, and who, being now old men devoured by envy at the true discoveries of youths, will be ashamed, together with all the other sectaries of Galen, that they have been hitherto so purblind failing to notice what I now set forth, yet arrogating to themselves a mighty reputation in the art . . ."

One might continue indefinitely with a description of this remarkable publication. Before moving on, there are two things more to which attention should be drawn. One concerns Vesalius' capacity for taking pains which is nowhere better shown than in the explicit directions printed at the top of the unnumbered leaf m3 (Fig. 57) which may be translated as follows:

"Leaf containing some small figures, which are to be pasted on to the figure prepared to show the arrangement of the combined veins and arteries, on page (signed) m3, numbered 313. In order to paste the figures impressed on this leaf more conveniently to their places, and to make them more useful, first paste a backing-sheet under this leaf and cut the individual figures out of the superfluous paper.

"*Prima*, showing the distribution of the unpaired vein [azygos], should be attached at the back of the large figure, where the trunk of the (vena) cava gives rise to this vein, this place being marked by the letter *o* in both figures.

"*Secunda*, having been cut away from the superfluous paper, will consist of two parts; the upper part shows the vein and artery of the right side, which go, under the pectoral bone, towards the upper part of the abdomen. The letter *q* marked on this part should be affixed to the letter *q* marked on the large figure; and the asterisk * should be affixed to the branch which runs toward the right side *z* and *m* on the large figure. The lower part showing the vein and artery which are distributed to the lower part of the abdomen should be affixed (to the larger figure) where their roots may be seen on the right side close to the letter *l*.

"*Tertia*, more important than the others, shows the distribution of the portal vein, together with the concomitant arteries, a large part of the omentum, and the spleen; it should be affixed to the concave surface of the liver in the large figure, where υ, φ and ς, and some neighboring letters (of the alphabet) may be seen in both figures.

"*Quarta,* showing a portion of the curved surface of the liver, would be most usefully pasted at the point where the letter A stands between the letters *s* and *F* on the large figure.

"*Quinta,* showing, besides the testicles and their envelopes, and the urinary passages, the seminal veins and arteries, should be placed where the letter η is seen in both figures, *i.e.,* where the seminal vein first joins the artery and both are met by the seminal ducts.

"*Sexta* should first be pasted under *Septima,* which shows the anterior surface of the bladder and the penis, together with the 'vessels' [ligaments] which we associate with the umbilicus. In *Sexta* we have shown the under surface of the penis so that its whole outline can be constructed from these two, which can then be pasted to *Quinta* by superimposing the two letters φ . . .

"*Octava* shows the bladder and umbilical 'vessels' [ligaments] of a woman, as well as a portion of the ureters. It should not be added to the large figure, but to the one printed on the verso of the leaf showing the uterus and its veins, arteries, and 'seminal' vessels [ovaries and tubes]. It should thus be joined to that small figure at the point η, where the seminal vein joins the artery, only the ureters being pasted on and with due regard to the relative position of the bladder."

And before leaving the first edition of the *Fabrica* to pass on to one by comparison wholly uninteresting because it lacks the illustrations, we may for a moment return to Calcar, hat in hand like Galen at the bedside. After Dr. Jackschath of Tilsit had pointed out in 1903 (212) that the series of fourteen full-page muscle figures in *Liber* II had a continuous landscape in their background, the figures were removed from the back of my copy of Roth and arranged in two sequences as here shown (Figs. 58 and 59). That the landscape panorama has since been identified as in the Euganean Hills a few miles to the south and west of Padua has already been told. Of the fact that this panoramic background was drawn by Calcar there is little doubt. The same general outlines, roughly indicated, appear also on the three muscle figures that form part of the Glasgow Codex. The suggestion has been made that their purpose was to disarm criticism on the part of those prejudiced against dissection of human bodies by physicians.

Finally a word may be said of the remarkable woodcut initials which portray scenes from the dissecting room as disarmingly played by young children and "putti." As interestingly described both by Lambert (unpublished) and Rosen-kranz (340), they are of two sizes: the four larger initials I, O, Q and T are approximately 7.5 centimetres square and correspond to fourteen lines of type as can be seen in the initial letter Q which starts the dedication to Charles V (Fig. 60A); the seventeen smaller woodcut initials, chiefly used for chapter headings, are approximately 3.6 centimetres square and correspond to seven lines of type. Their detail is such that Vesalius used two of them (the capital letters F and E) in *Liber* IV (p. 329) to illustrate the text (Fig. 60B).

That the printers of Lyon were partial to pocket editions of the medical classics has been emphasized in connection with Guillaume Roville's edition of the Giunta Galen, and it was to be expected that the practice would be imitated in the case of the *Fabrica*. So when the French King's ten-year privilege expired in 1552, the following two-volume Latin 16mo edition was printed at Lyon by the first Jean de Tournes who was soon to be appointed royal printer at Lyon. Vesalius in any event appears to have had nothing to do with de Tournes' venture and at that particular time he was probably on active service with Charles V, for another war was on with France, this time between the Emperor and Henry II. The text of the first volume is merely preceded by the following brief *Typographus lectori*:

"The foremost part of medicine, candid reader, was most commodiously arranged, illustrated, and perfected with dexterity of mind and elegance, by that most expert physician so well deserving of medicine, Andreas Vesalius, in the book which he entitled: 'On the fabric of the human body,' whether you look at it from the point of view of the order in the composition thereof, or of vivid-ness in speech, so as to leave nothing for those who would come after him, one might think. And indeed he gained great praise for it. At the request of many friends we undertook to commit this work to our types and to publish it, think-ing that it will be welcome and necessary to all candidates of both the art of Machaon [son of Æsculapius and the first surgeon] and of philosophy. The utility of this new edition, we submit, lies in its size; you now can easily carry about with you this (originally) immense volume, here compressed into the size of a convenient handbook, and divided into two or three volumes; added to this is a great reduction in price. We offer the text entire, excepting that which per-tains to the understanding of the pictures, as it was impossible to include that in such a small volume. Farewell."

FABRICA Unillustrated pocket edition *Lyon,* 1552

Title of Vol. I (Fig. 61): Andreæ / Vesalii Brvxel⸝ / lensis, de Humani cor⸝ / poris fabrica, / Lib. VII. / * / Ad Carolum Quintum / Imperatorem. / [Ornament] / Tomvs. primvs. / De Ossibus, & Cartilaginibus, Lib. I. / De Ligamentis & Musculis, Lib. II. / [Printer's "Deux vipères" device] / Lvgdvni / apvd Ioan. Tornæsivm / [rule] M. D. LII.

Vol. II: Same, with minor changes (see Fig. 61).

Collation Vol. I: 16mo; italic type in eights, 28 lines to the page; a⸝z⁸, A⸝I⁸, aa⸝zz⁸, A⸝M⁸, N⁴; 458 pp., [27] *ll.*, 523 pp., [22] *ll.*

Vol. II: a⸝z⁸, A⸝Z⁸, aa⸝ll⁸; 833 pp., [39] *ll.*

Paper: Chain⸝lines *ca.* 3.3 cm. run across pp. No watermarks.

Contents Vol. I: a1a title; a1b the typographer to the reader; a2a⸝F5b *Liber I*, text paginated 458 pp. (four illustrations of skull on pp. 130, 131, 132, much reduced from originals); F6a⸝I8a index, not paginated; I8b blank; aa1a⸝K6a *Liber II*, text paginated 523 pp.; K6b blank; K7a⸝N3b index, not paginated; N4a blank; N4b printer's "prism" device

Vol. II: a1a title; a1b able of Books III⸝VII; a2a⸝k5a (pp. 3⸝153) *Liber III*; k5b⸝q5a (pp. 154⸝249 [wrongly numbered 349]) *Liber IV*; q5b⸝M1b (pp. 250⸝546) *Liber V*; M2a⸝V5b (pp. 547⸝682) *Liber VI*; V6a⸝gg1a (pp. 683⸝833) *Liber VII*; gg1b⸝ll6b index for Vol. II; ll7a blank; ll7b printer's device; ll8 blank.

Note: This pocket edition follows the 1543 edition closely, even repeating the error of numbering the last chapter of *Liber I* as LX [De ossium numero].

Copies: Louvain [burned Aug. 1914]; London (BM); Paris (BN); Oxford (B); Munich; Buda⸝pest (UL); Waller; Cushing; PPCP; NNNAM [vol. 1 only]; Clendening; DLC; DSG; MiU (Crummer, Pilcher). W. M. Voynich in 1925 had a perfect pair priced $200. Perfect pairs are some⸝what rare; individual copies, often with Tomus I or Tomus II erased, are less so.

Copies used: Cushing; *Vol. I,* bought from C. J. Sawyer, London, Oct. 1912, for 25 shillings. Bound in contemporary stamped pigskin on boards with clasps; measures 12.4 by 7.5 cm., and in thickness 4 cm. without the binding. Provenance: Former owner's name (illegible) and date 1563.

Vol. II, bought from R. Lier, Cat. XII, 1929, for Swiss frs. 135. Bound in contemporary stamped vellum; edges stained red and goffered; measures 12.3 by 7.4 cm., and in thickness 3.8 cm. Prove⸝nance: "Bibliothecæ S. Dorotheæ Wrat." (St. Dorothea's Library, Breslau).

Jean de Tournes' venture could scarcely have been a profitable one, for the *Fabrica* without Calcar's illustrations was not the same book by any means. Only the year before, the fourth Latin edition of Vesalius' *Paraphrasis* had come from his press, but what is more important, he had for a decade been in close touch with other Lyon printers who for the benefit of those unable to read Latin had been printing French translations of the medical classics. In 1552 he had already issued a miscellany of medical tracts translated, among others, by Pierre Tollet and Jean Canappe whose French translation of the Anatomy of Loys Vassé had but recently appeared. Had he only seen fit to persuade Canappe, for the benefit of the barber surgeons, to put *en françoys* the pocket *Fabrica*! Well, in that case probably *no* copies would have survived to tell the tale. The two Paris editions of Paré's *Briefve collection de ladministration anatomique* of 1549 and 1550, though also unillustrated, are now impossible to find and the pocket *Anatomie universelle du corps humain* of 1561 for which fragments of Calcar's woodcuts were copied has become one of the rarest of books in the field of medicine.

Roth quotes Gesner's reference to a second edition of the *Fabrica* of 1554 (probably an error for 1555) and assumes (345, p. 224) that Vesalius was at work on a second edition in October, 1551, some considerable portion of which had been issued in the Spring of 1552. If this is true, no such fragmentary issue has ever been recorded.*

SECOND BASEL EDITION OF THE 'FABRICA'

What influenced Vesalius to make the comparatively unimportant alterations in the text of the *Fabrica,* and what encouraged Oporinus to undertake the printing in 1555 of a still more sumptuous volume than that issued in 1543 is not entirely clear. The printer's termagant wife would scarcely have favoured it, for as a business venture it was certainly unpromising, since by 1555 there were already numerous publications in England and on the Continent in which the plates had been copied and the sales value of the book must in consequence have been greatly reduced.

Nevertheless a new edition was lavishly prepared for. The paper was to be heavier and the type larger, with only 49 instead of 57 lines to the page, thus necessitating the recutting of all the small initial letters so that they would now fit seven lines of the new type. Indeed, an entirely new wood-block was cut for the frontispiece to the considerable loss of its beauty and for no other reason that one can see unless to save the nun's embarrassment by clothing the naked figure. The head of Vesalius at the dissecting table, however, is more vigorously portrayed than in the first folio. The former scroll at the bottom of the

* Oporinus's catalogue of May 1552 indicates that five of the seven books had already been run off and were for sale but, as Dr. Cushing points out, no copy of this fragment appears to have survived. A letter from Oporinus to Conrad Hubert of Strassburg gives insight into the difficulties under which the edition was brought out and accounts for the long delay. An English translation of this letter is given by Fisch (137, p. 254): "Shortly before your letter came I had written to Michael Toxites to secure for me from the guardians of Dryander's children the moulds and tools for the large types in which he had had some things of Plutarch and others printed by Augustine Fries. Dryander himself had previously lent me the moulds to make the types for the second edition of Vesalius's Anatomy. But now some of the types are so worn from use that I must have more cast in order to finish the Anatomy which I started long ago and I cannot do so without the moulds and tools. I could easily get them again from Dryander if he were still living. But if the guardians will not let me have them for the asking, I shall gladly buy them at a fair price, just to be sure of their being sent to me promptly, by the next post despatched to me at my expense. I had rather lose two or three florins than be without them longer and go on day after day being prevented from finishing a work begun three years ago. I beg you, Conrad, to see that I get them, and that they reach me quickly."—Ed.

CHARTA PARVAS ALIQVOT FIGVRAS COM

PLECTENS, QVAE FIGVRAE AD COMMONSTRANDAM VE narum arteriarumq; simul commissarum seriem paratae, ac in pagina m 3, aut numero 313 insignita obuiae, ueniunt agglutinandae.

PRIMA. **TERTIA.**

SEXTA.

SECVNDA. **QVARTA.** **SEPTIMA.**

QVINTA. **OCTAVA.**

VT figuras hæc chartæ impreſſæ commo dè ſuis ſedibus glutines, illaſq; ualidiores redda tur, primùm præſenti chartæ membranam ſub glutinabis, ſingulasq; fi guras à ſuperflua papy ro reſecabis. PRI MA, quæ uenæ pa ri caruris diſtributio nem proponit magnæ fi guræ tergo illic uenit co mittenda, ubi caua cau dex eam uenam promit. ac o in utriſque figuris ſcribitur ſpectatur. SE CVNDA, ubi à redundanti papyro cir cunciſa erit, duas partes conſtituet, quarum ſupe rior uenam arteriam que dextri lateris exprimit, ſub pectoris oſſe ſuperio rem abdominis ſedem pe tentes. Huius itaq; par tis q̃ ad magnæ figuræ q̃ figetur, cr * ad ra mum qui ad dextrum la tus ⁊ cr m in magna figura occurrit. Cæte rum humilior pars uenæ arteriamq; exprimens, quæ inferiorem abdomi nis ſedem implicant, illic eſt iungenda, ubi earum radices iuxta l in dex tro latere ſpectantur.

TERTIA cæteris dignior, uenæ portæ diſtributionem ſi mul cũ arterijs illam con comitantibus, magnã que inferioris membranæ o menti portione cr liene pariter exprimens, ad ca uam iecoris ſedem maiori figuræ nectetur, ubi v φ, ſ, cr contermini ali quot characteres in utriſ que figuris ſpectantur.

QVARTA portionem gibbæ ſedis ie coris proponens, nõ inu tiliter ueluti ex puncto il l c glutinabitur, ubi A inter ſ cr F maioris figuræ conſiſtit.

QVINTA præter teſtes ipſorumq; inuolucra, cr urinarios meatus, uenas arteriasq; ſeminales oſtendens, illic eſt committenda, ubi n in ambabus figuris obuium eſt, aut ubi uena ſeminalis arteriæ primùm iungitur, meatusq; urinarij illis ſubijciuntur.

SEXTA primùm ſub SEPTIMA uenit glutinanda. Septima enim ueſicæ cʒ penis anteriorem ſedem proponit, unã cum ua ſis quæ umbilico aſſcribimus. Sexta autem humiliorem penis ſuperficiem in hoc expreſſimus, ut tota figura ex ambabus illis conſurget, charactere φ ſuper quinæ figuræ φ nectit queat, ac poſtmodum penis inſtar S implicari.

OCTAVA figura mulieris ueſicam cr umbilici uaſa, urinariorumq; meatuum portionem continens, maiori nõ eſt committenda, ſed illi fi guræ quæ in chartæ tergo ubi maior impreſſa eſt, uterum ipſius, uenas cr arterias ſeminariaq; uaſa commonſtrat. Iungetur itaq; octaua ad paruam illam figuram ubi n occurrit, uenaq; ſeminalis arteriæ committitur: nexus ueró fiet urinarijs tantum meatibus, proportione à ueſicæ ſitu ſumpta.

m 3

FIGURE FIFTY-SEVEN

The unpaginated sheet m3 from the 1543 *Fabrica* [X2 in the 1555 ed.] with figures to be cut out and superimposed on a preceding plate.

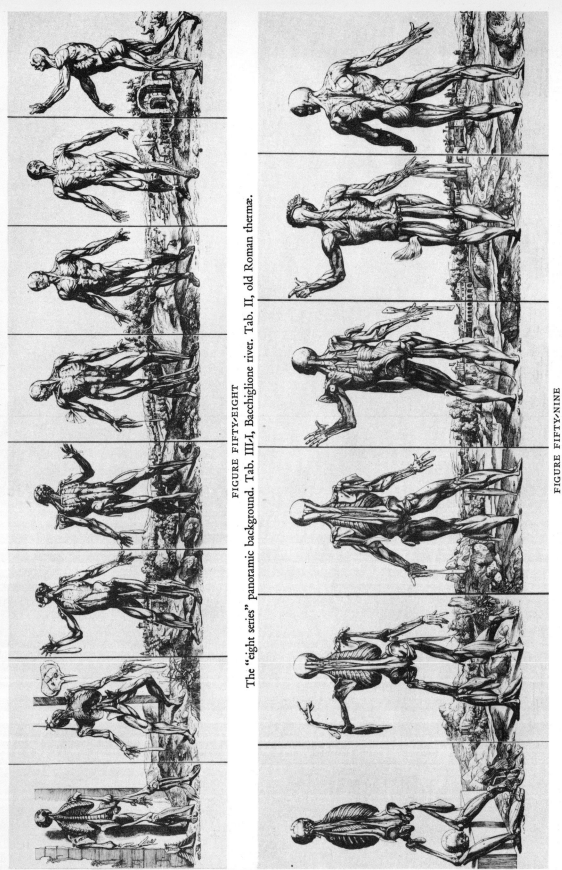

FIGURE FIFTY-EIGHT

The "eight series" panoramic background. Tab. IIII, Bacchiglione river. Tab. II, old Roman thermæ.

FIGURE FIFTY-NINE

The "six series" panoramic landscape. T. II, XIII, XII, Euganean Hills; T. XLX, thatched farm houses and bridge similar to those still extant.

V A
dis
tur
clei
diu
disc
mu
tis
dif
un
ipf
que
ac
art

teras quidem ſilentio prætereram, & de ea qu
monem inſtituam, profectò in hac tametſi rel

nagisꝗ attentam requirit mentem, quàm ſi

le
ꝗ
s.
ni
ue
ui

x?
os
m
it.
m
e
m
æ
s,

QVONIAM
Galenus in horum neruo-
rum deſcriptione, quemad-
modum & nonnunquam a-
libi, mentionem facit inſtru-
menti gloſsicomi, nos lecto
ri non incommodaturos du
ximus, ſi hunc characte-
rem F, in quo id inſtru-
mentũ obiter exprimitur,
hìc interijceremus: unà cũ
E, quo inſtrumentum deli-
neatur brachij, ſed potiſsi-
mum femoris luxationibus
reſtituendis idoneum. Li-
cet hæc alio libro ac argu-
mento tractanda pu
temus.

tibus obuius, ipſi arteriali uénæ adnaſcitur,

FIGURE SIXTY

Initials from the *Fabrica* (1543). Above (A), the first capital in the book, showing viviſection of a pig, from
the prefatory dedication to Charles V *(f. *2a)*. Below (B), capital initials F and E used in text of Liber IV,
page 329, to illustrate use of the glossocomium of Galen.

ANDREAE
VESALII BRVXEL-
lensis, de Humani cor-
poris. fabrica,

Ad Carolum Quintum
Imperatorem.
❦

TOMVS II.

*Quibusq; reliquos libros complectens, quorum
materiam sequens pagina docet.*

LVGDVNI
APVD IOAN. TORNAESIVM.
M. D. LII.

ANDREAE
VESALII BRVXEL-
lensis, de Humani cor-
poris fabrica,
LIB. I II.
*
Ad Carolum Quintum
Imperatorem.
❦

De Ossibus, & Cartilaginibus, LIB. I.
De Ligamentis & Musculis, LIB. II.

LVGDVNI
APVD IOAN. TORNAESIV M.
M. D. LII.

FIGURE SIXTY-ONE

Title-pages of the pocket *Fabrica* of 1552.

FIGURE SIXTY-TWO

Title-page of *Fabrica* of 1555.

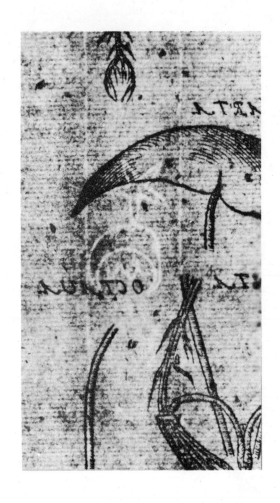

FIGURE SIXTY-THREE

Star-and-crescent watermark with 2.5 cm. chain-lines in the *Fabrica* of 1555.

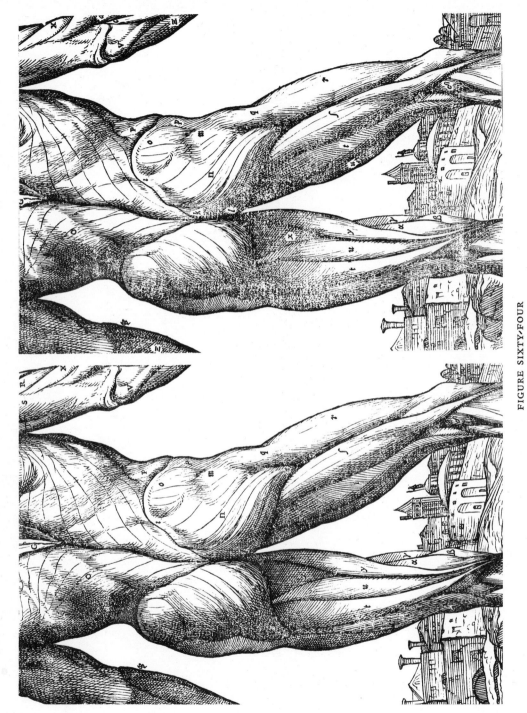

FIGURE SIXTY-FOUR

Showing the greater clarity of the lettering in the plates of the 1555 edition.
Note circumferential removal of shading around the lettering.

ANDREAE
VESALII
BRVXELLENSIS,
INVICTISSIMI CAROLI V. IMP.
MEDICI,
DE HVMANI CORPORIS FABRICA
LIBRI SEPTEM.

Cum Indice rerum & uerborum memorabilium locupletißimo.

VENETIIS,
Apud Franciscum Franciscium Senensem, & Ioannem Criegher Germanum.
M D LXVIII.

FIGURE SIXTY-FIVE (*above*)
Title-page of *Fabrica* of 1568.

FIGURE SIXTY-SIX (*below*)
Watermark of 1568 Venice edition of *Fabrica*.

frontispiece containing the privilege has been transformed into the top of an animal operating table (Fig. 62). The skeleton now carries a scythe and the ser- vants are bringing in a goat as well as a dog. The Oporinus *phi* monogram has been omitted as the licence now appears on the title-page.

VI.A.—3

FABRICA   2nd folio (3rd ed.)   *Basel,* 1555

Title (Fig. 62) [upper shield]: Andreæ Vesalii / Brvxellensis, invi- / ctissimi Caroli V. Imperatoris / medici, de Humani corporis / fabrica Libri septem. / [Privilege] Cvm Cæsareæ / Maiest. Galliarum Regis, ac Senatus Veneti gratia & / priuilegio, ut in diplomatis eorundem continetur. / [below wood- cut] / Basileæ, per Ioannem Oporinum.

Colophon: Basileæ, Ex Offici- / na Ioannis Oporini, An- / no Salutis per Christvm partæ M D LV. / Mense Augusto.

Collation: Fol. Rom. and ital. types; a-z⁶, A-V⁶, X³, Y-Z⁶, aa⁶, bb⁸, cc-zz⁶, Aa⁸, Bb-Ee⁶; [6] *ll.*, 824 pp., [24] *ll.*

Contents: a1a frontispiece-title; a1b blank; a2a-5a preface to Charles V dated Padua, August 1, 1542; a5b-6a letter to Oporinus, August 24th *(nono Cal. Sept.)*; a6b portrait woodcut.

Liber I, b1a-t2b, 41 chapters on bones and carti- lages (pp. 1-208), the last chapter on instruments for dissection having been moved up from Book II; the wrongly numbered Ca. LX of the 1543 edition on the number of bones has been rewritten to include the cartilages and has changed places with Chapter XXXIX.

Liber II, t3a-P2a, 62 chapters on ligaments and muscles (pp. 209-435); text considerably altered; same 14 full-page muscle figures, lettering on wood- cuts made more clear by circumferential removal of shading (Fig. 64).

Liber III, P2b-X2, 15 chapters on bloodvessels (pp. 436-505); ends with folding plate, sig. X1 (p. 505) and unpaginated leaf, sig. X2 [p. 506], of figures to be superimposed. Same as leaf m3 in the 1543 edition.

Liber IIII, Y1a-bb5b, 17 chapters on nerves (pp. 507-552); ends with folding plate, sig. bb6-7 (pp. 553-4).

Liber V, bb8a-oo5a, 19 chapters on abdominal organs (pp. 555-697).

Liber VI, oo5b-tt3b, 16 chapters on thoracic organs (pp. 698-754).

Liber VII, tt4a-Aa8b, 18 chapters on brain and special senses, ending with Chap. XIX on vivi- section (pp. 755-824).

Errata leaf, Bb1a; *Index* in 3 columns, BB1b- Ee5a; *register,* EE5a (below); *colophon,* Ee5b; Ee6a blank; Ee6b printer's device.

Note: Pagination of the text begins on sig. b and, in contrast to the *ed. princeps,* continues to p. 824, the end of Book VII, without a fault. The preliminary six and the final 24 leaves are unpaginated. In addi- tion, quire X (a "*semiternio*") has only two page numbers instead of six, and the folding leaf bb6-7 has only two page numbers instead of four. Hence with 71 gatherings in sixes, two in eights, and quire X with three leaves, there are estimated to be 445 leaves or 890 pages. This contrasts with the estimated 359 leaves and 718 pages of the 1543 edition.

Paper: heavier than the 1543 edition. Watermark: star and crescent (Fig. 63); chain lines 2.5 cm.

Copies: As with the 1543 edition, the known copies are too numerous to list. We have record of some 25 copies in the United States and many abroad.

Copy used: H.C., gift of Howard A. Kelly, 1905. Name of 16th century owner on flyleaf. Bound in contemporary stamped pigskin on boards with clasps, etc., dated 1558. Measures 41.8 by 28 cm.

Vesalius made some definite improvements in the text which have been cited by Garrison (164a, pp. 219-20), such as concern the ethnic aspects of craniology [p. 23, lines 12-29], but more particularly in connection with his physiological observations in the last chapter, *viz.,* (i) the effect of nerve section [p. 810, lines 22-34], (ii) persistence of life after splenectomy [p. 820, lines 26-31], (iii) collapse of the lungs on puncture of the chest [p. 821, lines 25-31], (iv) aphonia from section of the laryngeal nerve [p. 823, line 11], (v) prolongation of life by artificial intratracheal inflation of collapsed lungs [p. 824, lines 8-14].

We shall see that in 1564, the year of his death, Vesalius stopped in Venice on his way to the Holy Land and submitted his last book, a reply to Fallopius, to the printer Francesco Senense (Franciscus de Franciscis) for publication. This same printer, four years later, in collaboration with a Pomeranian engraver, Joannes Criegher, whose name he generously coupled with his own as printer, ventured to print a complete text of the 1555 *Fabrica* in smaller format and with all of the wood-blocks recut in smaller size. The skeletal and muscle figures, for example, were reduced about ten centimetres in height, to about two-thirds their former size, and their panoramic landscape background was replaced by something simpler. New woodcut capital initials of two sizes were especially engraved for the book, though they are inferior to those of the Basel editions. The new woodcuts for the illustrations, however, were so well executed that the engraver might almost have passed for the same person who in Venice at the behest of Vesalius had cut the original blocks for the larger work.

It must have been not only an expensive undertaking but a venturesome one, since the Vesalius plates by now had been re-engraved and printed not only by Geminus in England whence they had spread to Lyon with an edition in 1567, but also by Valverde whose first edition, published in Rome in 1556, had been promptly imitated by Plantin at Antwerp in 1566 and 1568. One can only conjecture that even after the death of Fallopius there must still have been a student demand for the Latin text and illustrations of the *Fabrica* which could be profitably met by a less costly edition than the ponderous 1555 reprint of Oporinus. The printer's brief dedication is to his Ferrara friend, Monticatinus.

VI.A.—4

FABRICA Posthumous 4th ed.   *Venice,* 1568

Title (Fig. 65): Andreæ / Vesalii / Brvxellensis, / invictissimi Caroli V. Imp. / medici, / De Hvmani Corporis Fabrica / libri septem. / Cum Indice rerum & uerborum memorabilium locupletissimo. / [Printer's device] / Venetiis, / Apud Franciscum Franciscium Senensem, & Ioannem Criegher Germanum. / M D LXVIII.

Collation: Fol. Rom. and ital. types; *⁶, A⁄Z⁶, Aa⁄Yy⁶, Zz⁸; [6] *ll.,* 510 pp., [23] *ll.*

Contents: *1a title; *1b blank; *2a⁄5a dedication to Charles V dated August 1, 1542; *5b⁄6a Oporinus to reader, and Vesalius' letter to Oporinus; *6b printer's dedication to Antonius Monticatinus; A1a⁄ L4a (pp. 1⁄127) *Liber I;* L4b⁄Z5a (pp. 128⁄273) *Liber II;* Z5b⁄Dd5 (pp. 274⁄322) *Liber III,* last leaf being plate with cuts for superimposition, verso blank; Dd6a⁄Gg2b (pp. 323⁄352) *Liber IIII;* Gg3a⁄ Oo1b (pp. 353⁄434) *Liber V;* Oo2a⁄Qq6a (pp. 435⁄467) *Liber VI;* Qq6b⁄Vu3b (pp. 468⁄510) *Liber VII;* Vu4a⁄Zz8a *index* in three cols. ital. (22 unnumbered *ll.*); Zz8a *register;* Zz8b blank.

Note: The book is set up with marginal notes exactly as in VI.A.3. It is well printed on durable paper evidently supplied by the same paper maker we have met before, if the watermark means a trade⁄ mark rather than an indication of the quality of the paper (Fig. 66).

Copies: Louvain; Munich; London (BM); Waller; Cushing; Fulton; CtY; van Wagenen; Trent; CaMM⁄Os; MH; PPCP; NNNAM; ICU; DSG; NIC; NNC⁄M; MdBJ⁄W; MBM; Ca⁄ TAM; IEN⁄M; NN; NPV; MiU (Crummer, Pilcher); Clendening; Fisher; CU⁄M.

Copy used: Cushing; gift of Wm. Osler, August 6, 1909. Original leather covers, rebacked; measures 31.8 by 21.5 cm.

This edition was a foreign book and was printed by Francesco Senense without licence, there being no regulation at the time (1568) to prevent this and it was a common enough practice. His sons, Giov. Antonio and Jacopo de' Franceschi, who carried on the press, soon printed a book on Thomas Aquinas, permission to publish which the Venetian censors had given provided certain passages were omitted. This was resented at Rome and the Congregation of the *Index* ordered the passages restored and made some additional regulations as a penalty, thereby directly punishing Venetian subjects in violation of the Con⁄ cordat. It was at this juncture that Fra Paolo Sarpi entered in as mediator in the quarrel, all of which lies beyond our present story except to show what diffi⁄ culties confronted the contemporary Venetian printers.

The sons of Francesco Senense must have come into possession of Criegher's carefully engraved wood⁄blocks and when in 1604 their father's edition of 1568 presumably became sold out, they decided to issue another in precisely the same format (Fig. 67). Indeed, more than a casual examination of the two books is necessary to make certain that the type has been completely reset, so closely, page for page and line for line, does it follow the 1568 edition. Fabricius of Acquapendente was by now professor of anatomy at Padua, and it was in all likelihood the student text he recommended. Additions to the book were a title⁄page handsomely engraved on copper and an additional series of anatomical tables with a new title⁄page and privilege giving the date of publication which was absent on the frontispiece.

VI.A.—5

FABRICA   Posthumous 5th ed.   *Venice*, 1604

Engraved title within elaborate copperplate border (Fig. 67): Andreæ Vesalii / Anatomia / Venetiis apvd / Ioan: Anton: et Iacobvm / de Franciscis.

Half-Title (*1*a): Andreæ Vesalii / Anatomia: / Addita nunc postremo etiam /
Antiquorum Anatome.

Title of Rufus appendix: Vniversa / Antiquorum / Anatome / Tam ossium, quam partium & externa-rum, & internarum: / Ex Rvfo Ephesio / Medico Antiquissimo: / Tribvs Tabellis explicata / per / Fabivm Pavlinvm. / Qvibvs accessit qvarta ex Sorani / Medici Antiquissimi Fragmento Græco non antehac Latino facto. / De Matrice. / Cvm privilegio. / [Printer's device] / Venetiis, M DC IIII. / [rule] / Apud Io. Antonium, & Iacobum de Franciscis.

Collation: Fol. *⁴, A-Z⁶, Aa-Yy⁶, Zz⁸; [4] *ll.*, 510 pp., [23] *ll.*

Appendix: a², b-c⁴; [10] *ll.*

Contents: *1a half-title; *1b blank; *2a engraved title (Fig. 67) signed by F. Valegio; *2b blank; *3 dedication to Duke of Urbino; *4a printers to reader; *4b Greek and Latin laudatory verses by Fabius Paulinus; A1a-Zz8b as in VI.A.4. *Universa Antiquorum* Contents: a1a title; a1b blank; a2a address to medical students; a2b arrangement of tables; b1a-c2b tables of bones, and of external and internal parts; c3a-4a table of the uterus from Soranus; c4b blank.

Copies: Louvain; London (BM); Waller; Cushing; van Wagenen; CaMM-Os; MH-M; PPCP; NNNAM; DSG; NBMS; NNC-M; MdBJ-W; MBM; MnU; ViRA; MiU (Crummer, Pilcher); Fisher; CU-M; PU.

Copy used: Cushing; purchased in January, 1907, from Martin Boas, Berlin, for M.60; measures 31.9 by 22 cm.

The *Fabrica* has never been printed in a language other than Latin. The vain regret has been expressed that Jean de Tournes did not persuade Canappe or Pierre Tollet to put the two-volume edition of 1552 into the vernacular for the benefit of the barber surgeons, a practice employed by many of the Lyon printers somewhat to the horror of the conservative Paris medical faculty. Almost four centuries elapsed when, if I have the story straight, G. van Rynberk, the professor of physiology at the University of Amsterdam, suggested to the Dutch Society of Sciences at Haarlem and the Society of Natural Sciences, Medicine and Surgery at Amsterdam that they publish a French translation of the *Fabrica*. Funds were collected for beginning the work in the hope that with international collaboration the enterprise might be brought to a successful end. Professor Verschaffelt of the University of Ghent, a physicist and not a physician, was engaged to do the translation from the 1555 edition.

Beginning with the text of *Liber* I (Fig. 68), the first six chapters were translated and forty leaves of text with the marginal notes and illustrations were set up in type and superbly printed by the famous Enschedé Press of Haarlem on paper of the first quality. The cost of proceeding thus far proved to be eighteen hundred dollars, at which rate to complete the book would have required in the neighborhood of $40,000 and the project, alas, was abandoned and there is little hope of its resumption. As it stands, the fragment is now little more than a bibliographical curiosity. Are there not, even now, forty people in the world who would be glad to give a thousand dollars to possess a French or English translation of this work to read, if only for historical purposes?

VI.A.—6

FABRICA French fragment [Haarlem, 1924]

Head-title (p. 1, *cf.* Fig. 68): André Vésale / La structure du corps humain / Livre premier, consacré aux organes / . . .

Collation: Fol. 1 *l.*, 40 pp.

Contents: Prelim. leaf corresponding to a6 of the 1555 ed., with portrait on verso; pp. 1-4 *Livre premier . . . Les os, leur utilité et leurs différences. Chapitre I*; pp. 5-6 *Chapitre II*; pp. 7-16 *Chapitre III*; pp. 16-24 *Chapitre IV*; pp. 24-29 *Chapitre V*; pp. 29-40 *Chapitre VI* (incomplete).

Note: The translation was made from the 1555 edition by Prof. J. E. Verschaffelt, a physicist, for the *Hollandshe Societeit van Wetenschappen te Haarlem* and the *Genootschap voor Natuur- Genees- en Heilkunde te*

Amsterdam under whose auspices it was printed by J. Enschedé & Sons of Haarlem in 1924 (the date verified in a letter from the printer to the New York Academy of Medicine, 18 April, 1933).

Copies: CaMM-Os; NNNAM; Trent; Fulton; Cushing.

Copy used: H.C.; gift of B. W. Th. Nuyens of Amsterdam, October 1932; in blue paper covers, measures 40 by 27.5 cm. untrimmed. Paper carries watermark "Van Gelder Zonen."

Other Fragmentary Renderings

Several sections of the *Fabrica* have been translated into English, and there have been many proposals to issue a complete English text. Prior to his death in 1937, the late Professor William Wright of London had made some progress toward rendering the 1543 text, but he had published nothing. Dr. M. F. Ashley-Montagu of Philadelphia had proposed to translate and collate the 1543 and 1555 texts in time for the commemoration year, 1943, but this project was abandoned for lack of financial support. Finally, Professor J. B. deC. M. Saunders of San Francisco, who expects to issue English translations of the Venesection and the China-root Epistles in 1943, has also completed translating a large part of the text of the 1543 *Fabrica* and hopes ultimately to issue it after the fashion of the Hoover *De re metallica* of Agricola, complete with plates and other illustrations. The five fragments which have come to our notice are as follows:

VI.A.—7

FABRICA English fragment 1931

Title: The last chapter of the *De Fabrica* of Vesalius entitled Some observations on the dissection of living animals. Translated from the Latin by Benjamin Farrington. *Trans. roy. Soc. S. Africa,* 1931, 20:1-14.

VI.A.—8

FABRICA   English fragment   1932
Title: The Preface of Andreas Vesalius to *De Fabrica Corporis Humani 1543.*
    Translated by B. Farrington (Cape Town). *Proc. R. Soc. Med.,* 1932,
    25:1357-1366.

VI.A.—9

FABRICA   English fragment   1935
Title: A reading from Andreæ Vesalii, De humani corporis fabrica liber VII
    de vivorum sectione nonnulla caput XIX. [Translated] By Samuel W.
    Lambert. *Proc. Charaka Cl.,* 1935, *8*:3-21.

VI.A.—10

FABRICA   English fragment   1936
Title: [Same as VI.A.9.] *Bull. N. Y. Acad. Med.,* 1936, 2d s. *12*:345-385.

Note: The original text has been included in both Lambert translations. In VI.A.9, seven pages (818-824) of the 1555 edition have been reproduced in collotype and tipped in (folded once) between the pages of the *Proceedings*. In VI.A.10, the translation is printed on recto pages, opposite the Vesalian text which has been set up after the fashion of the 1555 edition. The translation alone has been reprinted (pp. 142-151) in Logan Clendening's *Source book of medical history*, New York, P. B. Hoeber, 1942, xiv, 685 pp. In Dr. Cushing's collection is an unpublished MS. translation of a part of the vivisection chapter by Cecil K. Drinker of Harvard (see X.115).

VI.A.—11

FABRICA   English fragment   1942
Head-title: Preface. [From *The Fabric of the Human Body.*] To the Divine Charles
    the Fifth, Greatest and Most Invincible Emperor. The preface of Andrew
    Vesalius to his books On the Fabric of the Human Body.

Note: In: Clendening, Logan. *Source book of medical history.* New York, P. B. Hoeber, 1942. This translation appeared in Chapter XV (pp. 128-141). It was made by W. P. Hotchkiss, Associate Professor of History and Political Science, University of Kansas City. A footnote states that "The Prefaces of the editions of 1543, 1555 and the Venetian edition of 15[68], have all been collated to make this translation. Many passages are obscure and it has been thought best by Professor Hotchkiss and the editor to allow quite a loose translation in order to bring out any kind of sensible English meaning."

Since this purports to be a *bio*-bibliography, it has already seemed advisable
to make certain departures from de Feyfer's bibliographical sequence, as in the
case of the plagiators of the *Tabulæ sex*. So also at the present juncture, further
consideration of his subsections VI.B, VI.C with its 37 items, and VI.D with
66 more will be postponed in favour of something of more immediate interest:
namely, the subsequent history of the wood-blocks from which, despite repeated
use, perfect impressions after an interval of four centuries have recently been printed.

THE FATE OF THE WOOD-BLOCKS*

The Vesalian wood-blocks proved to be more enduring than brass as a monument to the unknown engraver (or engravers) who doubtless were hard driven
by the impetuous author. He admits having often been so sorely plagued by his
artists and engravers that he considered himself more miserable than the bodies
from tombs or executions he perforce was obliged to keep in his bedroom for
weeks. If this confession on Vesalius' part, made at the end of the China-root
Epistle, gives a true hint of the surroundings in which temperamental craftsmen
were expected to do their work, it can be easily imagined that conflicts with their
employer often arose. With the publication of the 1555 edition of the *Fabrica* and
the abortive attempt in the same year to issue an epitome bearing the same date,
all further interest in the wood-blocks must have ceased. There was little likelihood, owing to their forbidding size, that they would ever be used again, and
they doubtless remained in the possession of Oporinus at whose press during the
twelve-year interval they had of course been stored.

Which one of the Basel printers may have succeeded to or have purchased
the stores and apparatus along with the printing rights after Oporinus' death in
1568 is not clear, but it was probably the son of Jerome Froben who in 1588
finally succeeded in the face of great opposition in getting permission to print the
Hebrew Talmud, in the prolonged squabble over which Oporinus had previously been engaged. In 1583 Ambrose Froben had printed for Felix Platter his
De corporis humani structura et usu—a work which is divided into three books.
The last of the three has its own title-page and begins with a brief letter to the
reader in which Platter, lest he be accused of plagiary, frankly states: "As up to
the present time the plates of Vesalius are the best that have ever been offered, and
as it would be almost impossible to surpass them, I would have willingly added
them to this volume introducing a few slight changes (because the opportunity
presented itself for buying them), if I had not been prevented from this intention
by the necessity of adopting under the circumstances a volume of so large a size
it would be inconvenient for students. That is why I have had the plates of
Vesalius engraved on copper in reduced size and with slight changes; and to
them I have added a few others." Like his predecessor, Platter also seems to have
had trouble with his engravers, for he goes on to say: "I am forced to confess

* This section was written by Dr. Cushing several days before his death. He had not designated where
it was to be placed in the MS., but since the Maschenbauer, Leveling and New York Academy *Icones* all
used the original blocks of the *Fabrica*, it has seemed logical to include them in VI.A. Modified versions of
Vesalius' text (*e.g.*, Boerhaave's *Opera*) which did not use the original wood-blocks will be placed in VI.D
and arranged alphabetically.—Ed.

that, without my wish or negligence, but due to the malevolence of certain men, whom I do not care to name, many (plates) have been executed less perfectly, and some have even been spoiled; these, however, may be easily corrected from Vesalius' drawings, of which so many editions are extant—I have not the least desire to keep students away from these drawings by means of this my work— since I have used almost everywhere the same characters as Vesalius; as for my own newly-made plates, which were for that reason delineated more carefully, they too might be juxtaposed and compared with those of Vesalius."

From what Platter says to the reader, it is evident that though the wood-blocks were still available and for sale, he decided that his purposes could be best served by having the illustrations re-engraved. He does not say that he actually purchased the wood-blocks, as seems to have been inferred. Had he done so, their final resting-place, in view of his loyalty to his birthplace and admiration for Vesalius, would doubtless have been Basel rather than Munich. It seems far more likely that from the third generation of Frobens who apparently went out of business in 1603, the wood-blocks passed to the König family of Basel typographers whose firm at about the same time also purchased the business of the Petris. Evidence of this is shown by the fact that in 1603 when Ludwig König printed the second edition of Platter's work, the Froben device appears at the end of the second book, whereas the third book containing the illustrations has again a new title-page but with no further evidence of participation by the Frobens.

While the assumed possession of the wood-blocks by the Königs is of course conjectural, their Basel printing-house prospered during the seventeenth century and since we have begun making assumptions, it would take only one more to bring their business to a close with possibly a public sale of the many useless but nigh indestructible old wood-blocks inherited through the Frobens from Oporinus and still stored in their warehouses. So in this manner, unless some better explanation can be offered, let us imagine that the 150-year-old blocks came into the hands of a certain Andreas Maschenbauer, printer and publisher of Augsburg, who either got wind of the sale or happened at the time to be in Basel on some other business. Maschenbauer must have known what he was buying; indeed, the parcel may well enough have been clearly marked and sold as the celebrated Vesalian wood-blocks, some of which, as he shrewdly realized, could be used in a book for painters and engravers. He was probably unaware of the Calcar tradition and even had he known of it, the name of Titian added to his title-page would certainly have a greater sales value.

FIGURE SIXTY-SEVEN

Title-page of the 1604 *Fabrica*.

ANDRÉ VÉSALE
LA STRUCTURE DU CORPS HUMAIN
LIVRE PREMIER, CONSACRÉ AUX ORGANES
qui foutiennent et fupportent le corps tout entier, et par lefquels tout eft
confolidé et auxquels tout s'attache.

LES OS, LEUR UTILITÉ ET LEURS DIFFÉRENCES.
Chapitre I.

*Ce chapitre premier fe rapportant également bien à tous les os, il n'eft précédé d'aucun deffin; d'ail-
leurs, pour la même raifon, il n'a pas befoin d'une figure particulière, à moins qu'on ne juge peut-être
qu'il faudrait mettre ici en évidence toutes les figures qui devront néceffairement être ajoutées aux
chapitres fe rapportant aux divers os, et celles par lefquelles le fyftème entier et complet des os,
avec tous leurs noms, fera repréfenté à la fin de ce premier livre. Mais les reporter toutes en cet
endroit-ci ne conviendrait vraiment pas bien, parce qu'alors les mêmes figures et des figures fembla-
bles fe retrouveraient çà et là et rempliraient un trop grand nombre de pages; en outre, en permet-
tant au Lecteur de regarder à fon aife les images de tout l'ouvrage et d'examiner rapidement toute
la fucceffion des livres et des chapitres, avant de lui donner une leçon férieufe, nous paraîtrions
avoir, dès le début, bien peu de confiance dans fon zèle et fon application.*

S (L')eft de toutes les parties du corps humain celle qui reffemble le plus à de la
terre; auffi eft-il très fec et très dur. La
fubftance qui le conftitue, Dieu, l'artifan
fuprême des chofes, la créa avec raifon de
manière à pouvoir foutenir le corps tout
entier comme un fondement. Car ce que
font les murs et les poutres dans les maifons,
les pieux dans les tentes, la quille avec la
membrure dans les navires, la fubftance des
os le fait dans le corps humain. De ces os,
en effet, les uns font formés pour la folidité
comme des fupports du corps; de ce nombre font les os des jambes et des cuiffes,
les vertèbres du dos et prefque tout le fyftème offeux. D'autres, outre qu'ils
fervent de foutien, font encore mis par la Nature devant les autres parties du
corps comme moyens de protection, auffi fûrs que des remparts et des murs;
tels font le crâne, les épines des vertèbres et leurs faillies tranfverfes, l'os de la
poitrine, les côtes. D'autres encore, dont la partie principale s'eft développée
dans les tendons, font placés devant certaines articulations des os pour contri-
buer d'une façon convenable à la force des tendons et font chargés de régler
en quelque forte l'ample mouvement des articulations. C'eft dans ce but que
la ᵃrotule fe trouve dans le genou et que de même ᵇces petits os, que les experts
en diffections ont comparés à une graine de féfame, font placés contre la feconde
phalange du pouce de la main, et les premières phalanges des quatre autres
doigts et auffi contre les premières phalanges des cinq doigts du pied. Les dents,
par contre, fervent fpécialement à couper, rompre, broyer et moudre les
aliments, et de même ᶜles offelets des deux organes de l'ouïe fervent à un ufage
particulier: ils font chargés de l'audition. D'ailleurs l'office principal de chaque
os fera amplement expofé dans les chapitres dans lefquels nous décrirons les
divers os; il fuffira donc pour le moment de mentionner leur utilité générale,
qui eft (je le dis une fois pour toutes) de fervir de foutien à toute la maffe du
corps, à la façon d'un fupport auquel croiffent, fe fixent et fe fufpendent tous
les

Nature des os.

Utilité des os.

*Différences entre
les os d'après leur
utilité.*

*a. Voir les
deux fig.
chap. 32 et
pl. 8 des
mufcles k.*
*b. fig. 1.
chap. 25,
T, V, X.
fig. chap. 28.
fig. 1, chap.
11, y, w.*
*c. fig. chap.
1.*

FIGURE SIXTY-EIGHT
First page of the projected French translation of the 1555 *Fabrica* issued at Haarlem in 1924.

FIGURE SIXTY-NINE

The Maschenbauer title-pages: left (A), the first edition of 1706; right (B), the second edition of 1723.

FIGURE SEVENTY

Watermark from the Maschenbauer edition of 1706.

Maschenbauer's first edition printed in 1706 begins with a flowery and pompous dedication to the printer's patron, Gottfried Amman, dated December 14, 1705. This is followed by an address to the reader in which, after dwelling on the importance to artists of precise anatomical knowledge, he goes on to mention the publications in French by François Tortebat (1667) and in Italian by Giacopo Moro (1679)* which were based on the Vesalian plates and similarly designed for artists and sculptors. Neither of his predecessors, however, had at his disposal the original wood-blocks concerning whose provenance he says:

"In this work are published the figures executed by the Italian, Titian, of the house of Vecelli, a man phenomenally famous through Europe; and these illustrations he had made for the works of that famous anatomist Andreas Vesalius, the originals of which happened to fall into my hands by special chance. To estimate how highly and rightly this man was thought of during his lifetime, it may serve to state that the world-monarch Charles V wished to be painted by no one else than Titian, and that he not only made this artist a noble by the personally bestowed dagger, and made him a Count Palatine but honoured him with unusual privileges . . .

"He had the honour of staying often at the court of this world-ruler; occasionally accompanying his majesty to Augsburg, so that our art-loving and art-exercising Fatherland enjoyed the advantage of not only seeing him in person but of seeing some examples of work done by his incomparable hand and left to be placed in highly esteemed conservation. No potentate or sovereign was then living who did not want to be perpetuated by Titian, and even to-day his originals are esteemed almost as highly as gold . . ."

VI.A.—12

MASCHENBAUER   1st ed.   *Augsburg*, 1706

Title (Fig. 69A): Andreæ / Vesalii / Bruxellensis, / Dess Ersten, Besten / Anatomici, / Zergliederung / Dess / Menschlichen Cörpers. / Auf / Mahlerey / und / Bildhauer-Kunst / gericht. / [Wood-block from *Fabrica*] / Die Figuren von Titian gezeichnet. / [ornamental rule] / Augspurg, gedruckt und verlegt durch Andreas Maschenbaur, 1706.

Collation: Large fol. [*³], A-F², G¹; 16 unnumbered *ll.* gathered in twos. Large oval watermark (Fig. 70).
Contents: [*]1a title-page with five-skull woodcut (from 1543 *Fabrica*, p. 18); [*]1b blank; [*]2a-3a

dedication; [*]3b to the reader; [A]1a half-title: *Verfass / der / Anatomiæ / In so fern Dieselbe / Mahlern und Bildhauern, / Ja insgesamt allen und jeden / Künstlern, / Welche nach der Natur, und von Bildern / was Aufzureissen und zu Zeichnen haben, / dienlich und erwünscht ist;*

* See below, VI.D.18a and VI.D.26-31.

[A]1*b* (above in 2 columns) *Von denen Gebeinen dess Menschlichen Cörpers,* (below in 3 columns) table of lettering, *i.e.,* "characters" for the three skeletal figures from 1543 *Fabrica* pp. 163-165; A2*a* front view; A2*b* post.-lat. view; B1*a* side view; B1*b* legend for Plate I; B2*a* first muscle figure from *Fabrica,* p. 170; B2*b* legend for Plate II; C1*a* second muscle figure from *Fab.* p. 174; C1*b* legend for Plate III; C2*a* third muscle figure from *Fab.* p. 178; C2*b* legend for Plate IV; D1*a* first figure from *Epitome* I*b*; D1*b* legend for Plate V; D2*a* ninth muscle figure from *Fab.* p. 194; D2*b* legend for Plate VI; E1*a* third figure from *Epit.* H*b*; E1*b* legend for Plate VII; E2*a* second figure from *Epit.* I*a*; E2*b* legend for Plate VIII; F1*a* fourth figure from *Epit.* H*a*; F1*b* nude male figure from *Epit.* K*b*, without text; F2*a* nude female figure from *Epit.* L*a*, without text; F2*b* legend for final plate; G1*a* five cranial woodcuts from *Fab.* pp. 20, 22, 23 and 48; G1*b* blank.

Copies: Waller; DSG; NNC-M; MiU (Crummer); Cushing; Trent; van Wagenen.

Copy used: H.C.; bought from R. Lier, 1931, for 200 Swiss frs. Pasteboard covers on vellum spine; no provenance. Measures 44 by 28.5 cm.

As can be gathered from the table of contents, Maschenbauer selected from among the wood-blocks only those which pertained to the surface anatomy, nineteen in all. Twelve of them had been used exclusively in the *Fabrica,* four exclusively in the *Epitome,* and the lateral view of the skeleton in both. Six of the blocks from the *Fabrica* had to do with the anatomical configuration of the skull. While in his *Erklärungen* facing the successive woodcuts he was obliged to use the same "characters" (lettering) that Vesalius had employed, he made no attempt to account for all the characters as Torinus had done but only those having to do with muscles affecting the surface anatomy. He evidently had a font of Greek type at his disposal. Latin synonyms are occasionally used, but most of his are in the German vernacular and he borrowed little if anything from Torinus.

VI.A.—13

MASCHENBAUER   2nd ed.   *Augsburg,* 1723

Title (Fig. 69B): Andreæ / Vesalii / Bruxellensis, / Dess Ersten und Besten / Anatomici, / Zergliederung / Dess / Menschlichen Cörpers, / Oder Verfass / Der / Anatomiæ, / In so fern dieselbe / Mahlern und Bildhauern, / Ja insgemein allen und jeden / Künstlern, / welche nach der Natur, und von Bildern was aufzu- / reissen und zu zeichnen haben; / Ingleichem auch denen der / Medicin und Chirurgie / Zugethanen / sehr dienlich und erwünscht ist. / [Line] / Diese Figuren sind von dem berühmten Mahler Titian gezeich- net. / [ornamental rule] / Augspurg, gedruckt und verlegt durch Andreas Maschenbauer, 1723.

Collation: Large fol. A-O¹; [14] *ll.*
Contents: A1*a* title-page without woodcut; A1*b* blank; B1*a-b* letter to reader; C1*a* prefatory note on anatomy; from C1*b* to O1*a* the arrangement of *Erklärungen* on verso pages facing woodcuts on recto pages is the same as in 1706 edition; O1*b* *Erklärung* and the cranial plates, two of those showing base of the skull having been omitted to make room for the group of five crania on the title-page of the 1706 edition.

Note: Cheaper paper than in the 1706 edition, with large watermark; woodcuts less sharp.

Copies: Louvain; Munich; CaMM⸍Os; NNNAM; Cushing; Trent.

Copy used: H.C.; bought from L. Rosenthal, June 1907, for M.18. Cut down in binding to measure 43.5 by 27.5 cm., with large nude figures folded at bottom of page.

Sir William Osler's copy (CaMM⸍Os), given to him in 1910 by Dr. Cushing, is a defective, composite copy made up of eleven leaves, six of them from the 1706 edition and five (including the title) from the 1723 edition.

The New York Academy (NNNAM) copy corresponds in every detail to the H.C. copy.

This second edition, issued after an interval of seventeen years, largely due to the fact that the dedication was omitted, has only fourteen instead of sixteen leaves. The letter to the reader, who now becomes the venerated reader, ends with this additional paragraph: "In conclusion it may be mentioned that because in an Italian edition printed in Venice there are more figures than in this reprinted work of Vesalius, I have decided to add also a special part, hereafter, for painters; particularly for the reason that not only are these original figures drawn by the famous Titian and highly esteemed by all experts of art, but also because they are as useful for painters, sculptors and similar artists who have to draw, as are those in the present anatomical work. Furthermore, I intend to add to this other part of Vesalius instruction for surgeons, arranged so that it may be used to great advantage in surgery. That is what I wish to tell the kind reader and I herewith commend myself to his constant favour."

Maschenbauer's allusion to an Italian edition containing more figures than he himself employs refers undoubtedly to the Giuseppe Montani volume [see below VI.D.18A] published at Venice in 1679, in which were engravings of the contour drawings of many of the Vesalian plates in their original size drawn by Giacopo Moro for the benefit of artists and sculptors. His intention to add at some future time instructions for surgeons was apparently never fulfilled.

Sixty years pass before we again have news of the wood⸍blocks which until this time have presumably remained in Augsburg. Their re⸍discovery is fully accounted for in the preface to what is practically a condensed edition of the *Fabrica*, edited by the much betitled Bavarian anatomist and surgeon, H. P. Leveling of Ingolstadt. The illuminating preface is dated January 10, 1783, and begins thus:

"A fortunate chance led the 'kurfürstlichen baierischen Protomedikus und wirklichen Geheimen Rath' Herr von Woltter to discover the original plates of the anatomist Vesalius' great work as well as those of the *Epitome*, which had been preserved for some years in Augsburg. At the same time the congenial Bavarian Æsculapius, as an intelligent statesman, decided to purchase them, and already in 1774 he published his intention, in his scientific papers, of re-printing the plates contained in the larger work, together with a German explanation for the purpose of making them in this way more useful for general consumption.

"He entrusted me with the carrying out of this plan. To please this man (who had been the greatest of friends with my deceased parents and who had continued the friendship in my case to such an extent that it is to his kindness that I owe everything) was my duty, and my eternal thanks are due to him for conferring upon me the honour of editing this relic of the sixteenth century, with a German explanation. I am writing this at the time that this truly great man is living in retirement from the world, tired out by age and work, surrounded by a circle of a few remaining friends, for the rest of his days."

Leveling then proceeds to discuss the question whether the wood-blocks are the original ones, and he assembles proof to show that they must be. He tells of making a careful comparison of the woodcuts in the 1543 and 1555 editions and calls attention, for the first time, I believe, to the fact that in the latter the lettering in many of the cuts had been made more clear by cutting away the shading. He also states that while some of the smaller blocks must have been lost, they had been replaced by others, newly engraved, probably while in Maschenbauer's possession. That was notably true of the eighth muscle plate (*Fabrica,* Liber II, p. 192) which had been recut by an incompetent engraver on a new block directly from a print and so when struck off was reversed. Emphasizing the admiration the woodcuts had aroused on all sides, he discusses their common attribution to Titian and quotes Albrecht von Haller's conviction, that Vesalius would certainly have mentioned Titian's name had he in any capacity taken part in preparing the illustrations.

Of Wandelaar's new engravings for the *Opera omnia,* printed with "typographical splendor" at Leyden in 1725, he speaks admiringly, and after quoting Boerhaave's glowing tribute to Vesalius, he finally describes his own problem as follows:

"With these costly plates in my possession it was important to plan how to give interpretations worthy of their dignity, and make them more generally useful. I considered it unnecessary to translate Vesalius literally, but would accomplish what I wished by using only the brief explanation of each figure in Vesalius' great work, and instead of the text of the seven books merely taking what immediately follows each heading. This method I followed in six books.

"In the first book, however, I was obliged to retain the order of the chapter headings because in this book Vesalius had determined the order of his figures by these chapters; while in the other books the figures simply followed each other, and not in the same order as the chapter of each book but rather according to the number in which they follow. However, this subdivision of the figures of the first book according to chapters—in which first the sutures and then the foramina, etc., are especially described—prevented me from following my plan as in the other six books, namely to give a direct explanation of them [the illustrations] aside from the explanation of each part [in the text]; which I tried however to replace by a similar arrangement to that in the first book."

He then goes on to say that for the descriptions he has borrowed fully from Winslow, who himself was a follower of Vesalius, and had once intended editing a *Vesalius renovatus*. This he found so difficult that in the end he extracted only those portions of the German edition of Winslow's Anatomy, Basel, 1754, which referred to the letters of the illustrations. What is more, since Haller and others had pointed out mistakes made by Vesalius, these things he had to correct, and he makes a plea for the employment of German terminology, asking: "Has not the German language in common with the Greek the advantage of being a mother tongue?... Why should not Germans say *Fortsatz* instead of apophysis, and *Ansatz* instead of epiphysis?"

There is much more of this, all most interesting to the present-day reader, particularly in view of what is known as the B.N.A. [Basel Nomina anatomica] which came into being in 1895. But Herr von Woltter's intention, he says, was to give Bavarian surgeons a useful anatomical textbook and thereby to please the Germans with no thought of profit which would have been larger had the text been printed in Latin.

"I had intended [Leveling continues] to have this work printed in 1776 and sent out an announcement to the scientific public, choosing the subscription method, though this was not entirely successful. Herr Geheimer Rath von Wolter was very interested in the edition and therefore did his best to find a publisher for it, which he did in Herr Crusius of Leipzig. Accordingly I sent him the work, together with the plates, in August of 1777, but they were soon returned to me with the excuse that the expenses of printing this edition were too great for him to undertake. This circumstance retarded the accomplishment of my plan; I lost courage, and did not think any more about having it printed.

"It was only my due respect to the 'Geheimer Rath and Protomedikus' von

Woltter that moved me in 1780 again to announce the edition, and the success of this gave sufficient prospects of trying the publication as it is presented here without danger of great financial loss. Connoisseurs may judge from the number of the subscribers that it will remain a success even with the expense necessary for the producing of the plates and printing of the work. Nevertheless I have had 1500 copies printed, and perhaps now that the work is finished and is already in the hands of the scientific public in four parts, it will be valued more highly and have a wider sale . . ."

Leveling must have found the wood-blocks in surprisingly good condition considering the fact some of them had been used four times. Only one serious defect appears: namely, in the left hand of the cut which though destined for the *Epitome* first appears on the folded plate, m3, of the *Fabrica.* It already showed wear on its third usage in the German *Epitome* of 1543, where the thumb has been sheared off; but here it has been obliquely sheared off at the wrist as though in the grain of the wood, leaving behind only the vessels of the little finger. And having found them in good condition, Leveling left them equally so, as proved one hundred and fifty years later.

VI.A.—14

LEVELING Anatomische Erklärung *Ingolstadt,* 1781

Title: Heinrich Palmaz Leveling / [five lines of titles] / anatomische Erklärung / der / Original-Figuren / von / Andreas Vesal, / samt / einer Anwendung / der / Winslowischen Zergliederungslehre / in sieben Büchern. / [ornamental rule] / Ingolstadt, / Zu finden bey Anton Attenkhouer, der hohen Schule Buchbinder. 1781.

Collation: Fol. [†]^{2},)(^{2},)(^{2}, [✤]^{1},)(-)( )(^{2}, A-Z^{2}, Aa^{1}, Bb-Tt^{2}, Uu^{1}, Xx-Zz^{2}, Aaa-Mmm^{2}, *^{2}, Nnn-Zzz^{2}, Aaaa-Oooo^{2}, *^{2}, **^{1}; [11] *ll.*, 328 pp. 2 *ll.*, [3] *ll.*

Contents: [†]1*a* title-page; [†]1*b* blank; [†]2*a* dedication to Karl Theodor (laid out in 14 lines rather than 18 lines as in 1783 ed.); [†]2*b* blank;)(1*a*-2*b* dedicatory epistle;)(1*a*-2*b* list of technical terms; [✤]1*a* dedication page identical with that of 1783; [✤]1*b* blank;)(1*a*-)( )(2*b* preface dated 10 January, 1783; A1*a*-Oooo2*b* text, as in VI.A.14 except for insertion of *1*a*-2*b*, shorter list of subscribers, between Mmm2 and Nnn1; *1*a*-**1*b* longer list of subscribers.

Note: Dr. Max H. Fisch, Curator of the Army Medical Library, who has examined the rare 1781 edition and compared it with that of 1783 offers the following suggestions:

"Our 1781 copy is crudely put together throughout, and there seems to be some scissors-and-paste work on the signatures preceding the main text. The present board binding may very well be the original binding of 1783 or shortly thereafter, but it was certainly not bound by the printer.

"As you have probably noted, the shorter list of subscribers contains some names which do not appear in the longer list.

"My own theory is that the work was issued in four parts to the original subscribers, as follows:

"Part I: Title I [see VI.A.15], Title II with date 1781, dedication in 14-line form, dedicatory epistle, shorter list of subscribers (?), and pages 1-94 (Book I). [1781]

"Part II: Pages 95‑168 (Book II). [1781 or 1782]

"Part III: Pages 169‑228 (Books III‑IV) (perhaps the shorter list of subscribers was issued for the first time with this part). [1782]

"Part IV: Pages 229‑328 (Books V‑VII), prob‑ably accompanied by Title II with date 1783, the dedication in 18‑line form, the preface, the list of technical terms, and the longer list of subscribers. [1783]

"I think it probable that Leveling had had 1500 copies run off of the parts as issued, and that when Part IV was issued to his subscribers there were about 1180 copies remaining, which he then had his printer bind up and publish in single‑volume form, using Title II with date 1783, and the dedication in the 18‑line form. But it is barely possible that only enough copies were originally run off to supply his subscribers, and the forms kept intact, and an edition of 1500 copies run off in 1783. (This is made im‑probable not only by the cost of preserving the forms, but also by the fact that the distribution of the watermark and the CFK initials is the same in the 1781 and 1783 copies.) In either case, the rarity of copies with the 1781 Title II would be accounted for by the supposition that only the original sub‑scribers received Title II with that date, and that of the 240 or so copies, only a few were ever bound up,

whereas there were from 1180 to 1500 copies bound up with the 1783 Title II. It is further possible that even the original subscribers received the 1783 Title II with Part IV, and bound it in instead of the 1781 Title II which they had previously received, for the reason that the later Title II carried the portrait of Leveling, or because they had lost the earlier one."

Copies: DSG; MB.

Copies used: Army Medical Library. Dr. Cushing was aware that a 1781 issue had been listed, but he was doubtful of its authenticity. The full description of this copy can leave no doubt that a preliminary issue intended to enlist subscribers does exist, as with the 1724 Boerhaave‑Albinus Vesalius, VI.D.7

The Boston Public Library copy has a much simpler collation: [†]³,)(², *², A‑Z², Aa¹, Bb‑Tt², U¹; [7] *ll.,* 168 pp. It has both the engraved title‑page without date from the 1543 *Fabrica* (lacking in the Army Medical Library copy and tipped in here) and the printed title‑page with the date, 1781, fol‑lowed by the dedication to Karl Theodor;)(1a‑2b dedicatory epistle; *1a‑2b shorter list of subscribers; A1a‑Uu1b text of the first two books. The pages measure 41.7 by 27.4 cm., and the volume is bound in somewhat battered boards, rebacked. It was added to the collection on April 21, 1863.—Ed.

VI.A.—15

LEVELING Anatomische Erklärung   *Ingolstadt, 1783*

Title I Frontispiece from 1543 *Fabrica* (Fig. 71A): [in upper scroll] Des grossen Zergliederers / Andreas Vesals / anatomische / Original‑Figuren / in / sieben Büchern. [in lower scroll] Ingolstadt.

Title II (Fig. 71B): Heinrich Palmaz Leveling / [five lines of titles] / anato‑mische Erklärung / der / Original‑Figuren / von / Andreas Vesal, / samt / einer Anwendung / der / Winslowischen Zergliederungslehre / in sieben Büchern. / [Portrait decoration] / [ornamented rule] / Ingolstadt, / zu finden bey Anton Attenkhouer, der hohen Schule Buchbinder. 1783.

Collation: Fol. [†]³,)(²,)(¹,)( )(², *², A‑Z², Aa¹, Bb‑Tt², Uu¹, Xx‑Zz², Aaa‑Zzz², Aaaa‑Oooo², (2 folding leaves inserted between Iiii 1 and 2),)(², *², **1; [11] *ll.,* 328 pp., [5] *ll.*

Contents: [†]1a frontispiece from 1543 *Fabrica*; [†]1b blank; [†]2a title‑page (Fig. 71B) with portrait of Leveling and date of birth, 27 Sept. 1742; [†]2b blank; [†]3a dedication to Karl Theodor; [†]3b blank;)(1a‑2b dedicatory epistle, dated Ingolstadt, 3 November 1780;)(1a‑)( )(2b preface dated at In‑

golstadt, 10 January 1783; *1a‑2b alphabetical list of ca. 240 subscribers; A1a‑Aa1b (pp. 1‑94) *Book I,* on the bones; Bb1a‑Uu1b (pp. 95‑168) *Book II,* on he muscles; Xx1a‑Eee2b (pp. 169‑199) *Book III,* on the veins and arteries; Fff1a‑Mmm2b (pp. 201‑228) *Book IV,* on the nerves; Nnn1a‑Yyy1b (pp. 229‑266) *Book V,* on the abdomen; Yyy2a‑Bbbb2b (pp. 267‑280) *Book VI,* on the thorax; Cccc1a‑Hhhh2b (pp. 281‑304) *Book VII,* on the head; Iiii1a‑Oooo2b (pp. 305‑328) summary;)(1a‑2b list of technical terms (German and Latin); *1a-**1b list of sub-scribers (enlarged to about 300).

Note: The book is printed in German gothic type on two runs of paper: one with large watermark, the other with initials CFK (Fig. 72).

Copies: Louvain; Klebs; Waller; Cushing; Fulton; CaMM-Os; MH-M; PPCP; NNNAM; ICU; DSG; CSt-L; NNC-M; ICJ; MdBJ-W; MBM; IEN-M; MiU (Crummer, Pilcher); CtY; Fisher; CU-M. A considerable remainder of the 1500 printed copies was found in Leipzig some years ago and they were sold by Speyer and Peters. The sheets uncut and deckle-edged measure 45.6 by 29 cm.

Copies used: (i) Cushing; bought from L. Rosen-thal, Munich, in 1906 for M.15. Bound in paper-covered boards, rebacked, measuring 39 by 26.5 cm.; the preliminary and final leaves have been mis-bound out of usual sequence. (ii) Fulton; with 9 preliminary leaves (the shorter list of subscribers being absent) and 5 leaves at end; measures 40.2 by 27.2 cm.

In his illuminating preface dated January 10, 1783, Leveling speaks of his friend and patron, Herr von Woltter, as though he had not long to live. He tells us also that the wood-blocks had once been shipped to Leipzig for the inspec-tion of the printer Crusius; but what happened to them after von Woltter's death is unrecorded, though presumably they were deposited in the Library of the local University. When in 1800 Ingolstadt was taken by the French, the University was transferred to another old Bavarian city, namely Landshut on the Isar. There it remained for another twenty-six years until it was transferred to Munich. The wood-blocks, long accustomed to travel, were doubtless carted along on these successive migrations. Obviously unsuited for bookshelves, the Munich librarian of the day must have been puzzled to know what disposition to make of them; so they were probably hidden away and promptly forgotten for the next sixty-seven years. It was not until 1893 that the then University Librarian, Dr. Hans Schnorr von Carolsfeld, in the course of an inventory came upon a cache of them in a long-unused cupboard.

This rediscovery of the Vesalian wood-blocks after an interval of eleven decades was brought to the attention of Professor Roth of Basel whose biography had been published only the year before. His interest was naturally aroused and in Virchow's *Archiv* for 1895 (347) he published a detailed account of the 159 recovered pieces which with Teutonic thoroughness were listed in three tables showing just where they had been used in the 1543 and 1555 *Fabrica* editions, as well as in Leveling's book, presumably the last for which prints from them had been struck off.

Once more their very existence for well nigh thirty years was forgotten. However, when Spielmann's *Iconography* (371) came to be published in 1925 under the auspices of the Wellcome Historical Medical Museum, the editor, Mr. C. J. S. Thompson, discovered that the wood-block of the re-engraved frontispiece of the 1555 *Fabrica* was in the possession of a Mr. Firens of Antwerp, who subsequently presented it to the rehabilitated Louvain Library. Mr.

Thompson was generously permitted to take prints from it, which when folded were enclosed in an envelope with the printed volume. No information concerning the past history of this isolated wood-block could be elicited, but its discovery in the Netherlands was enough to lend support to the view, often expressed, that the wood-blocks had passed to the heirs of Vesalius after his death. What the heirs of any Flemish ancestor could possibly do with several hundred pounds of old wood-blocks, except to burn them in the Vesalian manner, is not easily answered; but from the lot one or two important pieces might have been rescued for sentimental reasons, and there was naturally hope that some day the block on which the portrait had been cut might also turn up, possibly along with those carrying the engraved initial letters.

When in 1932 Dr. S. W. Lambert of New York became interested in making a study of the capital initials, it was suggested by the late Leonard L. Mackall that a renewed search might be made for the wood-blocks in the Munich Library. Though these initial blocks were not found, the search unexpectedly disclosed the full-page blocks engraved for the *Epitome* which, because of their large size, had been separately stored. At the request of the New York Academy of Medicine, permission was given by the Munich authorities to have prints struck off from all of the original blocks that had so far come to light for the purposes of an Atlas to be issued by Dr. Willy Wiegand at the celebrated Bremer Presse at Munich.

This *de luxe* publication, printed on paper "specially made from the best hempen fibres," possibly serves to overemphasize the part played by Jan Stephan van Calcar and to minimize that of Vesalius, though to be sure the colophon on this occasion, were there one, should have read *"sumptibus Academiæ Medicinæ Nova-Eboracensis"* rather than *"sumptibus Stephani Calcarensis."* From the estimated 277 original wood-blocks, only 50 were missing, including the portrait which has been reproduced in facsimile. For ease of comparison, the two frontispieces from the 1543 and 1555 editions are printed *en face,* the wood-block for the latter having been loaned for the purpose by the Louvain Library. A photograph of the two blocks as they lay together in the frame of the hand-press at Munich was given to me by Dr. Wiegand.

VI.A.—16

ICONES ANATOMICÆ   *New York & Munich,* 1934(-35)

Title (Fig. 73): Andreæ / Vesalii / Bruxellensis / Icones / Anatomicæ / [short rule] / Ediderunt Academia / Medicinæ Nova-Ebora- / censis et Bibliotheca / Universitatis Monacensis / MCMXXXIV.

Collation: Atlas fol. 189 *ll.* without signatures, of which 130 and XIII pages are interspersed and numbered.

Contents: ll. [1-2] blank; *l.* [3] half-title; *l.* [4] title; *l.* [5] woodcut portrait of Vesalius in facsimile; *ll.* [7-8] title-pages of 1543 and 1555 editions; *ll.* [8-9] letter to Oporinus; *ll.* [10-46] *Tabulæ libri primi,* including pp. 1-31, explanatory text for plates; *ll.* [47-81] *Tab. lib. secundi,* incl. pp. 33-62 text; *ll.* [82-92] *Tab. lib. tertii,* incl. pp. 63-72 text; *ll.* [93-101] *Tab. lib. quarti,* incl. pp. 73-79 text; *ll.* [102-120] *Tab. lib. quinti,* incl. pp. 81-96 text; *ll.* [121-126] *Tab. lib. sexti,* incl. pp. 97-100 text; *ll.* [127-140] *Tab. lib. septimi,* incl. pp. 101-109 text; *ll.* [141-165] the *Epitome,* incl. pp. 111-130 text; *ll.* [166-167] half-title and reproduction of azygos plate from *Epistola docens; ll.* [168-174] *Tabulæ* [*sex*] *anatomicæ simulatæ; l.* [175] blank; *ll.* [176-180] folded facsimiles of the designs for the original title-page; *ll.* [181a-187a], paged [I]-XIII, *Index tabularum; ll.* [187b-188a] *Ad lectorem*; l.* [188b] colophon.

Note: The book, dated 1934, was not issued till 1935, as is mentioned in the colophon. It reproduces all the illustrations and their explanations from the works of Vesalius. The letterpress is in Latin throughout save for "Printed in Germany" on the verso of the title-page. Three types of paper are used: (i) 103 folia of deckle-edged paper with two different watermarks appearing on nearly alternate leaves— (a) with Vesalius' coat of arms taken from the cartouche of the *Fabrica* frontispiece (Fig. 74) and (b) with NYAM in shield and "1933" below. On

* A supplementary leaf with English translation, "To the Reader," and with "Printed in Germany" on the verso was issued in 1936 and properly belongs with the volume.

the sheets of this heavy paper cuts from the original blocks are printed on one side only, so placed that figures usually face one another. (ii) 74 folia of thinner, unwatermarked paper, 65 of which are interleaved with the watermarked folia and bear the text of the *characterum indices,* explanation of the plates, copied from the 1555 ed.; these leaves are paginated 1-130. The remaining folia of thin paper are used in the *index tabularum.* (iii) 12 folia of unwatermarked paper of still different sort, better suited for the collotype prints of the *Tabulæ sex* and designs for the title-page.

In the highly informative index the printer, Dr. Wiegand, has given a painstaking citation in tabular form of all the places identified by *Liber,* page, folium and signature where prints from the 227 surviving blocks have been used: *viz.,* in the present *Icones,* the 1543 and 1555 *Fabrica,* the Latin and German *Epitomes* of 1543, Maschenbauer's editions of 1706 and 1723, and in Leveling's edition of 1783.

The colophon states that the work was in progress from 1932 to 1935; it gives the individual number of the 615 copies, and identifies the work as Vol. 3 of the New York Academy's "History of Medicine" series. It does not mention the principal editors, Drs. Wiegand, Lambert, and Archibald Malloch. The edition is still in print, obtainable from the New York Academy of Medicine for $100.

Binding: quarter white pigskin over dark grey boards with label and date stamped on spine; signed "Frieda Thiersch" on inside of back cover. Folia measurements: 54 by 37.5 cm.

Copies: CaMM-Os; DSG; NjP; MH; PPCP; ICU; CSm-H; MdBJ-W; NN; OClM; Cushing; Trent.

Copy used: H.C.; No. 48, with colophon autographed "Willy Wiegand, 7th December 1936."

Time alone can tell what in another four centuries may happen to these historic wood-blocks, which at Venice in August of 1542 were carefully wrapped and labeled by Vesalius and his young friend, Nicolaus Stopius, preparatory to their long journey over the Alps to Basel. Something has recently happened at Munich, where they now remain, which may again alter the map of Europe and change the course of history. But let us hope that by A.D. 2342 peace and goodwill among the nations will have come to stay and that someone interested either in the engraver's art of the late renaissance, or in medical history of that time, will again rediscover and print from them another memorial volume, possibly in some universal language as yet unknown to us. But this is looking toward a Utopian future; and just now, being obliged in an agonizing world to face the present day with its strange behaviorisms, I shall, in the words of the radio announcer, "now return you to Basel," where in June of 1543 the Latin *Epitome* had just come off the press of Oporinus.

B. THE *EPITOME*

Fully convinced of the importance of anatomical diagrams for teaching purposes, and in view of his crowded classes, believing that the larger the figures the better, Vesalius had long determined to issue a series of plates to serve as an illustrated epitome of all that was contained in the larger work which he refers to as the "Seven Books" and we call briefly the *Fabrica*. This intention was announced as follows in the dedicatory preface addressed to the Emperor:

"In arranging the order of these [seven] books I have followed the opinion of Galen, who after the account of the muscles, considered that the anatomy of the veins, arteries, nerves and then of the viscera should be handled. But with very good reason it will be urged (and especially in the case of a beginner in this science) that the study of the viscera ought to be combined with that of the distribution of the vessels, a course I have followed in the *Epitome*. This latter I have made to be as it were a foot-path beside the highway of the larger book, and as an index of what is set forth in it."

For the purpose of the *Epitome* he had selected a series of nine engraved woodcuts some six centimetres taller than those in the *Fabrica*, in which only two had been used, *viz.,* those on the folded leaves signed m3, showing the blood-vessels, and p4, showing the peripheral nerves. They as a matter of fact had been originally prepared for the *Epitome* and had been used in the *Fabrica* as an afterthought. Since the same frontispiece used for the *Fabrica* was again employed for the title-page, enough room was left below the engraving for the following explanatory note to the reader, with the translation of which certain bracketed liberties have been taken in the hope of making it less confusing should anyone desire to check it with a copy of the book in hand (Fig. 75). It states that the reader may take his choice of approach either to begin reading the text, or to begin with the plates in which latter case he is advised to start with the nude male figure and work backward toward the front of the book so as to follow the muscle dissections from superficial to deeper layers. Unfortunately a textual error seems to have been made in the serial enumeration. That this has been highly puzzling to others is shown by the efforts of a former owner of one of my copies to enumerate the leaves backward.

"To the Reader.* The Compendium which we present of the books on the Fabric of the Human Body is divided into two parts. One of these, in six chapters [sigs. Ba-Ga], comprises a very succinct account of all the parts; the other [sigs. Gb-Ma], in many plates, sets forth a delineation of the same, together with an index of the characters [sig. Lb] by which they are marked. Therefore, estimating our sequence of plates (which we have selected from various ones as most suitable to the form of the impression and the method of composition) as highly as it seems to deserve, according to your own judgment of it, you will begin either with the description of the parts, or with the illustrations and their explanations [sig. Lb], starting the latter with the figures representing a nude man [sig. Kb] and woman [sig. La], where will be found the names of the surface regions, like an index to those figures.

"The figure printed on the back [recto] of the leaf with the nude male figure presents the entire structure of the bones [sig. Ka]; although in fact the figures, especially the fourth and fifth ones, drawn to the same proportion as that of the nude man, and, so to speak, named explicitly as illustrations of the muscles, also present the bones in the sequence of dissection.

"The delineation of the muscles and ligaments must be sought first from that figure [sig. Ib] which we place opposite the figure portraying all the bones [sig. Ka], and on this account it is specified as the first figure of the muscles: after this [working forward to the left] comes the one which is called the third [? second, sig. Ia], and then the fourth [? third, sig. Hb] and fifth [? fourth, sig. Ha and then the fifth, sig. Gb]. The organs of nutrition, the heart and the parts aiding its functions, are represented, and the series of nerves are shown in the figures following the nude likeness of a woman, where also there are seen the female instruments of generation; equally as the male generative organs occur in the figure to be cut and pasted to the plate [Gb] of the fifth muscle layer.

"In addition to the plate provided to demonstrate the nerves [sig. M], the muscle plates depict adequately those things which are comprised in the skull. And first comes the head of the first figure [sig. Ib showing the meninges], then of the second [sig. Ia showing falx, etc.], then of the fourth [sig. Ha showing cerebral ventricles, etc.], together with the representations which the hands of this figure hold [cranial fossæ, etc.]; and following these, there comes the depic-

* For an excellent analysis of this prefatory note and of the make-up of the *Epitome*, see W. G. Spencer's article (369) in Sudhoff's *Festschrift*.

tion seen in the left hand of the fifth figure [sig. G*b*, cerebellum and brain stem], and the other lying on the ground [cerebellum removed] in that place, besides the likeness of the parts of the eye. Farewell, and make good use of our well-intended efforts."

The dedication to Prince Philip dated Padua, August 13, 1542, and written in the customary laudatory manner, draws to an end with this statement:

". . . I certainly have not assumed the necessity of demonstrating here how negligent we are in learning anatomy, the basis and foundation of the entire medical art, and how highly essential knowledge of the human parts is to us, who have given authority to medicine; because the intellect of each one of us abundantly confirms the fact that, in curing diseases, this knowledge deservedly claims the first, second, and third parts, and is sought especially in the affected seat, which also indicates (besides other things) the proper use of remedies. Nay indeed, those who are dedicated to the old medicine, which now is restored almost to its pristine glory in many schools, are beginning to understand sufficiently that far too little energy and sweat have been expended in anatomy, from the time of Galen until the present; for, even if Galen is easily the foremost of the masters of this subject, still he never applied himself to the human body, and it is concluded now that he described (I shall not say, imposed on us) the anatomy of the ape rather than of man, although the former differs in structure from the latter in many parts . . ."

VI.B.—1*

EPITOME 1st ed.   *Basel,* June 1543

Title (Fig. 75): [upper scroll in frontispiece] Andreæ Vesalii / Brvxellensis, scholæ / medicorum Patauinæ professoris, suorum de / Humani corporis fabrica librorum / Epitome. / [lower scroll] Cvm Cæsareæ Maiest. Galli-arum Regis, ac Senatus Veneti gra-/ tia & priuilegio, ut in diplomatis eorundem continetur. / [below frontispiece] Lectori. / [12 lines in ital.] / Basileæ.

Colophon: [M*a*] Basileæ, ex officina / Ioannis Opo-rini, Anno M D XLIII. / Mense Iunio.

Collation: Large fol. A-M¹, [N-O¹]; 14 unnum-bered *ll.*

---

    * Since VI.B is a separate publication, a deviation from de Feyfer's enumeration seems advisable. Our VI.B.1 he listed as VI.B.6 in continuation of the *Fabrica* editions.—H.C.

Contents: A*a* frontispiece, title, privilege and address to reader.

    A*b* dedication to Prince Philip dated August 3, 1542.

    B*a-b* Chapter I on bones and cartilages.

    B*b-*D*a* Chapter II on ligaments and voluntary muscles.

    D*a-*E*a* Chapter III on organs of nutrition.

    E*a-b* Chapter IV on the heart and its function.

Eb-Fb Chapter V on the cerebrum and its nerves.

Fb-Ga Chapter VI on organs of generation. Directions follow on *Ga* running across page which read: "End of the enumeration of all the parts included in the Fabric of the Human Body. It is followed (*excipit*), as far as possible, by their full and entire delineation in the following pages, which should be consulted in the order prescribed in the prefatory note." On lower half of *Ga* is a woodcut portrait of Vesalius measuring 194 by 145 mm.

Gb front view of skeleton, largely denuded, showing deep or fifth muscle layer; skull and brain accessories. Lettering and legends to left and right of figure including directions for cutting and mounting of figs. from the last two unsigned leaves.

Ha back view of third and fourth layers of deep muscles. Lettering and legends to left and right.

Hb third muscle layer, from in front, with lettering and legends.

Ia first and second muscle layers from behind with lettering and legends.

Ib first and second muscle layers from in front, with lettering and legends.

Ka lateral view of celebrated thinking skeleton from the *Fabrica*, with the inscription on pedestal changed to a mournful Latin pentameter distich which may be paraphrased:

"All splendor is dissolved by death, and through the snow-white limbs

The Stygian colour lays waste the beauty of the form."

Kb nude male figure holding skull, designed to show the surface anatomy. Descriptive text.

La nude female figure, same purpose, with text.

Lb index of characters (lettering) marking all figures.

Ma chart of brain and nerves [used in *Fabrica*, sig. p4]; also errata, register with directions for binding, and colophon. The register and directions read in translation as follows: "*Series chartarum.* A B C D E F G H I K L M, in addition to two unsigned leaves; from one of these is to be prepared a figure to be pasted to he figure on the verso of leaf G; from the other is to be prepared a figure to be pasted to the figure shown on this page [*Ma*]. The remaining 12 leaves may be bound as one deems best. It is best to join A with M, B with L, C with K, etc., so that the Epitome would consist of a quire in-six, and might thus be made into a book."

Mb blank.

[*Na*] "*Figuræ ad tabulam aptandam paratæ, illi agglutinandam*" [*i.e.,* separate figures to be cut out and mounted—see note on sig. m3 of the *Fabrica*].

[*Nb*] blank.

[*Oa*] "*Charta, ex qua figuram parare convenit,*" etc.

[*Ob*] blank.

Note: The text is printed in roman type, two columns, 75 lines to a page; the explanations of the plates in italic. The leaves usually are (or have been) folded across centre. Two large capital initial letters (T and O) and six small ones (L, Q, O, C, I, H) from the *Fabrica* are used. The paper is heavy and durable, evidently of German make in view of the large (16 cm.) double-eagle watermark (Fig. 76) and shield counter-marks (all unrecorded).

Copies: Louvain; London (RCP); Venice (2 copies, one bound with *Tabulæ sex*); Amsterdam (2 copies); London (BM); CaMM-Os; DSG; MH; PPCP; NNNAM (in Streeter Collection, with two plates cut and superimposed); NBMS; NNC-M; MBM; MiU (Pilcher); Cushing (2 copies); Clendening; Trent. Three copies at least were printed on *vellum*. One, formerly in the library at Louvain, was destroyed by fire in August 1914. It had the plates superimposed, though I do not recall that the figures were hand-coloured as stated by de Feyfer. Another, formerly in the possession of Richard Mead, was sold May 8, 1755, to "Ball" for £8.12s.6d. and is probably the copy now in the British Museum. A third copy on vellum is in the Hunterian Library at Glasgow.

Copies used: H.C. (first copy), bought from Hirschwald, Berlin, November 1930, for RM.2800. Bound in contemporary pigskin stamped "*Compendium Vesaly*" and dated 1550. Separate leaves gathered and mounted for binding in the manner suggested by Vesalius. *Provenance:* signatures of previous owners dated 1636 and 1827. Margins of sheets show deckle edges and appear to be untrimmed. They measure 56.5 by 40.5 cm. The two unsigned folia are intact. All sheets show evidence of folding across middle.

For some years I have taken pains to measure copies as they were encountered. The greatest height of the leaves, 57.1 cm., occurs in the Streeter copy at the New York Academy of Medicine; the greatest width, 42.5 cm., was in a copy reported by Dr. Kurt Schwarz of Berlin in 1934. It is safe to say hat anything over 55 by 40 cm. in a bound copy approximates the original size. Copies of the 1543 Latin and German editions bound together and measuring 54 by 38 cm. were sold at auction by Karl and Faber on April 25, 1931, for RM.5000 ($1437).

H.C. (second copy), in a modern binding, measures 48.3 by 33.4 cm. and carries the following note: "In Sept. 1909 I purchased an imperfect but very clean copy from Rosenthal in Munich for Mk.150. In July 1911 for 500 francs I secured a complete copy in paper covers from C. Lang in Rome. The missing leaves C, G, L, together with the two final plates were added to the Rosenthal copy and bound by Riviere in London, August 1913. The rascals cut it down to this size."

Two months after the Latin *Epitome* had appeared, Oporinus completed the printing on August 9, 1543, of a German translation by Albanus Torinus, the Rector of the University, who at this very time must have been assembling the material for his *Opera omnia* of Rhazes, printed two years later at Basel by Heinrich Petri, in which Vesalius' *Paraphrasis* of the ninth book [*cf.* I.3] was incorporated.

The German edition of "Albanus züm Thor," as he signs himself, is far more rare than the Latin issue and is placed by de Feyfer under his group VI.C, on the grounds that it is a combination of VI.A and VI.B; but that is in a sense true also of VI.A.1, which has two figures from the *Epitome*. It contains a dedication by Torinus to the Duke of Württemberg emphasizing the importance of the work for German students and reiterating the statement of de Necker: namely, that Vesalius had compressed in these few pages all that Galen had spread over seven and twenty books. The dedication is dated August 5th, four days before the date of the colophon.

In the arrangement of the plates and the textual material, this German edition conforms with its predecessor so far as the use of gothic type permitted. As this takes up more running space than roman type, it was necessary to use 19 sheets instead of the 14 previously used, even with 92 lines instead of 75 to the printed page. To print Chapter I, for example, in roman type required 200 square inches of paper in contrast to 240 square inches required for the gothic type. As before, the separate sheets were evidently issued unbound, though in this instance no suggestions for binding were supplied. Various ways of saving space were employed. The copious marginal Greek synonyms, for example, were omitted probably for reasons easily conjectured, leaving only occasional Latin ones for the German anatomical terms. Whereas the legends for the lettering in the Latin issue could be squeezed in on the same plate to the right and left of each figure, this would have been impossible for the German text, so that an extra page facing each figure when possible had to be utilized for this purpose. As this provided a little more space than was needed, some extra figures not in the Latin issue were borrowed from the *Fabrica* to fill out the pages. All things considered, it must have presented a considerably more difficult task for the compositor even than the Latin issue which, as we have indicated, was highly complicated and confusing in itself. The wood-blocks in the German *Epitome* are the same as those in the Latin *Epitome* save for those taken from the *Fabrica*.

VI.B.—2

GERMAN *EPITOME*   Basel, August 9, 1543

Title (Fig. 77): [upper scroll in frontispiece] Von des menschen cörpers Anatomey, / ein kurtzer, aber vast nützer ausszug, auss D. An / dree Vesalii von Brussel Bücheren, von ihm / selbs in Latein beschriben, vnnd durch / D. Albanum Torinum / verdolmetscht. / [lower scroll in frontispiece: privilege in German] / [below frontispiece] / Dem gütwilligen läser / [13 lines of text.]

Colophon [2nd P*a*]: Gedruckt zü Basel, bey Johann Herpst, ge/nant Oporino, vnnd vollendet am neünten tag des / Augstmonat, nach der geburt Christi im̃ M D Xliii Jar.

Collation: Large fol. [*]¹, AP¹, P¹+ [3] *ll.* without sig., the last blank; 20 unnumbered *ll.*

Contents: [*]1*a* frontispiece with address to reader below in German; [*]1*b* woodcut portrait of Vesalius measuring 19 by 14 cm.

A*a* Vesalius' dedication to Philip in German; initial T of Latin issue replaced by gothic initial W.

A*b* Torinus' dedication to the Duke of Wurttemberg, dated August 5, 1543 and signed "Albanus Züm Thor."

B*a*G*a* the six chapters of text enumerating all the parts.

G*b* front view of largely denuded skeleton (*Die fünfft Figur*) showing deep (5th) layer of muscles, etc., as in Latin ed. but without marginal notes.

H*a* German text of marginal lettering and legends for the opposite figure on G*b*, together with directions for cutting and mounting thereon female organs, etc. from the 2nd of extra leaves. Below are four small woodcuts of fœtus taken from page 382 of *Fabrica*.

H*b* lettering with German legends in two columns for the figure showing the deep muscle layers from behind. Below, to fill space, are 4 heart figures from pp. 56567 of *Fabrica*.

J*a Die vierdt Figur* showing deep muscle layers from behind [fol. H*a* of Latin *Epit.*].

J*b Die dritt Figur* showing third muscle layers from in front [same figure as on H*b* of Latin *Epit.* but without letters and legends to right and left].

K*a* German lettering and legends for *die dritt Figur* on J*b*. Below, small figures of uterus and ovaries [from p. 380 of *Fabrica*].

K*b* lettering and legends in German for *die ander Figur* on opposite page [sig. L*a*] with additional figure of abdominal dissection [from p. 377 of *Fabrica*].

L*a Die ander Figur:* back view of muscle man showing first and second muscle layers [same as I*a* in Latin *Epit.* without lettering and legends].

L*b Die erste Figur:* anterior view of muscle man [*prima figura* from sig. I*b* of Latin *Epit.*] without lettering and legends to right and left.

M*a* above: German rendering of lettering and text taken from left side of skeletal figure (K*a* in Latin *Epit.*], awkwardly placed, as this figure does not appear until sig. N in German *Epit.*; below (lefthand corner): abdominal dissection from p. 378 of *Fabrica*, with German legend.

M*b* German text in two columns corresponding with Latin lettering and text taken from right and left sides of *prima figura* in Latin *Epit.* [sig. I*b*]. Below, woodcut of the mesentery [from p. 364 of *Fabrica*].

N*a* skeletal figure [from K*a* of Latin *Epit.*] without lettering and legends. Figure of uterus and vagina from p. 381 of *Fabrica* placed on outer margin of page. Below, an explanatory legend.

N*b* nude male figure [from K*b* of Latin *Epit.*] with German translation of text; marginal Greek synonyms omitted.

O*a* female nude figure [from L*a* of Latin *Epit.*] with German text.

O*b* continuation of text for nude figure (on N*b*

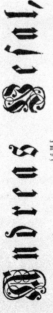

FIGURE SEVENTY-ONE

Title-pages of the Leveling Vesalius, 1783: right (B), engraved frontispiece from the 1543 *Fabrica*; left (A), with portrait of Leveling.

FIGURE SEVENTY-TWO

Left (A), showing large watermark in the Leveling Vesalius, 1783;
right (B), CFK watermark from nude-female plate.

ANDREAE VESALII BRUXELLENSIS ICONES ANATOMICAE

—

EDIDERUNT ACADEMIA MEDICINAE NOVA·EBORA· CENSIS ET BIBLIOTHECA UNIVERSITATIS MONACENSIS

MCMXXXIV

FIGURE SEVENTY·THREE

Title·page of *Icones anatomicæ*, 1934, issued by the New York Academy of Medicine and the Bremer Presse of Munich.

FIGURE SEVENTY-FOUR

Heavy-paper watermark in 1934 *Icones anatomicæ*.

ANDREAE VESALII
BRVXELLENSIS, SCHOLAE
medicorum Patauinæ professoris, suorum de
Humani corporis fabrica librorum
EPITOME

CVM CAESAREAE
Maiest. Gallorum Regis, ac Senatus Veneti gratia & priuilegio, ut in diplomatis eorundem continetur.

LECTORI.

QVOD nuns da ut librorum de Humani corporis fabrica Compendium, in duas partes dissectum est, quarum una sex tabulis complexa, succinctissimam omnium partium historiam complectitur altera in pluribus tabulis earundem delineationem simul cum characterum ga hos insignitus index proponit Quare tuo ipsius arbitratu nostrum ordinem: quem ex uar
rie... expressionum formam, compendiorū tat orem commodissimum sulgeantes tant quare: sum ere pendens, aut partium descriptionem aut designationem, notarumq indicem primum eg
gredientur, cum omnina a figuris nudas uin mulieris imagines proponim has asspicabere, ale externarum sedum appellationes, crustarum imagnum index, occurrent. Integrum ossium
corpla remossit reliqua... uirit erg o impressa, quaepia & figure ad uriillius proportione delineate, ac telas musculorū tabule inscripte eram sectiones serie ossa proponento & præcipul
corum quarta & quinta. Musculorum item in hg amentis tenenda est uirum ab illa tum i regione figure omnia essa experimentis locum us, ob idq prime musculorum figura
insurdi tur, cui succede que teria nominatur, dein quarta & quinta. Naturis rnes que cibo pota ue suborgane, & deni cor parters que ipsius manus sudferuerunt, simul cum neruorum
serie proponantur figuras nudam mulieris imaginem subsequent lus, ubi & mulierum genera conissellaneta instrumenta, perinde et uirorum organa occurrent in figure que uer musculorum tabule agglutinata. Eorum que caluaria comsellantur imaginem, preter tabulam neruis communibus descriptis sequantur, musculorum f que re satis absolute referrunt ac primum quidem ca
put prima figure, dein secunde, uot quate, simul cum imaginibus quas teus figure menus emptet nautis. & has subsequitur que in sinistra quinta
figura manu est obuia, al esq inch preter oculi part un essig em homo decumbens. Vale, &
nostris conat has cand de, uti offeruntur sisere.

A

BASILEAE.

FIGURE SEVENTY-FIVE
Title-page of the first Latin *Epitome* issued in June 1543.

FIGURE SEVENTY-SIX

Double-eagle watermark, 16 cm. tall, used in both the Latin and the German *Epitome* of 1543.

and O*a*) followed by the lettering and legends ("*Büchstaben*") [*Characterum Index* from L*b* of Latin *Epit.*] for figures on last two leaves to be cut and superimposed.

P*a* continuation from O*b* of *Büchstaben*, i.e., lettering and legends.

P*b* lettering and legends [from M*a* of Latin *Epit.*] to confront last figure of brain and peripheral nerves which here is without lettering and legends.

2nd P*a* figure of brain and peripheral nerves [from folded *l.* p4 (p. 354) of *Fabrica*]. Colophon. Register and suggestions for binding omitted. 2nd P*b* blank.

Two unnumbered leaves follow, both with verso blank. They show the woodcut from the folded leaf m3 of the *Fabrica* surrounded, one by 9 smaller figures including female organs, and the other by 10 including male organs to be cut out and mounted

according to directions (on H*a*) either on the deep muscle figure G*b* or on the figure of the nervous system on 2nd P*a*. There is a final blank leaf.

Note: The book is set in gothic type, 2 columns, 92 lines to the page; in copy used, all leaves at one time have been folded across centre. One large capital initial (I) and 4 small initials (D, S, A, E) taken from the *Fabrica* are used. Same paper with double-eagle watermark as used in Latin edition.

Copies: Louvain; DSG; MH; MBM (a fine copy, measuring 52 by 38.2 cm., bought in 1904 from the Tiedemann collection); NNC-M; MdBJ-W; CSt-L; Cushing.

Copy used: H.C.; bought from Ludwig Rosenthal, Munich, September 1909, for M.250; uncut, loosely bound in modern vellum, measures 48 by 35.5 cm., leaf N wanting, supplied in photostat.

VI.B.—3

EPITOME 2nd Latin ed.   *Basel, 1555*

Title: Frontispiece: Collation: Contents: same as Latin *Epitome* of 1543 (*cf.* VI.B.1).

Note: The only difference in the two issues lies in the last leaf M (Fig. 78), the type of which has been entirely reset and the date changed from *M D XLIII Mense Junio* to *M D LV Mense Aprili.*

Copy: A copy of this issue which appears to be unique and which came from the library of Antonio Scarpa is now in the possession of Dr. Erik Waller of Stockholm, Sweden. It has been carefully examined by competent bibliographers; and were there any doubt whether the sheet M had been set up and printed at Basel in 1555 by Oporinus, this would be dispelled by the watermarks on the paper. An examination of the leaves has shown that the newly printed leaf M is on the same paper as that used for

the 1555 edition of the *Fabrica* and shows the star-and-crescent watermark (*cf.* Fig. 63) of the paper used for that issue, whereas all the other sheets show the watermarks of three types that are found in both the German and Latin Epitomes printed twelve years previously.

The conclusion is inescapable that the text of the colophon-leaf M had been reset and printed on a sheet of the paper being used for the 1555 *Fabrica*. This newly printed colophon-leaf M has been substituted for the original leaf in a set of the leaves for the *Epitome* printed in 1543, possibly taken, as Dr. A. C. Klebs has suggested, from some unsold remainders.

It is peculiar that only one such copy should be known, but other examples may in time come to light. When one considers what stress was laid by Vesalius on the *Epitome* as a student's short cut to all that had been compressed into the larger work, it has always seemed strange that the 1555 *Fabrica* was issued without the companion volume. The natural explanation has always been that the press of Oporinus had exceeded its financial resources in publishing the handsome 1555 edition with its heavier paper, new type, re-engraved title-page, capital initials, and so on, and hesitated to become more deeply involved should an *Epitome* having the same date be required. They may therefore as a trial balloon have made up a few copies with the new colophon leaf, only one of which has survived. Or there may be some better explanation.

The history of paper making and its watermarks is highly complicated and obscure. The writer consequently has hesitated to stress even such a matter as the identical watermark on the sheets of the *Tabulæ sex* and the Glasgow codex, thereby bringing them both into relationship with Calcar. Even more hesitation was felt in regard to the significance of the watermarks on the paper used by Chrestien Wechel in the 1543 edition of Tagault's Surgery. In the instance of this unique 1555 *Epitome*, however, the watermarks provide evidence, more than circumstantial, that the last leaf of the book was printed in 1555. The matter has been gone into more deeply by Dr. Waller in his interesting description of the volume (417).

There were many subsequent reprintings of the *Epitome's* text, some unillustrated like that incorporated in the *Chirurgia magna* of Borgarutius in 1568, also that in the Dutch edition of Jan Wouters the following year, and in the subsequent 1603 Wittenberg edition. Others were accompanied by reproductions of the Vesalian plates, as were the Anatomies of Geminus (1545), Valverde (1556), Felix Platter (1583), Caspar Bauhin (1588) and many more. Some of these publications de Feyfer thought best to include in his subsection VI.B, but the larger number of them fall in his next subsection VI.C, wherein he lists publications in which the *Epitome* and *Fabrica* are more or less combined.

Indeed, on the basis that Albanus Torinus, in order to fill out his pages, had borrowed certain woodcuts from the *Fabrica* which were unused in the Latin *Epitome,* de Feyfer looked upon this as a combination of the two works and consequently placed it in his subsection VI.C. On these slender grounds the *Fabrica* itself might almost be put in the same category in view of the two folding plates that were intended for the *Epitome*. De Feyfer's subsection VI.C therefore starts out with the German *Epitome* (VI.C.11) and continues with a series of 34 items up to and including the *Opera omnia* of Boerhaave and Albinus(VI.C.45).

[The texts of the unillustrated Epitomes were not available to Dr. Cushing and he had been unable to examine them. Vander Haeghen (37) gives a full description of the editions of 1560, 1569, 1582 and 1603. The text of the 1560 edition has been obtained in photostat from the Army Medical Library and the Vander Haeghen description verified. The other three entries are based directly on Vander Haeghen.—Ed.]

VI.B.—4

EPITOME without illustrations   *Paris,* 1560

Title: Andreæ / Vesalii Brvxel╱ / lensis, Scholæ Me╱ / dicorum Patauinæ profes╱ soris, / suorum de humani corpo╱ / ris fabrica librorum / epitome. / [Printer's device] / Parisiis, / Apud Andream Wechelum, sub Pegaso, / in vico Bel╱ louaco. / 1560.

Collation: 8°. A╱I⁸; 142 pp.

Contents: A1*a* title; A1*b* blank; A2*a*╱3*b* dedication to Prince Philip II; A4*a*-I8*b* text.

Note: The book is printed in italic type and has no illustrations. It contains the six chapters of the *Epitome* and the chapter, *Externarum humani corporis sedium partiumue citra dissectionem occurrentium appella╱ tiones,* which in the 1543 edition accompanies the Adam and Eve plates. The Greek words which formerly appeared in the margins are now incorpo╱ rated in the text.

Copies: London (BM, RCS); Paris (BN); Munich; DSG; MiU (Pilcher).

Copy used: Photostat of copy in Army Medical Library; it does not have the unnumbered prelimi╱ nary leaf which Vander Haeghen mentions as being blank on the recto and having a note "to the reader" on the verso.

VI.B.—5

EPITOME. Dutch   *Bruges,* 1569

Title: Dat Epitome Ofte Cort Be╱ / griip Der Anatomien, Andr. Vesalii. Wt. Het / Latijn in neder╱duudsch naer den oprechten zinne ouer╱ghestelt, door / M. Ian Wouters, ghegagiert Medicijn ende Chirurgijn der stede vander / Vere in Zeelāt: eñ wort ghedeelt in zes capittelen met zijn additiē. / [Wood╱ cut with two anatomical figures, one lying down, the other standing] / Te Brvgghe, / Inde peerde strate bij my Pieter de Clerck, Ghezworen Drucker der / Con. Maiesteyt. Anno 1569. Eñ daer vijntmen (*sic*) se te coopen. / Cum Gratia & Priuilegio.

Colophon: Brugis Flandrorum excudebat Petrus Clericus / Typographus à Regia Maiestate admissus / Anno M. CCCCC. LXIX. / Cum Gratia & Priuilegio.

Collation: 4°. [8] *ll.,* 105 (wrongly numbered 104) pp., [2] pp. + 1 blank.

Contents: The preliminary leaves consist of the fol╱ lowing: title╱page, with half╱length woodcut portrait and coat of arms of Jean Wouters on the verso; dedicatory epistle dated Veere, 26 October 1569; letter of translator to Jean Pelsers, pensionary surgeon at Bruges, dated Veere, 31 October, 1569; Dutch verses *Tot den beminden Leser;* Latin preface of trans╱ lator; two bits of Latin verse, one by Arnold Man╱ lius, the other anonymous; and an alphabetical index of Dutch technical terms with their interpreta╱ tion in Latin or Greek. The main part of the book contains: pp. 1╱94 *Dat Epitome;* pp. 95╱102 *De Naemen Van De Butenste Steden, Plaetsen, Ofte Deelen. Haer Naectelicken zonder Anatomizerijnghe openbarende eñ verthoonende;* pp. 103╱104 woodcut followed by explanatory text. The two unnumbered pages at the end contain the list of errata, the appro╱ bation dated [Bruges], 14 May 1569, the privilege dated Brussels, 20 May 1569, and the colophon.

Note: The main part of the text is a translation of the 1543 *Epitome.* The old division into seven chapters is retained, but the chapters have been subdivided by Wouters. The second part is a translation of the explanatory text which accompanies the two nude drawings. The woodcut representing the table of instruments used in anatomical dissection is reduced and reversed from that appearing in the *Fabrica* (both 1543 and 1555) and in the 1545 *Compendiosa* of Geminus (VI.C.2). The number 63 is used twice in the pagination; from this point on, the even and odd numbers occupy respectively the recto and verso of the pages.

Copies: Van der Haeghen quotes only one copy, in the University Library at Ghent.

VI.B.—6

EPITOME without illustrations　　　　　　　　　　　*Wittenberg,* 1582

Title: Andreæ Vesalij / Brvxellen- / sis, Scholæ Medico- / rvm Patavinæ Pro- / fesso- / ris, suorum, de humani corpo- / ris fabrica, librorum / epitome, / Ex Editione / Hvivs Posteriori, In / vsum artis medicæ studio- / sorum, correc- / tiùs / impressa. / [Device] / VVitebergæ, / Typis Zachariæ Lehmani, / M D LXXXII.

Collation: 8°. 1 *l.*, 108 pp.

Contents: l. 1 title-page; on verso, Latin distich: "Corporis ignari, mortem inter / prandia cœnant: / Quare corpus, homo discito, / nosse tuum." pp. 1-6 (in roman type) dedication to Prince Philip of Spain; pp. 7-108 (in ital. type) text of which pp. 99-108 contain *Externarum humani corporis sedium partiumve . . . appellationes.*

Note: The book is unillustrated and the contents correspond with VI.B.4. The Greek words in the text have been omitted as in the (Geminus) London edition of 1545.

Copies: Darmstadt (Bibl. gr. duc.); Bonn (Bibl. univ.); Breslau (Bibl. univ); Vienna (Bibl. imp.).

VI.B.—7

EPITOME without illustrations　　　　　　　　　　　*Wittenberg,* 1603

Title: Andreæ Vesalij Brvxellensis, Scholæ Medicorvm Patavinæ Professoris Svorvm, De Hvmani Corporis Fabrica, Librorvm Epitome, Ex Editione Hvivs Posteriori, In usum artis Medicæ studiosorum, correctiùs impressa. [Device] Witebergæ, Impensis Bechtoldi Raben, Typis M. Georgij Mulleri, M. DC. III.

Collation: 8°; 110 pp.

Contents: pp. 1-6 contain title, Latin distich and dedication to Prince Philip; pp. 7-110 text, of which pp. 101-110 contain the text that went originally with the Adam and Eve plates.

Note: The book is without illustrations and is a reprint of VI.B.6.

Copies: Breslau (Bibl. univ.); Königsberg (Bibl. univ.).

*　　　　*　　　　*　　　　*

With the publication of the *Fabrica* and its *Epitome,* so far as concerns a bio-bibliography of Vesalius, we reach a definite fork in the road. Turning one way, we might follow the footsteps of his later career which takes him to court and the further campaigns of the Emperor, but this distinctly falls off in biblio-graphical interest. On the other hand, we may follow, as de Feyfer has done, the subsequent history of both *Fabrica* and *Epitome,* which would keep us more alive to the tradition of the artist but will cause us for the moment to lose sight of the author. The latter seems preferable to me in view of what is now generally conceded: that Calcar's contributions, even though done under Vesalius' direc⁄tion, were as much a factor in the great and enduring success of the work as what Vesalius had dangerously said in his text. There was no adverse criticism of the woodcuts made from Calcar's drawings; the only criticism—and that came from Vesalius himself—was that they were everywhere promptly copied and reduced in size.

C. GEMINUS*

As will have been noted, the three highly informative letters written to friends by Vesalius all came to be printed at Basel. The first on the venesection con⁄troversy was sent from Padua on January 1, 1539, to Nicolaus Florenas; the second, concerning the *Fabrica,* forwarded from Venice to Oporinus was dated August 24, 1542; while the third, sent from Regensburg to Joachim Roelants on June 15, 1546, was the China⁄root Epistle. The last of the three, from a biographical standpoint, provides the greatest amount of source material; and while it was obviously written to clear himself before the bar of public opinion from the charges of the Galenists, he at the same time took occasion, as he did in the letter to Oporinus, to lay bare some of his minor grievances as an author.

To one of these grievances, which concerned a book published in England only the year before, attention may now be drawn. In the preface to the China⁄root Epistle which Franciscus Vesalius addressed to Duke Cosimo, he speaks disparagingly of the plagiary of his brother's *Epitome* by a certain Englishman, his one⁄time housemate at Padua, who had so completely spoiled the book that it no longer retained the slightest resemblance to the edition of Oporinus. And in the letter proper, Vesalius reverts to the subject himself as follows: "But who, I ask, can feel the faintest inclination to publish the results of his night⁄long studies, when there are people everywhere guilefully plotting to destroy the works of others? A case in point exists at present in England, where the figures of my *Epitome* have been copied very poorly and without skill in drawing—although not without expense to whoever will have to pay for them. And, indeed, I would be ashamed to have anyone think that I had published these illustrations in such form."

* In view of Dr. Larkey's (244) disclosure that the Geminus text of the English editions is drawn from Vicary and only the plates from Vesalius' *Fabrica,* it becomes impossible to classify the Geminus editions in strict accordance with the original de Feyfer scheme. On this account, Dr. Cushing had evidently set aside VI.C for Geminus, and had placed in section VI.D all other modified versions of Vesalius' anatomical texts (and plates). Dr. Larkey points out that the plate legends rendered by Udall are the first English translations of this part of the *Fabrica* to appear up to the present time.—Ed.

In view of his emphasis on the necessity of large plates if one were successfully to portray the finer anatomical details, it must have been a blow to Vesalius to see them reproduced in smaller size; but it would have been far better had he taken it as a compliment rather than a slight; for the engraver, who undoubtedly shows skill, makes no concealment of their source but accredits the work to Vesalius and draws with equal freedom upon both *Epitome* and *Fabrica*. As a matter of fact, the plates have been copied with accuracy and the new medium of copper has made possible a sharpness of line impossible for even such skilful wood engravers as cut the blocks for the *Fabrica*. As Vesalius hints, the publisher must have gone to great expense in getting them done, but the venture apparently proved successful, for copies of his three editions, particularly those with an English text, are far more rare than are copies of the 1543 *Fabrica* or *Epitome*.

The person referred to was of course Thomas Geminus, doubtless mistaken by Franciscus for John Caius who, as we have already stated, lived with brother Andreas at Padua when he was preparing his contributions to the Giunta Galen. There is no reason to suppose that Geminus had at any time been employed by Vesalius, though being an Italian and an engraver he might conceivably have been among those who worked for him on his plates. John Caius returned to England in 1544, the year after the *Fabrica* and *Epitome* were published; and two years later he was appointed Reader to the United Company of Barber Surgeons in which capacity he was called upon to give annual public dissections.

At about the time Caius returned, Thomas Geminus had apparently migrated to England probably in search of employment, and he first appears on the scene in connection with a certain Thomas Raynold (Raynald, Raynalde or Ray) who had undertaken to reprint the English translation of the *De partu hominis* (Frankfurt, Egenolph, 1532)—Rösslin's *Rosengarten*—a popular and oft reprinted work on midwifery which first appeared in German at Strassburg in 1513. The first edition in English, translated by Richard Jonas, appeared in 1540 with the title *The Byrth of Mankynde newly translated out of Laten into Eng-lysshe*. The book had a great vogue and it was Raynold's intention to add to his new edition a section on anatomy with illustrations of the female organs of generation. In Raynold's augmented edition of 1545, the text called for eleven figures, only two of which were included. They were copperplate reproductions, in identical size, of the first two figures in Liber V of the *Fabrica* (Fig. 79); one showed the outer peritoneal layer of the abdomen (as pointed out by Crummer [92] it is reversed), the other the viscera and omentum after reflecting the peri-toneum, both figures having the lettering used by Vesalius.

These prints are said to be among the first copperplate engravings in any English book; but that fact and the inappropriateness in the second print of using a male figure for a "Woman's book" is far from their only point of interest. The text calls for and describes nine other figures, evidently those pertaining to the female organs of sex which appear later on in Liber V. All of them are to be found in the many subsequent printings of the *Byrth of Mankynde*, of which Sir D'Arcy Power has made a detailed study (323).

Since this 1545 edition therefore begins the Geminus-Vesalius tradition and as Raynold's book was unknown to de Feyfer, it deserves a brief citation prior to a consideration of the three Geminus editions of the *Epitome*:

VI.C.—1

RAYNOLD-GEMINUS   Woman's book   *London,* 1545

Title (Fig. 79): The byrth of / mankynde, otherwyse named / the Womans booke. Newly / set furth, corrected and / augmented. Whose cō-/tentes ye maye rede / in the table of the / booke, and most / playnly in the / prologue. / By Thomas Raynold / phisition. / Anno. M.D.xlv.

Colophon: Imprynted at London by / Tho. Ray [Raynold].

Collation: 8vo. A⁴, B-I⁸, Hh⁸, Hhh⁶, K-Q⁸, R⁴, S-X⁸, Y¹⁰; [22] *ll.*, 162 *ll.* wrongly numbered; two groups of two plates each follow sigs. Hh8 and L8 respectively.

Contents: A1*a* title; A1*b* Latin introduction to reader; A2*a*-4*b* table of contents, calling for eleven figures on fol. 46; B1*a*-D2*a* prologue to women readers; D2*b* blank; D3*a*-Hhh6*b the fyrst booke.* On sig. Hh8*a* (fol. 46 for 54) begins the *"Declaratyon by letters of the fygures"* followed by two inserted leaves with figures *en face* apparently engraved on a single plate (*cf.* Fig. 79) copied from *Liber V* of the *Fabrica* (the text of the "Declaratyon" follows through sig. Hhh6); K1*a*-R4*b the second booke;* S1*a*-X4*a thyrde booke;* X4*a*-Y10*b fourth booke.*

Note: The book is printed in black letter type of two sizes, 22 and 26 lines to a page. The two Vesalian plates follow sig. Hh8; the two Rösslin plates follow sig. L8. Foliation begins on D3*a*, continues correct to 18*a* (ff. 1-46), becomes jumbled through sigs. Hh and Hhh to K1*a* where begins fol. 47, and continues reasonably correct though with a succession of minor errors to end at fol. 148.

Copies: London (BM, RCP); DSG [additional 9 plates cut and pasted in]; CSmH [has full sheet from Geminus folded in]; Cushing.

Copy used: H.C.; bought from W. M. Voynich, New York, *ca.* 1926, for $600. Contemporary Oxford binding. Former owner "W. Herbert 1781," with signature of W. H. Ireland (the Shakespeare forger). Measures 18 by 11.5 cm.

It can readily be seen from the peculiar construction of this 1545 Raynold volume that the insertion of signatures Hh and Hhh, which caused the compositors such confusion in their foliation, was an afterthought on the editor's part. Thomas Raynold was a somewhat mysterious person. It is quite possible that he may be not only the "Tho. Ray" who printed the 1545 *Womans booke*, but also the "T.R." who printed the 1540 Jonas edition in which occur two leaves with copperplate prints after Rösslin. Though Thomas Raynold describes himself as a physician, he does not, according to D'Arcy Power, appear to have been a member of the College. As a printer and editor it is conceivable that he had a falling-out with Geminus. The fact that two copperplates were noted in the inventory of his stock in 1540 shows that they had long been in his possession, if they were actually the two under consideration, as some believe, rather than the Rösslin plates.

It is quite possible that prior to 1545 Raynold made contact with John Caius who prompted him to undertake something on a far larger scale: namely, to issue an edition of Vesalius' *Epitome* with new copperplate illustrations. Such a publication would profitably be consulted by the students at his public anatomies. Some such explanation would not only account for the failure by Geminus to supply Raynold with the nine missing plates called for in his text, but explain why the two plates used by him were re-engraved for the *Compendiosa* of Geminus. To this work we may now turn.

VI.C.—2

GEMINUS, Compendiosa   *London*, 1545

Engraved title (Fig. 80): Compendiosa / totius Anatomie delineatio, ære / ex-arata: per Thomam Geminum. / Londini.

Head-title (A1*a*): Andreæ Vesalii Brvx / ellensis svorvm de hvmani corporis / fabrica librorvm epitome.

Colophon: Londini in officina Ioanni Herfordie: Anno Domini. / 1545. / Mense Octobri:

Collation: Fol., mostly in sixes; [*]², A-B⁶ (B4 has sig. 4 and 5 on same leaf), C⁵, D-G⁶, H³; [45] *ll.* of text and [40] *ll.* of copperplates (one folded), all blank on verso.

Contents: [*]1*a* engr. title with arms of Henry VIII; [*]1*b* blank; [*]2*a-b* dedication signed Thomas Geminus Lysiensis, London, September 28 (*Quarto calendas Octobres*), 1545; A1*a-*2*a* Chap. I, following head-title to text of *Epitome*; A2*a-*4*b* Chap. II; A4*b-*6*a* Chap. III; A6*a-*B1*a* Chap. IV; B1*a-*2*a* Chap. V; B2*b* Chap VI, followed by folding plate [pl. 1], nude figure; B3*a-b Externarum humani corporis sedium* [from *Epitome* K*b-*L*a*]; B3*b Brevis numeratio* [ab-stract from *De ossium numero* in *Fabrica*, Cap. LX (for XL)]; B4-5 index for 3 skeletal figs. [pl. 2-4]; B6*a-*D4*b* indices for 14 full-page muscle figures from Book II of *Fab.* [pl. 5-18]; D5-6 indices for two plates [19-20] of assembled muscle figures; E1*a-*3*a* indices for two plates [21-22] of venous circulation, portal and caval, from *Fab.*; E3*b-*4*b* indices for two plates [23-24] from *Fab.*, of arterial system; E5 index for plate [25] from both *Epit.* and *Fab.* of arterial and venous systems with figs. to be super-imposed (for variants of this plate *cf. infra*); F1*a-*3*b* index of nerve figs. on four plates [26-29]; F4*a-*G2*a* index of organs of nutrition with four plates [30-33] (pl. 30 has the two figures from Raynold re-engraved, the first now reversed to accord with *Fab.* woodcut); G2*a-*3*b* indices of female organs in one plate [34] which has the nine extra figures from the *Fab.* called for in Raynold's 1545 *Byrth of mankynde*; G3*b-*5*a* index of thoracic organs with one plate [35]; G5*b-*H2*b* indices of 19 brain figures from *Fab.* assembled in four plates [36-39]; H3*a-b* indices for miscel-laneous figures on last plate [40], with colophon on H3*b*.

Note: De Feyfer VI.C.15. The only references to Vesalius occur in a heading at the beginning of Chap. I (sig. A1*a*), the wording of which is indi-cated above under *head-title*, and in the dedication to Henry VIII in which Vesalius is given high praise (see Larkey [244, p. 369] for translation).

The text is printed in roman type, two columns to a page; watermarked paper.

Copies: Louvain; London (BM); CaMM⁄Os; Cushing [2 copies]; MH; OClM; NNNAM; Trent; DSG; CSt⁄L; MdBJ⁄W; MBM; NN; Clendening.

Copies used: (i) H.C., bought in 1910 from Maggs Bros. for 6 guineas. Title and dedication leaf in facsimile. Note of early owner on fly⁄leaf, "Ex Legato Jacobi Bartholomæi Beccarii Anno 1766." Contemporary vellum; measures 38 by 26.5 cm.

(ii) H.C., incomplete. Covers of early stamped French binding of *ca.* 1550 preserved; gilt fore⁄edges. Former owner's inscription erased, "*Ce livre appartient a* [indecipherable]. *Maistre Chirurgien à Orleans 1638.*" Measures 40.4 by 26.7 cm. Folding plate missing.

Briefly noted under *"Contents"* is the fact that one of the leaves with illustra⁄tions [pl. 25] shows innumerable variations. It carries prints of two separate copperplates; the larger, measuring 33.5 by 12.2 cm., shows the figures on the folded sheet m3 of the *Fabrica* (p. 313) intended for the *Epitome* and used there also; the narrower plate measuring 33.5 by 7.2 cm. carries the eight figures on the unnumbered m3 sheet of the *Fabrica* which Vesalius intended should be cut and superimposed on the other. There was a small *unnumbered* ninth figure of the uterus and ovaries on the verso of the folding sheet m3, so that in copy (1) the roman numeral is wanting; but in the other copy it has been engraved on the plate, *i.e.,* number IX is supplied. Sometimes the larger of these two plates, as in the British Museum copy, may be on the left rather than right side of the page.

There are many other peculiarities in the arrangement of the forty pages of copperplates to which serial numbers have been given herein to aid in identi⁄fication. Geminus has taken liberties in plate [1] with the celebrated nude figures from the *Epitome*, for the male figure in his cleverly copied plate now holds an apple instead of a skull. An enlarged skull is now on the ground with a serpent intertwined, thus emphasizing the Adam and Eve tradition. On plate [34] occur the nine figures of the female generative organs called for by Raynold in his 1545 edition of the *Byrth of mankynde*.

On all forty leaves of illustrations (excluding the title⁄page), the prints with few exceptions have been made from a single copperplate (*ca.* 33.5 by 18⁄21.5 cm.), the largest being that [1] with the nude figures which measures 34 by 32.5 cm. The copperplates for thirty⁄four leaves [1⁄19, 21⁄24, 27⁄37 and 40] are full page in size while there are five leaves [20, 25, 26, 38 and 39] with two copper⁄plates to the page. Plate [30] alone, on which the two re⁄engraved Raynold figures occur, shows impressions of three plates, all of which were perhaps originally engraved on a single plate. Certainly the plate on leaf No. 32 was a single large plate from which the *Undecima figura* has been cut out, re⁄engraved and re⁄inserted. The same thing has happened on leaf No. 33 with Figure XIX. Accompanying these illustrations are the descriptions from the *Fabrica* now for the first time rendered into English.

Each of the 83 leaves of the *Compendiosa* shows a watermark. In three different copies examined, they prove to be of three principal types: (1) an elaborated pitcher appears chiefly but not exclusively in all the copies on paper for the text leaves; (2) a gauntlet with star in one copy (Maggs) is used chiefly but not exclusively for the plates; (3) a letter P is used chiefly for the plates in another copy. In all three copies an occasional plate is printed on type (1) paper.

In 1552, as we have seen, there was published at Lyon by Jean de Tournes a small unillustrated two-volume pocket edition of the *Fabrica*. Though intended for students, the text, like the original, was in Latin. It could not have had a particularly warm reception for there was no second issue. In the same year Geminus, encouraged by the sale of his fully illustrated edition of the *Epitome,* despite its Latin text, was persuaded, possibly by John Caius, to print an edition in the vernacular. Not feeling competent to make the translation himself, he was constrained to seek the help of others, as explained in his preface. "Wherunto forasmuch as I am not my selfe so perfeict and experte in the Englishe tounge that I dare waraunt or trust myne owne dooynges, I have used the studious peines of Nicholas Udall and certain other learned men whose exercise in translacions and pennyng in this tounge hath ben (as I understande) not without some fruite to the common weale."

Who may have suggested and have brought him in contact with Nicholas Udall, one-time headmaster of Eton and now prebendary of Windsor, is uncertain. It may well enough have been John Caius again who for the past eight years at the command of Henry VIII had been lecturing on anatomy, possibly at Barber Surgeons Hall, to a group of students, few of whom could read enough Latin to understand the text even of the indices of the forty plates. What is more, the order of the text of the seven preliminary chapters covered the subject in a newfangled fashion rather than in the orderly method of conducting an anatomy prescribed by Mondino. This time-honoured method, indeed, was doubtless followed by Vesalius himself if one may judge from the frontispiece of the *Fabrica* where he starts his dissection with the abdominal viscera which for obvious reasons should first be removed.

For the benefit of the "unlatined surgeons" as Geminus calls them, a translation into the vernacular not only of the *characterum indices* for the Vesalian plates but also of some brief text more nearly in accord with the customary sessions of a three-day public anatomy than the Vesalian text of the *Epitome* was highly desirable.

Dr. Sanford Larkey has made the important disclosure that the text chosen as a substitute for that in the *Epitome* was similar to that used by Thomas Vicary in his *Anatomie of the bodie of man* (first published in 1548), but rearranged to follow the order of Mondino's Anatomy. In spite of the fact that he too, like Paré, was an unlatined surgeon, Vicary had come into royal favour for having once cured the "sore legges" of His Majesty and his consequent prominence may account for his having been depicted in Holbein's famous painting commemo⁄ rating the union of the Company of Barbers and the Guild of Surgeons which still hangs in Barber Surgeons Hall. He is shown kneeling at the King's left while Henry hands him the charter which indicates that, however unlettered, he was an important person.

The text of Vicary's book was traced in 1895 to the Surgery of Henri de Mondeville by the scholarly J. F. Payne (313), who came upon a fourteenth⁄ century MS. with an English translation by an unknown Londoner, much of which had been printed practically word for word by Vicary. This manuscript subsequently disappeared, but Sir D'Arcy Power wrote me on June 4, 1922, that he had "cleared up the Vicary mystery by finding an early translation of Henry de Mondeville." Whether this was the same MS. as the Peterhouse, Cambridge, MS. 118 mentioned eleven years later by S. V. Larkey in his informative essay given before the Bibliographical Society (244) I am unprepared to say. Here at all events were at least two early English renderings of de Monde⁄ ville, either of which Vicary might have seen and drawn upon for his text which was selected on the advice of someone, very possibly Caius, to replace the Latin text of the *Epitome*. Under these circumstances, with no translation to be done, just why it was necessary to drag in the gifted Nicholas Udall merely to translate the *characterum indices*, a task for which Caius would have been much better fitted, is not clear.

All editions of the *Compendiosa* of Geminus are rare, those in English espe⁄ cially so. The *Short⁄title catalogue* cites eight copies of five editions of 1545, 1552, 1553, 1557 and 1559. As the only copies of the 1552 and 1557 editions were credited to the Wellcome Historical Medical Museum, information was sought in 1929 from the Librarian and he replied that their three editions were these: (1) of 1545 (lacking one plate and with the title⁄page in reproduction); (2) of 1552 ("lacking the title⁄page but with that of the 1545 edition substituted"); and (3) of 1559. They were bound in one volume by Rivière and had been pur⁄ chased for £35. He felt confident that there were no 1553 or 1557 editions. However, he subsequently found an opportunity to collate their supposed 1552 W.H.M.M. copy with the first English edition in the British Museum and was surprised to find that they were identical except that the B.M. copy had the date 1553 engraved on the lower right corner of the framed title in the frontispiece.

There are, in other words, copies of what may be considered early stages of the 1553 edition which have the same undated title-page as the 1545 edition, the only date elsewhere being that at the end of Nicholas Udall's preface on the verso of the second leaf signed "at Windesore the .xx. of July 1552." On the recto of this second leaf occurs the dedication of Geminus *"To the moste hygh and re-doubted Prynce Edwarde the VI by the grace of God Kynge of Englande, Fraunce & Irelande"* [etc.] This must have been written before July 6th, on which date the sickly young King when only fifteen years of age ended his brief rule. It indeed was stated by Brunet that in the 1552 edition a portrait of Edward had been substituted for his father's coat of arms on the title-page. While no such copy is now known, it is surprising that Udall who must have known of Geminus' dedication, did not mention the fact of the young King's death when he dated his preface two weeks after it had occurred.

VI.C.—3

GEMINUS, Compendiosa   English ed.   *London,* 1553

Engraved Title: [identical with VI.C.2, with the date 1553 printed in some copies beside 'Londini'].

Colophon: Imprynted at London by Nycholas Hyll dwellynge/ in Saynte Johns streate, for Thomas Geminus [n.d.].

Collation: Fol. [*]², A⁶, B⁷, C-I⁶, K²; 39 (instead of 40) engr. plates not included in 59 unsigned *ll.* of text; gothic type; 2 cols.

Contents: [*]1a engr. title; [*]1b blank; [*]2a dedi-cation "To the moste hygh and redoubted Prynce Edwarde the VI" etc.; [*]2b Nicolas Udall "To the ientill readers and Surgeons of Englande," dated July 20, 1552; A1a-K2a text of "thys treatyse of Anatomie" [Vesalius nowhere mentioned]. The engraved plates are identical with those of the 1545 Latin edition (lacking one plate of the arteries) and they still retain their Latin lettering.

Note: Copies of this edition differ from one another in minor details. Plate 25 (before F4) exists in two states (as described in VI.C.2); and in the British Museum copy the date 1553 has been printed on the title to the right of "Londini." This work is the first to appear in English with the name of the engraver of the plates stated. No mention is made, however, of the originals from which the plates were engraved. Edward VI had died July 6, 1552, two weeks before the date of Udall's preface.

Copies: London (BM, W); Cushing; PPCP; NNC-M; MiU (Pilcher); CtY.

Copy used: H.C., bought from Voynich in Decem-ber 1928 for $600. Lacks Adam and Eve plate (as do B.M. and Wellcome copies).

The second English Geminus of 1559 is less rare than the first of 1553 and differs from it only in the addition of two folded woodcut leaves usually referred to as fugitive sheets and two explanatory leaves of text entitled "The Anatomie of the inwarde partes of man." Otherwise it is a re-issue, with the same setting of type save for the last page with the colophon. The engraved title is from the same plate as that of the 1545 and 1553 editions, save for the fact that the arms of Henry VIII have been replaced by an engraved portrait of Queen Elizabeth, thought to be the earliest known portrait of the Queen. In the Bodleian copy, however, there is a note in contemporary script stating that this portrait was intended to be Bloody Mary and not Elizabeth (who ascended the throne as the book was passing through press). The long four-page dedication of Geminus is likewise addressed to Queen Elizabeth.

Larkey (244) who has thrown so much light on the Geminus text writes as follows concerning the three editions of Geminus:

"The Compendium of Geminus and the two editions of the English translations were among the most important anatomical works in England of the sixteenth century. They must have been of tremendous value in the study of dissection, as conducted by John Caius at the Barber-Surgeons Company and in later dissections at the Royal College of Physicians. They meant that the young surgeons knew their anatomy from the best source, Vesalius, although the text was so arranged that it could be used in the dissecting room. This was probably a factor in the improved surgery of the Elizabethan period.

"Further, these works stand as an example of the broad interests of the scholars of early Tudor times. If Caius was really connected with the 1545 Geminus, this adds lustre to a name already great for its contributions not only to medicine but also to philology and education in general. It shows that he appreciated the importance of careful dissection and makes us realize that the 'anatomies' he directed were not simply a recital of the old authorities but were really in the spirit of investigation.

"The versatility of the school-master and dramatist, Nicholas Udall, is strikingly evident in his grasp of the problem. He realized the value of the illustrations of Vesalius, but also that the text of the *Epitome* was not suitable for teaching. His re-arrangement of the Vicary text along the lines of Mundinus was the form followed in a great many of the later anatomies. This type and the Vesalian Compendia following Geminus were the most popular in the sixteenth and seventeenth centuries. Udall's version, combining these two, possessed the merits of both, and was admirably suited for its purpose. As such, it was the first English dissecting manual.

"Perhaps we shall never know just what he added to the 1548 Vicary but there is a literary quality in his treatise that is probably the result of his own genius. His choice of this text shows the high regard for the work of this estimable surgeon of Barts. It is indeed unfortunate that there is no copy of the earliest version of Vicary, for it would be interesting to compare it with the text of Udall, the most important link in the long series of editions of Vicary.

"The value of this book in the spread of the Vesalian anatomy has been emphasized. It contains the only English translation of the descriptions of the drawings in the *Fabrica* . . .

"The entire translation of Udall is distinguished by its clarity, especially in contrast to the Payne manuscript, and should be of interest to students of literature since it provides another example of the work of this forerunner of the great Elizabethans. These books are in every way a delight, bringing before us a picture of the full life of those energetic times."

VI.C.—4

GEMINUS, Compendiosa   English 2nd ed.   *London,* 1559

Engraved title (Fig. 81): Compendiosa / totius Anatomie delineatio, ære / exarata per Thomam Geminum. / Londini. 1559.

Colophon: Imprinted at London within the blacke fryars: by Thomas Gemini. / Anno salutis. 1559. / Mense Septemb.

Collation: [*]⁶, A⁶, B⁷, C-I⁶, K²; 61 *ll.* of text; 2 folding woodcut plates; 39 engr. plates.

Contents: [*]1a blank; [*]1b half-title with Royal Arms facing title; [*]2a title; [*]2b blank; [*]3a-4b Geminus' dedication to Queen Elizabeth; [*]5 "Anatomie of the inwarde Partes of man"; folding woodcuts with flaps; [*]6a "Anatomie of the inward Partes of wooman"; [*]6b blank; folding copper-plate of Adam and Eve; A1a-K2a text as in previous edition; K2b blank.

Note: The peculiarities of this edition are described in the text above. The fugitive sheet of man and woman, with the flaps illustrating he anatomical layers, was described in 1925 by Crummer (91).

Copies: London (BM) [has leaf before title bearing royal arms and *"Honi soit qui mal y pense"*; missing in all other copies]; Waller; Cushing; PPCP; NBMS; MiU (Pilcher); Fulton; Harvey.

Copy used: H.C. The Wollaton Hall copy sold at Christie's, June 15, 1925, No. 366, for £72. Lacks [*]1. Repaired with title added from another copy and sold by E. P. Goldschmidt, also in 1925, for £240. Measures 37.5 by 26.5 cm.

Interest in the Geminus venture was such that his engravings were immediately copied in Germany (See *Anatomia Deudsch,* 1551, VI.D.4), and the original copperplates shortly fell into the hands of André Wechel at Paris, who brought out editions of the Geminus text and plates, both in Latin and French, under the editorship of the young French humanist, Jacques Grévin.

VI.C.—5

GREVIN-GEMINUS   *Paris,* 1564

Title: Anatomes / totivs, ære in- / scvlpta delineatio, / cvi addita est epitome innv- / meris mendis repvrgata, qvam / de corporis humani fabrica conscrip- / sit / clariss. And. Vesalius: / eiqve accessit / partivm corporis tvm simplicivm

/tum compositarum breuis elucidatio, per Iacobum Greuinum / Claro-
montanum Bellouacum, medicum Paris. / [device] / Lvtetiæ Parisiorvm. /
Apvd Andream Wechelvm, svb / Pegaso, in Vico Bellovaco. / M. D.
LXIIII.

Colophon: none.

Collation: Fol. *², A⁸, B-H⁶, I²; [2] *ll.*, 54 *ll.*, 42
inserted plates, each with blank leaf opposite.

Contents: *1a title; *1b large woodcut plate bearing
arms of Philippe de Boulainvilliers-Dammartin,
Comte de Courtenay et de Fauquembergues; *2
dedication to Count Philip signed by Wechel;
A1a-H6b text with plates interleaved; I1a-2b (*ll.* 51-
52) dissertation by Grévin.

Note: This is a Continental edition of the Latin
Geminus *Compendiosa* with occasional commentaries by the editor Jacques Grévin; the Geminus
text is set in italic throughout and Grévin's comments boxed in Roman. Wechel had somehow
acquired all Geminus' original copperplates. Probably Grévin himself had made the deal since he had
spent the year 1559-60 in England, and had there
become a protégé of Queen Elizabeth to whom
Geminus had dedicated the third edition of the
Compendiosa in 1559. Wechel had published the
unillustrated text of the *Epitome* in 1560 (VI.B.4),
but he was evidently dissatisfied with the lack of
illustrations and no doubt induced Grévin to undertake the more elaborate edition. In this connection it
is significant that Wechel, and not Grévin, signed
the dedication to Dammartin.

Jacques Grévin (?1538-1570), one of the found-
ers of the *théatre régulier* of France, also a poet and one
of the most distinguished medical humanists of
France, died at Turin at the early age of 32. He was
thus only 22 years of age when he was befriended by
the young Queen of England, and 26 when he

brought out this edition of Geminus (see Pinvert,
L., *Jacques Grévin (1538-1570). Etude biographique et
littéraire.* Paris, 1899.) Grévin's *Le chant du cigne*, a
poem of 238 lines, addressed to Queen Elizabeth in
January 1560, remained unpublished until discovered in 1899 by Pinvert, who issued the full text.
The original MS. is in the Bibliothèque Nationale,
Paris, MS. division, *fonds latin,* No. 17075, *ll.* 89-92.
As verse it is of middling quality, artless and im-
mature in places, but exhibiting a certain delicacy
and warmth of expression. The final verses run as
follows:

*Toutesfois je sentis vostre parolle humaine
Alenter doulcement ma doulleur et ma peine,
Lors qu'il vous pleut me veoir, me faisant cest honneur
D'avoir pour agreable ung mien petit labeur.
Ainsi donc, recouvert de ces plumes estranges,
Je laissay ma chanson pour dire voz louanges,
Pour anoncer au peuple et aux hommes sçavans
Qui vivent aujourdhuy et seront survivans,
Bref pour escripre au doz de vostre renommee:
La Royne Elisabet, princesse bien aymee.*

According to Vander Haeghen, copies of the
1564 edition exist in which the word "clariss." on
the title is misspelled "clariis." In the H.C. copy of
this edition, the word is correctly spelled.

Copies: Louvain; London (BM); Cushing; Trent;
NNNAM; NNC-M; MdBJ-W.

Copy used: H.C., from Dr. Henry Barton Jacobs,
22 October, 1910. Olschki in 1915 priced one at
$135, and Nourry of Paris offered a copy for 4000
francs in 1927.

VI.C.—6

GREVIN-GEMINUS   *Paris,* 1565

Title: [Identical with preceding except for new date, M. D. LXV.]

Collation and contents: identical with preceding, *i.e.,* a
page-for-page reissue from the original setting of type.

Copies: Glasgow; Waller; Cushing; MH; CSmH;
NIC; NNC-M.

Copy used: H.C., measuring 38.5 by 25.6 cm.,
bought from Lier in 1926. Olschki offered copies in
1931 and 1932 for $250 and $310 respectively, and
the Goldschmidt copy which measured 38.9 by
25.4 cm. was priced at £75.

GREVIN-GEMINUS.   French   *Paris,* 1569

Title: Les / portraicts anato- / miqves de tovtes les / parties dv corps hvmain, / gravez en taille dovce, / par le commandement de feu Henry huictiesme, / Roy d'Angleterre. / Ensemble / L'Abbregé d' André Vesal, & l'explication d'iceux, accompagnee / d'vne declaration Anatomique. / Par Iaqves Grevin, / de Clermont en Beauuoisis, / Medecin à Paris. / [device] / A Paris, / Chez André Wechel. / M. D. LXIX.

Colophon (p. 106): A Paris, / De l'Imprimerie d'André Wechel, rüe S. Iean de / Beauuais, au Cheual volant.

Collation: [*]⁴, A-C⁴, D-Z², Æ¹; [4] *ll.,* 106 pp., 40 plates inserted through text.

Contents: [*]1a title; [*]1b blank; [*]2a-4b Adver-tissement / de I. Grevin au Le- / cteur sur les noms / Francois imposez a quelques / parties du Corps humain; A1a-Æ1b (pp. 1-106) text.

Note: This is the first translation of the Vesalian text into the French vernacular. Grévin made the trans-lation himself from the text of the 1564-65 Latin edition.

Copies: London (BM); Waller; Glasgow; Cush-ing (2 copies, one lacking first four leaves); MH-M; NNNAM; DSG; NNC-M; MBM; MiU(Pilcher).

Copy used: H.C., from Lier & Co. in 1926 for 600 Swiss francs. Davis & Orioli offered a copy in 1926 for £32/10/-.

D. MODIFIED VERSIONS OF VESALIUS' ANATOMICAL WORKS (OTHER THAN GEMINUS)*

For more than three hundred years the *Fabrica* and the *Epitome* were plagiarized and copied, but it would far exceed the scope of a bio-bibliography to trace all of Vesalius' imitators or those who, spuriously, foisted writings on the world under his name. There are, however, many works which, with some basis, carried Vesalius' name and their respective texts were usually drawn either from the *Epitome* or the *Fabrica,* or from a combination of the two. These books would normally be indexed under Vesalius, and it becomes necessary in a compilation such as this to list them briefly. Those more remote from Vesalius, many of which de Feyfer included in his section VI.D. and which Dr. Cushing had himself collected, must be omitted and reserved for a more peaceful time when they can be studied and their relationships traced in detail. We have in mind such writers as Bartholin, Bauhin, Banister, Casserius, Crooke, Diemerbroeck, Guillemeau, Read, Paaw, Paré, Spigelius and others who, consciously or un-consciously, drew from the Vesalian texts or figures. The texts more immediately based on Vesalius, most of which carry in addition to Vesalius the name of an

---

* Compiled by the editors. Dr. Cushing had prepared many cards for this section but at the time of his death they had not been systematized or arranged, and none of the entries had been described bibliographi-cally. No census was taken of copies in this section.—Ed.

FIGURE SEVENTY-SEVEN

Title-page of the German *Epitome* issued August 9, 1543.

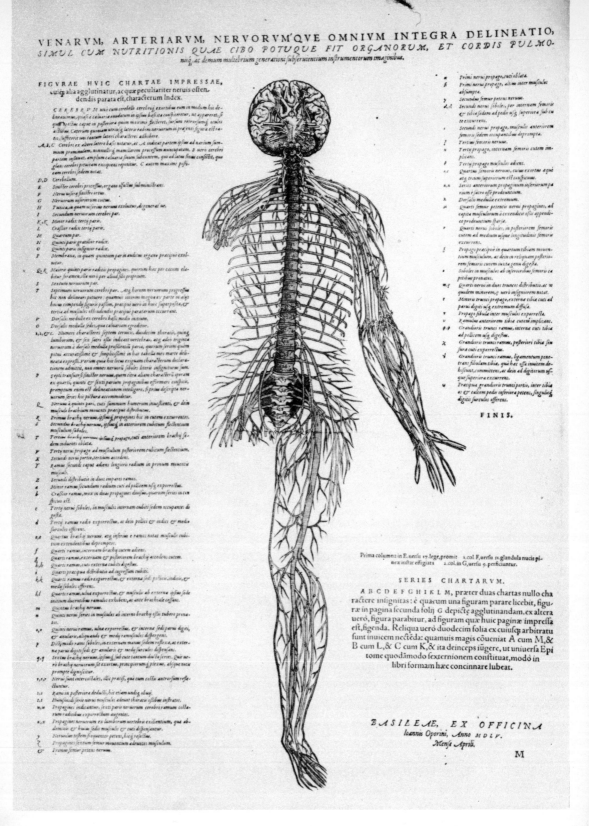

The colophon-leaf M of the 1555 Latin *Epitome* (*ca.* one-third natural size). Kindness of Dr. E. Waller.

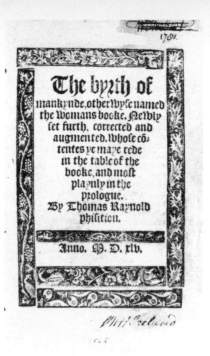

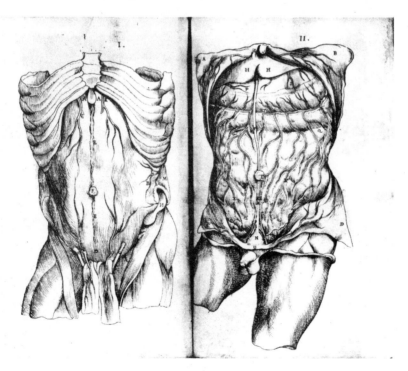

FIGURE SEVENTY-NINE

Title-page of Raynold's *Byrth of mankynde,* 1545, with the two torso plates lifted from Book V of the *Fabrica.*

FIGURE EIGHTY

Engraved title-page of the 1545 Geminus *Compendiosa*.

editor, follow an alphabetical sequence (of editors or publishers). A special development in which Dr. Cushing was greatly interested was the various adaptations of the Vesalian plates for the use of artists. It has been impossible to include them all since they carry down to the present day (many still being designated as executed by Titian); but attention should be directed to the three most famous artistic anatomies based on Vesalius: namely, those of Bonavera (VI.D.9), van der Gracht (VI.D.16-18) and Tortebat (VI.D.25-31) (see also Maschenbauer, VI.A.12-13). Materials about Vesalius and general commentaries are grouped in Chapter X (Vesaliana).

VI.D.—1

BAUDIN, Description.   German   *n.p.*, 1559

Title: Beschreibung und Anzeigung Mannes und Weibes innerlicher Glieder in 12 Kupfer-Figuren verfasst und gezogen aus der Anatomie A. Vesalii. 1559.

Note: This is said to be a folio with twelve figures taken from the Geminus *Compendiosa* of 1545. The title is taken from Haller (182, i, p. 184). No copy has been traced in the United States.

VI.D.—2

BAUDIN, Description.   French   *Lyon*, 1560

Title: Description et De-/monstration des membres interieurs de/ l'homme & de la femme, en douze Tables, tirées / au naturel, selon la vraye Anatomie de André Wesal, / Philosophe, & Docteur en Medicine [*sic*]. / Oeuure vtile & necessaire non seulement aux Medicins [*sic*] & / Chirurgiens, ains aussi aux Portrayeurs, & Architectes. / [device] / A Lyon, / Par Clement Bavdin, / M.D.LX.

Collation: 4°. 24 *ll.*, printed on one side only (except for first).

Note: According to Vander Haeghen (37, v109) who describes this edition in detail, it consists of 12 figures copied from Geminus with explanatory text also translated from the Geminus indices. Vander Haeghen lists the 12 plates but does not indicate from which of the 40 Geminus figures each is taken, *e.g.*, that of the genital anatomy of the female from plate [34] opposite *l.* G2*b* of Geminus, 1545. No copy traced in the U. S.

Copies: Stuttgart (Royal Library); Paris (BN).

VI.D.—3

BAUDIN, Description.   French   *Lyon*, 1567

Title: [as in preceding]

Note: This is a reissue of the 1560 edition with a redated title (Vander Haeghen).

Copy: Leningrad (probably now in Moscow). No copy traced in the U. S.

VI.D.—4

BAUMAN, Anatomia Deudsch   *Nürnberg,* Aug. 1551

Title: Anatomia / Deudsch, / Ein kurtzer Auszug der beschreibung / aller glider
    menschlichs Leybs aus den buchern des / Hochgelerten Hern D. Andree
    Vesalij von Brüssel . . . soderlich wundärtz / ten Deutscher Natiō zu nutz
    ins deutsch gebracht. / [Arms of the city of Nürnberg] / Gedruckt zu Nürn-
    berg beim Jul. Paulo Fabricio. / Anno salutis M D LI. Mense Augusto.

Collation: Fol. [*]², A-N⁶; [2], lxxviii *ll.*; 40
plates.

Contents: [*]1*a* title; [*]1*b* blank; [*]2*a* preface
signed 'Jacob Bauman, Wundartzt'; A1*a*-N6*a* (*ll.*
i-lxxviii) text with 40 engraved plates distributed
through text.

Note: From a bibliographical standpoint, this book
is something of a curiosity since it is printed on
single, unfolded sheets with adjacent pages of the
gatherings pasted together so as to facilitate assemblage. The chain lines, as Vander Haeghen has
pointed out, are horizontal, but this does not indicate, as he implies, that the book is a quarto. It is
made up of single sheets gathered in 6's, this being
true also of VI.D.5 and 6 as exemplified by the
Cushing copies. The 40 copper engravings are
copies, and poor ones at that, of Geminus' plates of
1545 with plate legends in German.

Copies: Louvain; Waller; Cushing; Fulton; MH-M;
NNNAM; DSG; Trent; NNC-M; MBM; MnU;
MiU (Pilcher).

Copies used: H.C., bought in 1907 from Ludwig
Rosenthal for M.55, measuring 38 by 28 cm.; J.F.F.,
bought in 1927 from E. P. Goldschmidt for £75.

VI.D.—5

BAUMAN, Anatomia Deudsch (variant)   *Nürnberg,* 1551

Title: [as in preceding save that after "ins deutsch gebracht" the phrase "durch
    Hieronymum Lauterbach" has been added].

Collation and contents: same as VI.D.4; a reissue.

Note: Jacob Bauman's collaborator, Lauterbach,
has not been identified (see *Janus,* 1909, 14:327-334).

Final leaf lxxviii is mounted.

Copy used: H.C., bought from Lier in March 1936
for Swiss frs. 700.

VI.D.—6

BAUMAN, Anatomia Deudsch   [*Nürnberg*] 1575

Title in red and black: Anatomia / Das ist, / Ein kurtze vnd klare beschreybung
    von der vss- / theilung vnnd zerschneydung aller glider dess Menschlichen
    Lybs, vss den / Bücheren dess Hochgeleerten D. Andree Vesalij Rö. Key.
    May. Leyb- / artzt, gezogen: . . . durch den wol erfarnen M. / Jacob Buw-
    mann Wundartzt zu Zürych in / Truck verfertiget. / [device] / Alles mit
    kunstlichen vnnd schönen figuren . . . M. D. LXXV. / [device]

Collation: identical with VI.D.4 except for added title-page.

Contents: same as VI.D.4, with added second title-page; final leaf lxxviii is mounted as in VI.D.5.

Note: This "edition" is in reality merely a reissue of the remaindered 1551 edition, with a second title inserted. Dr. Cushing's copy carries the 1551 title as well.

Copies: Louvain; Cushing; DSG; MiU (Crummer).

Copy used: H.C., purchased from Halle, Munich, in 1911 for M.180. Dated (1593) stamped pigskin binding with clasps bearing initials "G.M." and carrying an elaborate design of Nürnberg eagles.

VI.D.—7

BOERHAAVE-ALBINUS, Opera omnia (Vol. I)   *Leyden, 1724*

Title: Andreæ Vesalii / Invictissimi Caroli V. Imperatoris Medici / Opera Omnia / Anatomica / & / Chirurgica / Cura / Hermanni Boerhaave / . . . / & / Bernhardi Siegfried Albini / . . . / Tomus primus. / Tabulis æneis Pulcherrimis Ornatus. / [device] / Lugduni Batavorum / Apud { Joannem du Vivie, / et / Joh. & Herm. Verbeek. } / Bibliop. / MDCCXXIV.

Collation: Fol. [*]¹, A-Z⁴, Aa-Zz⁴, Aaa²,¹; [1] *l.*, 358 pp., 43 full-page copperplates.

Contents: [*]1*a* title; [*]1*b* note of publishers to subscribers, in Latin and Dutch; A1*a*-Aaa2*a* text which includes the first three books of the *Fabrica* with the 43 plates re-engraved on copper by I. Wandelaar; [Aaa]3 inserted leaf m3 of the *Fabrica*.

Note: A few copies of this preliminary volume bearing the date 1724 were issued, evidently for the purpose of getting an advanced subscription list for the two-volume edition published the following year.

Copies: MdBM; Trent; Cushing.

Copy used: H.C., bought of Davis & Orioli in December 1935 for £4/4/-; later restored by Zaehnsdorf.

VI.D.—8

BOERHAAVE-ALBINUS, Opera omnia   *Leyden, 1725*

Title in red and black (Tome I): Andreæ Vesalii / Invictissimi Caroli V. Imperatoris Medici / Opera omnia / Anatomica / & / Chirurgica / Cura / Hermanni Boerhaave / . . . / & / Bernhardi Siegfried Albini / . . . / Tomus primus. / [ornamental engraving] / Lugduni Batavorum, / Apud / Joannem du Vivie, / et / Joan. & Herm. Verbeek. / Bibliop. / MDCCXXV.
(Tome II): [identical with I, save for 'Tomus secundus.']

Half-title ([*]1*a*): Andræ Vesalii / . . . / in duos tomos distributa.

Collation: Fol. Tome I: [†]², *-********², A-Y⁴, Z², Aa², Bb-Zz⁴, Aaa-Bbb², Ccc-Rrr⁴, Sss-Ttt², Vvv-Zzz⁴, Aaaa-Ffff⁴, Gggg¹; [21] *ll.*, 572 pp. Tome II: Gggg⁵, Hhhh-Iiii⁴, Kkkk-Nnnn², Oooo⁴, [*¹], Pppp-Yyyy⁴, Zzzz⁴,², Aaaaa-Mmmmmmm⁴, Nnnnnnn-Bbbbbbbb²; [4] *ll.*, 577-1156 pp., *26 ll.*; "79 engr. plates" (*recte* 82; both vols.).

Contents (Tome I): The complete text of the 1555 *Fabrica* preceded by [†]1*a* half-title; engr. title-page (after the 1543 *Fabrica*); [†]2*a* printed title; *1*a-b* dedication; *2*a*-*******1*a* preface including life

of Vesalius; *******2*a-b* list of subscribers; ********1*a-2b* half-title of *Fabrica* and index of its chapters; A1*a*-3*a* dedication to Charles V; A3*a-b* letter to Oporinus; portrait facing A4*a* where text and page numbering begin.

Tome II: After 4 *ll.* of preliminary matter one finds the full text of the following:

1. The *Epitome* of 1543 (pp. 577-616)
2. The China-root Epistle (pp. 619-684)
3. Fallopius' letter to Manna (pp. 685-758)
4. Vesalius' *Examen* of Fallopius (pp. 761-830)
5. Cuneus' *Examen* (pp. 833-885)
6. *Chirurgia magna* (pp. 889-1156)

Note: In place of the triangular device on the title-page of the 1724 edition, Wandelaar has substituted in this his charming, engraved device in which the Vesalian skeleton leaning on a spade appears twice. This elaborate edition of Vesalius was put out without regard for expense. The typography is excellent and the plates skilfully engraved. It is not clear, however, why Boerhaave in an *Opera omnia* included the China-root Epistle and omitted the Venesection letter. The spurious *Chirurgia magna* is also included without explanation. There are 188 names in the list of subscribers, for the most part Dutch, some subscribing to as many as eight copies. There are a few English names such as Peter Sainthill of Bart's, Gideon Wells, Josephus Tanner, etc.

The text of the *Fabrica* of this edition as well as the figures are based on the 2nd folio edition of 1555. The figures are assembled partly in the text and partly out of sequence. The majority are copper-plates but a few of the smaller are wood-blocks. The inserted figures, 67 in number in Vol. I, all bear the name of Wandelaar, the engraver, and are numbered in order, and carry page-numbers to indicate their place in the text. Twelve additional plates, also in copper, occur in Vol. II, and have a page indication in reference to pages 595, 597, 599, 602, 604, 606, 608 (2), 614 and 616 (3).
Copies: too numerous to list.
Copy used: H.C., purchased from Martin Boas, Berlin, January 1907, for M.60.

VI.D.—9

BONAVERA, Notomie   n.p. [*ca.* 1670]

Engraved title: Notomie di Titiano . Dedicate / All' Ill.ᵐᵒ Sig.º Francesco Ghisi-lieri / Senatore di Bologna. / [no imprint]

Dedication on title-page: Perche grande Alessandro di merito, non concedeua / d'essere ritratto, che da celeberimo Pittore. / Perche non minore VS. Illᵐᵃ nel merito, non / douerebbe essere ritratto su' le carti[*sic*], che da / famoᵐᵒ Oratore. Quindi essendo a me negato / simile talento, e desiderando d'essere an- / nouerato fra di lei seruitori, ho' ricorso all' / arte, e ció che cellebrare non posso, di tribu- / tare ho' risolto. A gloriosi meriti adunque di VS. Illᵐᵃ / dedico la presente fatica, ritagliata ad utile, di / chi disegna, e la suplico a non isdegnarla, già che / da VS. Illᵐᵃ cosi prodigamente é mantenuta la pu- / blica Accademia del Disegno; nella quale ami- / rando ogn'uno il glorioso genio che VS. Illᵐᵃ pro- / fessa a uantaggi d'un arte cosi nobile meco si dedica / Di VS. Illᵐᵃ / Huᵐᵒ Deuᵐᵒ Obligᵐᵒ seruitore / Domenico Bonaueri.

Colophon: none.

Collation: Fol., no sigs. [1], 17 *ll.*

Contents: l. [1] engr. title; *ll.* [2-18] the 17 engr. plates, numb. 1-17; no text.

Note: Domenico Maria Bonavera, an Italian engraver, pupil of his uncle, Canuti B., was born at Bologna in 1640. Since the present volume is addressed to Ghislieri, the Bologna senator, it is reasonable to assume that the book was likewise published there. The figures measure *ca.* 33 cm., being approximately the same size as those of the *Fabrica,* but smaller than the Tortebat plates. Bonavera includes

the 3 skeletal plates and the 14 muscle plates, all re-engraved on copper (in reverse) directly from the *Fabrica* with the same landscape background. Each plate after the first is signed 'T.I.D.' and 'D.B.S.' which on the first plate is expanded 'Ticianvs Inventor et Delineavᵗ.' and 'Dominicus Bonauera [*sic*] sculpsit'—again indicating the belief still prevailing that Titian had executed the Vesalian plates (see Tortebat, VI.D.25).

In the 18th century, an undated English anatomy for artists appeared under the title, *An abridgment of Anatomy taken from Titian & other of the best Italian Masters and adapted to the arts of painting and sculpture,* dedicated to Sir Godfrey Kneller and issued by one Thomas Bakewell of Fleet Street. The title is an adaptation in English of the Tortebat and Bonavera brochures and was evidently based on them. There are four full-length Vesalian muscle figures, all as modified by van der Gracht in 1634, and are reversed from his plates III, IV, V and XI by the engraver, H. Hulsbergh.

Copies: no census taken.

Copies used: H.C. (3): (i) very large copy (47.4 by 35.5 cm.), from Lier in 1929 for Swiss frs. 350; (ii) smaller, waterstained copy bought in Florence in 1907 for 20 lire; (iii) small copy lacking first plate, from Lier in 1926 for Swiss frs. 125. Baer of Frankfurt a/ M. had a copy in 1919 for M.60, and Rappaport in Rome had one in 1911 for 120 lire.

VI.D.—10

BOTTER, Epitome (signed issue)   *Cologne,* 1600 [1601]

Engraved title: Andreæ / Vesalii / Brvxellensis / Suorum de Humani corporis / fabrica librorum Epitome: / Cum Iconibus elegantissimis iuxta Germanā / Authoris delineationem artifitiose iam⸝ / pridem ex ære expressis: . . . / Opus perinsigne, nunc primum in Germa⸝ / nia renatum, hac*que* forma quam / emendatissimè editum. / Anno / 1600. / [at bottom of vignette] / Colonie [*sic*] Vbiorv*m* Formis et Expensis Ioan. Bvxmacheri et Georgii Mevtingi.

Colophon: Coloniæ Agrippinæ, / Typis Stephani Hemmerden. / Anno M. DCI.

Collation: Fol. *⁴, A⁶, B⁵, C⸝G⁶, H⁴, 40 engr. plates; [4, 45] *ll.*, 40 pl. (on 39 *ll.*], lettered A⸝Z, a⸝r.

Contents: *1a engr. title; *1b blank; *2a⸝3b 'Epistola dedicatoria' dated Cologne '7 Calend. Septemb.' i.e., 26 Aug. 1600 and signed 'Henricus Botterus, D. ac facultatis Medicæ pro tempore Decanus'; *4a hexastich in honour of Vesalius; *4b engr. portrait of Vesalius; A1a⸝H4b text; 40 plates.

Note: This is an imitation of Geminus with a newly engraved portrait copied from that of the 1543

Fabrica. The full text of the *Epitome* is included with the figure legends; the plates are taken from the same copperplates Bauman had used for his *Anatomia Deudsch* (VI.D.4). Dr. Cushing noted that the plates in the signed issue are sharper than in the following unsigned issue; but it is not clear which was printed first. Vander Haeghen mentions a copy in which at the end of the preface 'Henricus' is misspelled 'Henricut.'

Copies: DSG; MiU (Crummer); Fulton.

Copy used: J.F.F. (Henricus correctly spelled), obtained from Le François, Paris, in 1923, for 80 French francs.

VI.D.—11

BOTTER, Epitome (variant)   *Cologne,* 1600 [1601]

Title: [Identical with preceding]

Collation and contents: as in preceding, except that dedication is signed 'Decanus facultatis Medicæ, in Academia Coloniensi.'

Note: Dr. Cushing corresponded with Prof. Dr. Keussen, *Stadtarchivar* of Cologne, concerning the time of Botter's tenure as dean of the medical faculty and received the following reply (6 July, 1925): "The library of this city owns two copies of the work, both *with* the name of Botter. I can prove he was dean in the years 1600, 1602, 1606, and 1607. Whether he occupied the position of dean throughout the whole year of 1600, I cannot ascertain. Apparently he is identical with the unnamed dean

who signed the Epistola on 26 Aug., 1600. I do not know how to solve the riddle which your variant issue presents. Perhaps your copy was a proof for correction in which the name was later put in. Possibly you could determine by inquiry at the larger libraries if there are more copies without the name of the dean. In that event, the solution I suggested would not be correct. B. after all had no cause to suppress his name in a work of which he might be proud and was proud. The question must be answered: *non liquet.*"

Copy used: H.C., inscribed: Baltimore, 1912. Bound with Eustacchio, *Tabulæ anatomicæ,* 1722.

VI.D.—12

BOTTER, Epitome   *Amsterdam,* 1617

Engraved title: Anatomia / Viri in hoc Genere Princip. / Andreæ Vesalii Bruxel⸝ / lensis; in qua tota humani corpo⸝ / ris fabrica, iconibus elegantissimis, / iuxta genuinam Auctoris delineatio⸝ / nem æri incisis, lectori ob oculos po⸝ /

nitur . . . / Opus perinsigne et utilissimum, nunc / primum quam emenda- tissime / editum. / Amstelodami / Excudebat Ioannes / Ianssonius 1617.

Colophon: Coloniæ Agrippinæ / Typis Stephani Hemmerden. / Anno M. DCI [altered in ink to read M. DC*XVII*].

Collation and contents: as in preceding save for altered dates (both in ink and doubtless made by the pub- lisher) at the end of the dedication and colophon.

Note: A clumsy reissue of the remaindered edition of 1600-01, with the same engr. title border from which the 1601 imprint at the bottom has been removed. The prefatory note is signed by Botter as Dean.

Copies: Louvain; Waller; Cushing; CaMM; DSG; PPCP; NNNAM; NNC-M; MiU (Crummer); Trent.

Copy used: H.C., from Lier in 1926 for 300 Swiss frs. Hertzberger had a copy in 1936 in which the dates had been altered in ink.

VI.D.—13

FONTANUS, Epitome   *Amsterdam, 1642*

Engraved title: Librorvm / Andreæ Vesalii / Brvxellensis / De Hvmani Corpo- / ris Fabrica / Epitome: / Cum Annotationibus / Nicolai Fontani / Amstel- redamensis / Medici. / [below in vignette] / Amstelodami, / Apud Ioannem Ianssonium. / M D C XLII.

Colophon: none.

Collation: Fol. *³, **⁴, A-I⁶, K²; [7] *ll.*, 112 pp., 40 plates.

Contents: *1a engr. title; *1b blank; *2 dedication to Frederick-Henry, Prince of Orange, dated Am- sterdam, September 10, 1642; *3a engr. portrait of Vesalius; *3b Fontanus to the Reader; **1a-**4b 'Drama Cercopithecium'; A1a-K2b text, with 40 plates inserted.

Note: A new edition of the Bauman-Geminus plates with text following the Botter editions of 1600-01 and 1617. There is an elaborate engraved title border, and in Fontanus' annotations to the *Epitome* there are three new figures (p. 14, showing the omentum of an infant; p. 20, a full-page plate of the viscera; p. 33, uterus and adnexa); otherwise the figures are all taken from Bauman's copperplates. In the preliminary matter there is a diverting piece en- titled "Drama Cercopithecium." It has to do with a wise but petulant monkey which put mankind to ridicule in the best Rabelaisian, or better, Jan- Steenian, manner. The Vesalius-Sylvius controversy is brought in by implication and Vesalius is made out a man who, unlike Galen who created men of monkeys, made monkeys of men (his contempo- raries who had not trained their eyes sufficiently to distinguish man from monkey). This gay and sar- castic Dutch whimsey ends with a Latin hexastich which has been rendered as follows:

Just as at night, the moon, when it is full,
 Outshines all her brother stars with her light:
Just so, this one book of Vesalius is superior to all others.
 It shows how skilfully the body is constructed.
There, students, you may learn the structure of your body:
 You will find that it is not your least honour.

The late Dr. LeRoy Crummer had the whole simian drama translated and presented a typescript of the rendering to Dr. Cushing in 1929.

Copies: Louvain; London (BM; RCS); Waller; Cushing; CaMM-Os; NNNAM; DSG; CSt-L; van Wagenen; NNC-M; MdBJ-W; MnU; RPM; MiU (Crummer).

Copy used: H.C., purchased in 1924 from Taeuber and Weil, Munich, for M.45.

VI.D.—14

FUCHS, Epitome, 2 vols.   *Tübingen, 1551*

Title (Vol. I): Leonhar- / ti Fvchsii Scholæ / Tvbingensis Professoris Pvb- / lici, de humani corporis fabrica, ex Galeni / & Andreæ Vesalij libris concinnatæ, Epi⁄/tomes pars prima, duos, unum de ossi⁄/bus, alterum de musculis, libros/complectens./ [device]/ Tvbingæ per Vlricvm Mor⁄/har⁄dum, Anno M. D. LI.

(Vol. 2): Leonhar⁄/ti Fvchsii . . ./ Epitomes pars altera, quatuor/ Libros complectens. / [device] / [no imprint].

Collation: 8°. Vol. I: a⁄z⁸, A⁄C⁸, D⁴, E⁸; 302, [8] *ll.*; Vol. II: A⁄Z⁸, Aa⁸, Bb⁴, Cc⁸; [1], 202 *ll.*

Note: Although de Feyfer did not include these volumes in his Section C, it seems essential to include them here since the text, as the title indicates, is drawn largely from the first edition of the *Fabrica,* and Vesalius' observations are quoted on almost every page. The Tübingen edition in two volumes is evidently a rare book, but the second edition published at Lyon in the same year is better known. The text may be regarded as Fuchs's own "epitome" of the *Fabrica.* There are no illustrations.

Copy used: H.C., purchased from Voynich for $160 (date not given). Lier quoted a copy in 1930 for Swiss frs. 200. Another copy had been quoted in 1927 for Swiss frs. 625.

VI.D.—15

FUCHS, Epitome, 2 vols. *Lyon, 1551⁄55*

Title (Vol. I): Leonharti / Fvchsii / de / Humani Corporis fabrica / Epitomes Pars / Prima, / Duos, unum de ossibus, alterum de muscu⁄/lis, libros com⁄plectens. / [device] / Lvgdvni, / Apud Antonium Vincentium. / [rule] / 1551.

(Vol. II): Leonhar⁄ / ti Fvch⁄ / sii, / * / De humani corporis fabrica, / Epitomes pars al⁄ / tera. / [fleuron] / [device] / Lvgdvni, / Apud Antonium Vincentium / [rule] / 1555.

Colophons: (Vol. 1) Lvgdvni, / Excudebat Ioannes / Frellonius. [rule] / 1551. / (Vol. 2) Lvgdvni, / Michaelis Sylvii / Typis, M. D. LV.

Collation: 8°.Vol. I: A⁄Y⁸; 338 pp., [7] *ll.*; Vol. II: A⁄T⁸, V⁴; 155 (wrongly numb. 159) *ll.,* 1 *l.*

Note: It is noteworthy that in this second edition, Vincent, the publisher, has entirely omitted the name of Vesalius from the title. This edition does not appear to differ textually from the Tübingen edition which appeared earlier in the year.

Copy used: H.C., purchased from Voynich for $200 (date not given). Lier quoted a copy in 1927 for Swiss frs. 325.

VI.D.—16

VAN DER GRACHT, MS of Anatomie [? 1634]

Title: [Anatomie, etc.] Manuscript of 22 leaves (plus 14 blanks) in low Dutch on watermarked paper measuring 43 by 28 cm.

Contents: No title; pp. 1⁄7 'Voorreden' signed (p. 7): '1 Septemb. 1634. Jacob van der Gragt'; pp. 8⁄9 contents; p. 10 explanation of skeletal plate; p. 11 drawing of anterior skeleton; pp. 12⁄72 text and 15 additional drawings on facing pages interleaved with 14 blanks.

Note: Dr. Cushing had made a detailed comparison of each of the 16 drawings in this manuscript with the plates of the *Fabrica,* those in the 1634 van der Gracht and those of the Vosmaer MS as described by de Feyfer (see next entry). The plates of the present MS are all somewhat taller than those of the

Fabrica and those of the printed edition of van der Gracht. Thus:

Plate I. Anterior skeleton not reversed. Background changed. (See 1543 *Fabrica,* p. 163.) Heights: H.C. MS, 37.5 cm.; *Fab.,* 34 cm.; Vosmaer MS, 33.5 cm.; van der Gracht, 33.5 cm.

Plate II. Posterior skeleton with addition of lying skeleton, not reversed. Heights: H.C., 37; *Fab.,* 32.5; V., not given; G., 33.8.

Plate III. First muscle plate, a new rendering with sensible and free combination of muscle plates 1 (p. 170) and 3 (p. 178) of *Fab.* Heights: H.C., 39; *Fab.,* 35; V., 36; G., 36.

Plates I and II (skeletons) are in black crayon, while the muscle series (Plates III-XVI) are in henna-red crayon with bones underlying still in black. In the edition of 1634, the first two plates are unnumbered, while the muscle series is numbered consecutively from I to XVI as in Lib. II of the *Fabrica;* all, however, omit the landscape background. Plate III of the H.C. MS thus becomes Plate I in the published edition. The other plates of the MS are as follows:

Plate IV. Second muscle plate, reversed from *Fab.,* p. 174; ht. 39.8; one arm missing.

Plate V. New muscle plate similar to *Fab.,* p. 170, but with hair on head; ht. 41.

Plate VI. Fourth muscle plate reversed from *Fab.,* p. 181; pectoralis minor missed; ht. 39.

Plate VII. Fifth muscle plate reversed from *Fab.,* p. 184; Vesalius' rectus abdominis blunder corrected; pectoralis mistake repeated; ht. 38.

Plate VIII. Sixth muscle plate reversed from *Fab.,* p. 187; monkey scalenus corrected and rt. leg more flexed; ht. 39.1.

Plate IX. Seventh muscle plate reversed from *Fab.,* p. 190, with omission of separate diaphragm; ht. 34.

Plate X. Eighth muscle plate reversed from *Fab.,* p. 192, posture of hands changed and flesh removed; ht. 41.5.

Plate XI. Ninth muscle plate reversed from *Fab.,* p. 194; ht. 38.5.

Plate XII. Tenth muscle plate reversed from *Fab.,* p. 197; ht. 40.5.

Plate XIII. Eleventh muscle plate reversed from *Fab.,* p. 200; ht. 39.

Plate XIV. Twelfth muscle plate reversed from *Fab.,* p. 203, and rendered to show bony relationships; ht. 38.5.

Plate XV. Thirteenth muscle plate reversed from *Fab.,* p. 206, with changed posture of legs; ht. 37.8.

Plate XVI. Fourteenth muscle plate reversed from *Fab.,* p. 208; ht. 37.5.

Van der Gracht thus corrected two of Vesalius' most serious errors (*e.g.,* the scalenus muscle and the rectus abdominis); he made his muscles more prominent (bulging) than had Vesalius and achieved conspicuous success in showing the relation of the muscles to the bony skeleton. Dr. Cushing concluded from his study of the plates that they were trial drawings given up (i) because they were too big and (ii) because reproduction in black and red did not prove feasible. The figures were evidently redrawn to essentially the size of those in the *Fabrica,* the changes of position being carried from the present coloured drawings to the final cartoons from which the blocks of the 1634 edition were made. It is therefore probable that the Vosmaer MS contains the final cartoons. A set of 14 van der Gracht drawings, presumably from that MS, was exhibited at Amsterdam, July 21-August 1, 1927, by Mme. Vosmaer-Roëll, on the occasion of the VIth International Congress of the History of Medicine at Leyden (Dessins, No. 88 in the exhibition catalogue). In a note inserted in the present MS, Dr. Cushing adds: "The drawings themselves cannot be too highly praised, and the idea of showing the bones in black is excellent. It's too bad that they could not have been done in red and black. Of the text I have some doubts. It looks as though some later owner had taken the legends from the back of the printed drawings and copied them on the back of the drawings. It could hardly have been done in preparing the original MS by van der Gracht—though possibly so. The paper, however, in the original seven leaves of text bears the same watermarks as that on which the drawings are made. It would be interesting to know the date and place of this paper."

Copy used: H.C., obtained from Menno Hertzberger in May 1927 for 250 guilders.

van der **GRACHT**, Anatomie   *The Hague*, 1634

Engraved title: Anatomie / Der wtterlicke deelen van het / Menschelick Lichaem. / ... / Aengewesen / door Iacob van der Gracht / Schilder. / Bequæm voor / Schilders, Beelt-houwers, Plæt-snyders, / als oock Chirurgiens. / Wtgegeven door den Auteur, / In s'Graven Hagæ. / Cum Privilegio. / 1634.

Colophon: none.

Collation: Fol. [*]¹, A-H⁴; [33] *ll.* (not paginated or foliated).

Contents: [*]1*a* title; [*]1*b* privilege, dated The Hague, September 22, 1634; A1*a*-2*b* preface; A3*a*-H4*a* text; H4*b* blank.

Page heading (G4*a*): Wt Het Kort / Verhael vande Boecken / Andreæ Vesalij. [The text of this section is taken directly from Vesalius' *Epitome*.]

Note: This unusual volume has aroused much interest because in his preface van der Gracht implies that some of the drawings were after Michelangelo. Actually there are 18 full-page skeletal and muscle engravings, all from Vesalius save the last two (showing the hand and foot) which he lifted from Casserius. Original drawings of the first 16 were acquired by Dr. Cushing in 1927 and have been described in the preceding entry. Other details of the book are given fully by de Feyfer (130), as follows: "We do not know much more about Jacob van der Gracht than this work. He was probably born at the end of the 16th or the beginning of the 17th century in The Hague and passed many years abroad, including Naples. From the preface of his work we take the following details: After giving a thorough discussion of the practical uses of anatomy for artists, designers and sculptors, he tells us that he studied anatomy intensively in Italy and that he had even made dissections on a number of cadavers. As he says himself, he did this in order to get a thorough knowledge of the different relations of the body, most necessary for the art of painting. He then states that he possesses some drawings which have been made after Michelangelo, others by Baccio Bandenelli, and which are said to be described by the most famous anatomists. He himself only wished once more to bring to light these works of art.

"This communication would have escaped us were not these drawings still in the possession of Prof. Dr. G. C. J. Vosmaer in Leyden, who inherited them from his father; and he describes them as follows: 'These are the original Italian drawings (by what artist?) which J. van der Gracht has reproduced in his Anatomy in 1634 and which he describes in his Preface, saying that he had got them in Rome.' Mr. C. Vosmaer bought them about 1880, I do not know where, at the same time that he got the charcoal drawings by J. Dilhoff (1760) from Rembrandt's *Anatomy* of Dr. Johan Deyman, now in fragmentary form in the Reichsmuseum in Amsterdam. Before speaking of these drawings, let us first examine the anatomical plates of van der Gracht: The engraved title-page shows an anatomy lesson, above the rectangular shield bearing the title. A cadaver is suspended in a sitting position, in a similar manner to that which Vesalius employed when demonstrating subjects to artists." De Feyfer then described each plate in the Vosmaer MS, and it is obvious that except for their smaller size and being uncoloured, they follow closely those of the H.C. MS (see previous entry).

Copies: DSG; Cushing.

Copy used: H.C., from Burjersdijk & Niermans in 1913 for 9 florins.

VI.D.—18

van der **GRACHT**, Anatomie   *Rotterdam,* 1660

Engraved title: [as in 1634 ed. with new imprint (preceded by "den tweden Druck")]—Wtgegeven door Quiryn Smits Boeck / vercoper woont Inde Vergulde / Boeck Cræm tot / Rotterdam / 1660.

Printed title: Anatomie/ Der wtterlicke deelen van het Menschelick/ Lichæm./ .../ Aangewesen door J.V.G./ Ende nu vermeerdert ende verbeetert met een Tractaat,/ van het verhaal van't Hart, waar in wert gesprooken,/ Van de Nieticheit der Geesten. Van de Bloetmaking./ Van de warmte der levende Lichaamen, etc./ In't einde een Byvoegzel voor den Omloop/ des Bloets, van Harveivs./ Bequaam voor Schilders, Beelt-houwers, Plaat-snijders,/ als ook Chirugiens. den tweeden druck, verciert/ met diversche koopere-platen./ [device]/ Tot Rotterdam./ Gedruckt by Hendrick de Bruyn, Boeckdrucker, ende/ Boeck-verkooper, woonende in de West-wage-/straet, Inden Koning David. Anno 1660.

Colophon: Tot Rotterdam./ Gedruckt by Hendrick de Bruyn, Boeck-drucker ende / Boeck-verkooper, Woonende inde West-/ waghe-straet, inden Koningh Davidt./ Anno 1660.

Collation: Fol. [*]², A-H⁴, A-G²; [48] *ll.*

Contents: [*]1a engr. title; [*]1b blank; [*]2a printed title; [*]2b blank; A1a-b preface; A2 [missing in H.C. copy; ? blank]; A3a-H4a text (including plates); H4b blank; A1a-F4a tract on the heart; F4b blank; G1a-2a appendix; G2b blank.

Note: The text is reset but the engr. title of the 1634 edition is used with changed imprint, and all 18 of the plates are used again. An anonymous Dutch translation of J. de Back's *Dissertatio de corde* (Rotterdam, 1648) is appended.

Copies: Waller; NNNAM; Cushing.

Copy used: H.C., from Burgersdijk & Niermans in 1907 for $3.00.

VI.D.—18A

MORO and MONTANI, Anatomia   *Venice, 1679*

Title: Anotomia/ Ridotta all' vso de' Pittori, e Scultori/ dal Signor/ Giacopo Moro:/ Consecrata/ All' Illustrissimo, ed Eccellentissimo Signore il Signor/ Gio: Andrea/ Raciborsko/ Conte di Morstin, &c:/ e Gran Tesoriero del Regno di Polonia./ [device]/ In Vinegia, M.DC.LXXIX. [rule] Presso Gio: Francesco Valuasense./ Con Licenza de' Superiori.

Colophon: None.

Collation: Fol. No signatures; 23 pp., 1 p., 15 *ll.*, 17-25 [28] pp.

Contents: p. [1] title; p. [2] blank; pp. 3-4 Giuseppe Montani's dedication to his patron, dated Venice, 10 April, 1679; p. 5-7, 'Montani allo studioso di Pittura,' p. 8 folding skeletal plate with explanatory legend; pp. 9-10 legend; p. 11 blank; p. 12 second folding skeletal plate with legend; pp. 13-14 legend; p. 15 third folding skeletal plate with legend; pp. 16-20 legends; inserted folding plate containing the three skeletal figures from the *Fabrica*; pp. 21-23 legend; [part 2 begins] *ll.* 1-15 legends with the 15 muscle plates opposite re-engraved on copper directly from *Fabrica*, plates 15 and 16 being combined in one; p. [26] instructions and corrections; p. [27] poem to the author; p. [28] blank.

Note: There are 19 plates in all, the first three skeletal plates being engraved on extra wide, numbered pages (pp. 8, 12 and 15) folded with the text and the other 16 are unfolded; all are beautifully executed copper engravings and each carries an elaborate monogram. Moro is evidently a descendant of the sixteenth century artist Antonio Moro (c. 1512-1575).

Cicognara writes: "Gius. Montani pubblicò questo lavoro del caval. G. Moro dilettante di simili studi; nel quale però sono copiate in contorno tutte le tavole anatomiche che Tiziano disegnò per la prima edizione di Vesalio, concentrando le figure in 19 tavole con molte chiare e buone illustrazioni. L'istruzione però per dipingere a fresco è quella prodotta dal P. Pozzi nel suo secondo volume della prospettiva, e nell'antologia dell'arte pittorica." (vol. 1, p. 339).

Copy used: H. C. Bought from Rappaport, Rome, in 1912 for 152 lire.

PAAW, Epitome   *Leyden, 1616*

Title in red and black: Andreæ Vesalii / Bruxellensis / Epitome / Anatomica. / Opus redivivum. / cui accessere, / Notæ ac Commentaria / P. Paaw Amstel-damensis / in Lugduno-Batava Academia / Professoris Anatomici. / [device] / Lvgdvni Batavorvm. / Ex Officina Ivsti à Colster. / Ann. M D CXVI.

Colophon (Ff2a): Lvgdvni Batavorvm, / Ex Officina typographica Ulrici Corn: Honthorstij. / Ann. M. D. CXVI.

Collation: 4°. *⁴, A-Z⁴, Aa-Ee⁴, Ff²; [4] *ll.*, 226 pp., 1 *l.*

Contents: *1a title; *1b dedication; *2a-4a dedicatory preface to the magistrates of Amsterdam; *4b poem to Paaw signed "Henricus Florentius Med. Doctor."; A1a-Ff1b text and running commentary; Ff2a errata and colophon; Ff2b blank. The book contains 12 copperplates incorporated in the text plus one folding plate marked "folio 67" and placed between pp. 66 and 67.

Note: This is a reprint of the Vesalian *Epitome* with "Commentaria" by Paaw; to it has been annexed as a seventh chapter, "De externarum humani corporis sedium partiúmve citra dissectionem occurrentium appellationes" (pp. 215-226). The 13 copper engravings scattered through the text are all fragments from the *Fabrica* (402) and the text is lifted largely from the *Epitome*. Each chapter is followed by Paaw's comments, but in fairness to him the following is translated from his preface: "Just how grateful (*i.e.,* for the *Epitome*) students of medicine were appears from the fact that it was translated into various languages and reprinted by many editors at different times and in different places, and was sought after by all nations. However, the Italians broke to some extent this wave of fame and prevented the rays of the sun reaching its object, by a cloud. As new things also are preferred to old by youth, as are foreign things to domestic, and as at the same time a book of similar purport was brought out by Realdus Columbus, these circumstances easily served to obliterate the memory of this divine work executed by him [Vesalius]. So that we, both pleased with the memory of that greatest of men, and resisting the attack of those of poor judgment, have produced for those honestly beginning the study of medicine that *Epitome* of the great work, drawn from obscurity, and afterwards having sought out [his work] again correctly, have re-established him in his former position of distinction so far as we could.

"For what could be more suitable to move us in this fashion than the superiority of the work? Then also, the name of the author is worthy of immortality. In addition, the zealous youth of anatomy which was wearied with error, seemed for long to desire a compendium of this sort. In order to make it more fully useful, I have undertaken to supply it with brief notes and commentaries where Vesalius seemed to me to be either brief or obscure." De Feyfer describes another issue of the same year having certain minor changes in the preface. A copy of this variant issue is at the University Library in Leyden. Since he does not list the changes, it has been impossible to distinguish the two issues in our census of copies.

Copies: Louvain; London (BM, RCS); Waller; Cushing; CaMM-Os; NNNAM; Trent; DSG; NBMS; ICJ; MdBJ-W; MBM; MiU (Crummer).

Copy used: H.C., purchased at "Sotheby's sale, Nov. 1921, very cheap."

VI.D.—20

PAAW, Epitome   *Amsterdam, 1633*

Title in red and black: Andreæ Vesalii / Bruxellensis / Epitome / Anatomica. / Opus redivivum, / cui accessere, / Notæ ac Commentaria / P. Paaw Amstel-damensis / in Lugduno Batava Academia Professoris Anatomici. / [device] / Amstelreodami, / Apud Henricum Laurentii. Bibliopolam. / M. DC. XXXIII.

Colophon: none.

Collation: 4°. *⁴, A-Z⁴, Aa-Cc⁴, D²; [4] *ll.*, 214 pp.

Contents: *1a title; *1b blank; *2a-3b preface; *4a Florentius' poem to Paaw; *4b blank; A1a-Dd2b text and commentary beginning on A1a with 'Andreæ Vesalii / Bruxellensis, / Suorum de humani corporis/ fabrica liberorum [*sic*] epitome.' The plates are the same as in VI.D.19.

Note: The preface is addressed to the benevolent reader rather than to the magistrates of Amsterdam, and it has a shortened ending which may be rendered as follows: "Certainly, O candid reader, these explanations of mine will be welcome to you. If any-

one is malicious or wishes to injure my name and fame, to him I oppose Vesalius himself and the knowledge of his good deed. He is secure in the saying that 'Virtue is its own reward.' If anyone calls the *Epitome* mean and not well done, he may have this from me, that there is contained here more of the marrow of Vesalius' Anatomy than of mine. Whoever reads, let him do so with intelligence. Farewell, candid reader."

Copies: London (BM, RCS); Cushing; MH-M; NNNAM; MdBJ-W; CaTAM; MiU (Pilcher).

Copy used: H.C., purchased in Paris in 1911 from L. J. Syme for 42 francs. Lier offered a copy in 1927 for Swiss frs. 300, which he described as having *two* folding plates plus the 12 other engravings.

VI.D.—21

PLATTER, De corporis humani structura   *Basel,* 1583

Title: De / corporis / hvmani / strvctvra et / vsv / Felicis Plateri Bas. / Medici Antecessoris / Libri III. / Tabvlis methodicè explicati, Iconibvs / accuratè illustrati. / [Froben device] / Ex Officina Frobeniana / Per Ambrosium Frob. / M D LXXXIII.

Colophon: none.

Collation: Fol. *⁴, A-Z⁴, Aa-Bb⁴, [1], 50 *ll.*; [4] *ll.*, 198 pp., 1 *l.*; [1], 50 *ll.*

Contents: *1a title; *1b 'Argumenta'; *2 dedication to Egenolfus signed Basel, 'Cal. Febr. Anni M D L XXXIII'; *3a-4a laudatory poems; *4b blank; A1a-S2b text of Book I; S3a-Bb3a text of Book II; Bb3b errata; Bb4a blank; Bb4b Froben device; 1 *l.* (title of Book III); 50 numb. *ll.* with plates on recto and explanations on verso.

Note: Book III has a separate title as follows: Liber / Tertius. / Corporis humani partium / per icones delineata- / rum explicatio. / [device] / Ex Officina Frobeniana/ M D LXXXIII. Book III with the 50 plates may therefore have been circulated as a separate item. Platter's illuminating preface to this book has been quoted above (p. 97). In referring to the plates he says: "Since it is difficult without seeing them to form a conception of the various shapes of

individual parts which we have described (above), and since dissection of the human corpse is rarely feasible, I have decided to add here the following drawings which set forth before our eyes that which has been described. . . . We have published the drawings separately in this book, so that should one desire it, it might be bound separately so as to be more convenient for use in reading the first part, and make it unnecessary when looking for an individual passage to go through the entire volume, which would have been the case had we inserted each plate in a separate place. For this reason I have placed the explanations of all the characters of each plate on the opposite page, so that one might have no need to turn the leaf." Of the 50 roughly engraved copper-plates, all but two (Nos. 2 and 3, both skeletal) are copied from the *Fabrica*.

Copy used: H.C., purchased from Davis & Orioli, Florence, in 1926 for Swiss frs. 400.

VI.D.—22

PLATTER, De corporis humani structura, 2nd ed.   *Basel,* 1603

Title: Felicis / Plateri Archiatri / et Profess. Basil. / de / corporis / hvmani / strvctvra / et vsv / Libri III. / . . . / Qui libri cùm Operi practico recens ab /

eodem autore edito / plurimùm / inseruiant, denuò sunt / publicati. / [orna‚
ment] / Basileæ, / Apud Lvdovicvm König. / [rule] / M. DCIII.

Colophon: none.

Collation and contents: same as preceding.

Note: This is a reissue of the edition of 1583 with new titles for the book as a whole, and for Book III which now reads: Liber / Tertius. / Corporis hu‚ mani partium / per icones delineata‚ / rum explica‚

tio. / [ornament] / Basileæ / Apvd Lvdovicvm König. M. DCIII. The same 50 copperplates were also used.

Copy used: H.C., from Pickering & Chatto in 1922 for £15/15/0; bound with the Ingrassia, *In Galeni librum de ossibus commentaria,* Palermo, 1603.

VI.D.—23

SANDIFORT, Tabulæ ossium   *Leyden,* 1782

Title: Andreæ Vesalii Anatomici Summi Tabulæ ossium humanorum, cum explicat. earum. edit. Sandifort. Lugd. Bat. 1782.

Collation: fol.

Note: De Feyfer (130) describes a copy with this abbreviated title as existing in the University Library at Leyden. It was examined at Dr. Cushing's re‚ quest by Mr. N. Posthumus of The Hague who states that this issue lacks the Sandifort preface "Auditoribus suis S.P.D. Eduardus Sandifort" and

the leaf with two plates of the skull bearing the legends 'Fig. 1. Tabulæ VIII. et IX.' and 'Fig. 5, Tabulæ VI. et Fig. 2. Tabulæ VIII' (see next entry). The abbreviation of the title was not verified. It is possible that this is a proof copy and not a genuine separate issue.

VI.D.—24

SANDIFORT, Tabulæ ossium   *Leyden,* 1782

Title: Andreæ Vesalii / anatomici summi / Tabulæ / Ossium / Humanorum. / Denuo edidit, earumque ex‚ / plicationem adauxit / Eduardus Sandifort, / … / [ornament] / Lugduni Batavorum, / Apud / S. et J. Luchtmans, / P. van der Eyk et D. Vijgh. / M D C C L X X X I I.

Collation: Fol. †², *², A‚N², 24 plates; [4] *ll.,* 50 pp., [1, 24] ll.

Contents: [†]1*a* half‚title; [†]1*b* blank; [†]2*a* title; [†]2*b* blank; *1*a*‚2*a* Sandifort to his *Auditores;* *2*b* list of plates; A1*a*‚N1*b* (pp. 1‚50) text; N2*a* list of Sandifort's other works; N2*b* directions to book‚ binder; 24 engr. plates on thicker paper containing *Tabulæ* numbered from 1 to 27.

Note: This is a reimpression of the Wanderlaar copperplates in Bk. I of the Boerhaave‚Albinus *Opera omnia* (VI.D.8). The sequence of the illustra‚ tions has been changed, the skull figures (Tab. VII et X) have been repeated and the legends are con‚ fused. On *l.* *2*b* the source of each figure from the

Boerhaave‚Albinus edition is given. This edition has been fully described by Vander Haeghen (37, V 122).

An edition of 1791 is recorded by de Feyfer who gives Vander Haeghen and Choulant as authority; but they do not record such an edition and we have concluded that it is a "ghost."

Copies: Louvain; London (BM); Cushing; PPCP; NNNAM; Trent; MBM; IEN‚M; MiU (Crum‚ mer, Pilcher).

Copies used: H.C. (i) from N. Posthumus of The Hague in 1928 for 16 florins; (ii) provenance un‚ recorded.

TORTEBAT, Abrégé   *Paris*, 1667 [1668]

Title: Abregé / d'Anatomie, / accommodé avx arts / de Peintvre / et de Scvlp-tvre, / . . . / Ouvrage tres-utile, & tres-necessaire à tous ceux qui font / profession du Dessein. / Mis en lumiere par François Tortebat . . . / [device] / Et se vendent / A Paris, / Chez ledit Tortebat, rüe Neufve-Sainte-Catherine. / [rule] / M. DC. LXVII. Avec Privilege de Sa Maiesté.

Collation: Large fol. (49.3 by 33 cm.). a⁴, A-[C]⁴; 4 ll., 16 ll.

Contents: a1a title; a1b blank; a2 Tortebat's dedication to the gentlemen of the Royal Academy of Painting and Sculpture; a3a-4a Tortebat to the reader; a4b blank; A1a half-title; A1b-[C]4a explanatory legends and plates; [C]4b privilege.

Note: Tortebat's 12 copperplates designed for artists are by common consent the most beautiful reproductions of Vesalius' illustrations ever to be made (402). The third plate is signed 'Franc. Tortebat del. sculp. et execu. Anno Dñi. 1668,' and at the end of the *Privilège* is the statement, 'Achevé d'imprimer pour la premiere fois le douziéme Ianvier 1668.' This undoubtedly accounts for the fact that many copies (both those of H.C.) of the 1667 edition have had a Roman 'I' added in ink to the M.DC.LXVII, making the date appear 1668 instead of 1667

Roger de Piles (1635-1709) used the pseudonym François Tortebat, if we can credit the statement in his *Cours de peinture par principes* (Paris, 1708, p. 153). The plates are all freshly engraved and reversed with new lettering, and many have the landscape backwards of the *Fabrica* plates (unlike those of van der Gracht). All from the *Fabrica* are enlarged by 15 to 20 per cent. Those from the *Epitome* are of approximately original size.

This is the second important anatomical treatise for artists, since van der Gracht had preceded Tortebat by some 34 years (see VI.D.17), but his *Anatomie* had had a very limited circulation. The Tortebat plates are as follows:

Plate I (A2a). Anterior skeleton from *Fabrica*, 1543, p. 163; heights: *Fab.*, 34.5 cm.; Tortebat, 40.0 cm., signed 'F. Tortebat delin. sculp. et excud.'

Plate II (A2b). Posterior skeleton from *Fab.*, p. 165; hts.: *Fab.*, 32.4; T., 37.5, signed 'F.T.'

Plate III (A3a). Thinking skeleton from *Fab.*, p. 164, with inscription 'Solidior corporis, pars est quam frequens usus agitat. Seneca.' followed by the dated Tortebat sig. mentioned above; hts.: *Fab.*, 33.5, T., 39.7.

Plate IV (Fig. 1). First muscle plate from *Fab.*, p. 170; ht. 40.3, signed 'F. Tortebat delin. et sculp.'

Plate V (Fig. 2). Second muscle plate from *Fab.*, p. 174; ht. 40.4, signed 'F.T.'

Plate VI (Fig. 3). First muscle plate from sig. I verso of the *Epitome*, 1543, with landscape added; hts. 42.2 in both, signed 'F.T.'

Plate VII (Fig. 4). Third muscle plate from sig. H verso of *Epit.*, slightly modified with landscape added; ht. 42.2, signed 'F.T.'

Plate VIII (Fig. 5). Ninth muscle plate from *Fab.*, p. 194, without change; ht. 40.2, signed 'F.T.'

Plate IX (Fig. 6). Second muscle plate from sig. I recto of *Epit.* with minor changes including addition of calvarium and landscape; ht. 42.2, signed 'F.T.'

Plate X (Fig. 7). Fourth muscle plate from sig. H recto of *Epit.*, also with calvarium and landscape added; ht. 41.2, signed 'F.T.'

Plate XI (on verso of Fig. 7). The naked Eve from sig. L recto of *Epit.*; ht. 42.7, signed 'F.T.'

Plate XII (facing Eve). The naked Adam from sig. K verso of *Epit.*; ht. 42.7, signed 'F. Tortebat.' In the upper right corner is the following: "Pour detromper ceux qui croyent, qu'on ne peut pas sçauoir l'Anatomie sans faire dur, jay bien voulu vous faire voir à la fin de ce liure les deux figures, que le Titien a mises a la fin de l'Epitome de Vesale: vous en jugerex." It was thus openly assumed that the Vesalian illustrations had been done by Titian (see also the preface, sig. a4a: "Pour ce qui est des Figures, elles sont d'apres celles, que le Titien avoit desseignées pour le Livre de Vesale; vous les trouverez asseurément fort justes; & je m'en suis servi, parce que j'ay crû qu'il estoit impossible de mieux faire pour le sujet").

Copies (no census taken): DSG; Cushing.

Copies used: H.C. (2): (i) a large (49.3 by 33 cm.), perfect copy obtained from Voynich in 1926 for $150 (bound with Bouchardon, *L'Anat. necessaire pour . . . dessein*, Paris, 1741); (ii) provenance unrecorded, lacks Plates XI and XII and measures 44 by 28 cm.

VI.D.—26

TORTEBAT, Abrégé.   German   *Berlin, 1706*

Title: Kurtze Verfassung / Der / Anatomie, / ... / Erstlich ans Licht gegeben von Francisco Tortebat, / ... / [device] / Berlin, bey Johann Andreas Rüdiger, 1706.

Collation: Fol. A⸍G², 12 inserted plates; [14, 12] *ll.*

Note: Contains a translation of Tortebat's preface and text of the 1667 *Abrégé* and all 12 of his figures re⸍engraved in a smaller size (31 cm. instead of 40). The preface is signed Johann Andreas Rüdiger, who is evidently both the printer and the translator. The third plate is signed "Lorentz Beger sculp"; others bear initials "L.B."

Copies: no census taken.

Copy used: H.C., provenance unrecorded.

VI.D.—27

TORTEBAT, Abrégé   *Paris, 1733*

Title: Abregé d'anatomie, accommodé aux arts de peinture et de sculpture, mis en lumière par Fr. Tortebat et M. de Piles. Paris, chez Jean Mariette, 1733.

Note: This edition is said by de Feyfer (130) to be a reprinting with the old plates (80, 402).

Copies: none traced.

VI.D.—28

TORTEBAT, Abrégé   *Paris, 1760*

Engraved title: Abregé / d'Anatomie, / ... / a Paris Chez. J. B. Crepy, / ... mis / en lumiere par Fran⸍ / çois Tortebat 1760.

Collation: Fol. [13] *ll.* (no sigs.)

Note: This is a little known issue with the first ten plates of the 1667 edition re⸍engraved to *c.* 24 cm. (Adam and Eve plates omitted in H.C. copy) and reversed back to the postures of *Fab.* and *Epit.* The landscapes are omitted throughout. The introduc⸍tion and explanation of the plates correspond with those of the 1667⸍68 edition.

Copy used: H.C., from Voynich for $35.

VI.D.—29

TORTEBAT, Abrégé   *Paris, [?1761]*

Title: Abrégé / d'Anatomie, / ... / par François Tortebat ... / Et mis dans un ordre nouveau ... / par de Piles. / ... / A Paris, / Du Fonds de Charles⸍ Antoine Jombert. / ... / [small rule] / 8.

Collation: Large fol. (43.7 by 27 cm.) [2, 8, 5] *ll.*; iv pp., [13] *ll.*

Note: Contains original Tortebat preface but the plates are placed in two groups, each with a separate sub⸍title page: the first, 'Myologie,' includes Figs. 1⸍7 (*i.e.,* Plates IV to X, of 1667 *Abrégé*), the second 'Osteologie,' includes Figs. 8, 9, 10 (Plates I to III of the 1667 edition). The original copperplates have been used. At the end of the preface to Pt. 2 one reads: "Cet abrégé d'Ostéologie est extrait du *Traité des Os,* par M. *du Verney,* lequel fait partie des *Œuvres anatomiques* de cet homme célèbre, imprimées chez *Jombert,* en 1761, en deux volumes *in⸍quarto,* avec beaucoup de figures."

Copy used: H.C., from Rappaport, Rome, 1930, for Swiss frs. 180.

VI.D.—30

TORTEBAT, Abrégé   *Paris, 1765*

Title: Abrégé / d'Anatomie, / . . . / Par M. de Piles. / . . . / Mis en lumiere par François Tortebat . . . / [ornament] / A Paris, Rue Dauphine, / Chez Charles-Antoine Jombert, . . . / [double rule] / M. DCC. LXV. / Avec approbation et privilege de Sa Majesté.

Collation and contents: as in [1761] edition.

Note: A reprint of 1761 edition with a new title in which "M. de Piles" is set down as the author and the book "mis en lumiere" by Tortebat (see note to the 1667 edition). The original copperplates are still used.

Copies used: H.C. (2): (i) from Halle, Munich, for M.24; (ii) from Dulau, London, 1925, gift of Dr. Edward C. Streeter (bound with Preister's *Abrégé de l'anatomie à l'usage des peintres,* Paris, n.d.)

VI.D.—31

TORTEBAT, Abrégé   *Paris, 1784*

Title: Methode pour apprendre le dessin. . . . Paris, chez L. Cellot, 1784.

Note: Listed by de Feyfer (130, p. 496), and said to contain 3 skeletal and 3 muscle plates much reduced and re-engraved by Poletnich. The figures measure 23 cm. No copy has been traced.

VI.D.—32

VALVERDE, Anatomia. Ed. princeps.   *Rome, 1556*

Engraved title: Historia / De la composicion del cuerpo humano, / escrita por Ioan de Valuerde / de Hamusco. / [below vignette] / Impressa por Antonio Salamanca, y Antonio Lafrerij, / En Roma. Año de M. D. LVI.

Colophon: Imprimiose la presente Obra en Roma / en casa de Antonio Blado Impresor/ de su Santidad. Año de/ M.D.LVI.

Collation: Fol. *⁶, ✚⁶, A-D⁶, E⁴, F¹⁰, G-L⁶, M²⁰, N⁸, O⁴, P¹⁰, Q-V⁶, X⁴, Y⁸, a-b⁶, c⁴; [12], 105 *ll.*; illustrations and their explanations bear signatures but not foliation; numbered leaves include text only.

Contents: *1*a* title; *1*b* dedication to Pope Paul IV signed at Rome, May 4, 1556, by G. Rotulus; *2 dedication to Cardinal Don Juan of Toledo; *3*a* to the reader; *3*b*-4*b* table of contents; *5*a*-✚6*b* index; A1*a*-2*b* prologue; A2*b*-c3*a* text; c3*b* register; c4*a* errata; c4*b* blank.

Note: Juan Valverde de Hamusco (also Amusco), a Spanish anatomist who flourished in the mid-16th century (dates of birth and death unknown), was a student of Realdo Colombo. He appears to have spent a number of years in Italy and save for his first published work, *De animi et corporis sanitate tuenda* which was issued in Paris in 1552 (also Venice,

1553), all were published in the first instance in Italy. He is best known for the present work, which was issued at Rome in Spanish. Of the 42 engraved copperplates, all but four appear to have been taken directly from the *Fabrica.* His original figures include an écorché muscle plate, the *motif* of which was evidently taken from Michelangelo's Last Judgment in the Sistine Chapel. His other original figures include the following: Lib. II, Tab. 15, Figs. 20 and 22; and Lib. III, Tab. 6, in which the pregnant woman suggests the nude figure in the *Epitome,* but the sitting fœtus at the bottom of the plate is entirely new.

In his *Examen* of Fallopius (IX.1), Vesalius inveighs against Valverde's plagiarism and accuses him of never having dissected. In referring to the Vesalian plates, Valverde in his preface states that it would have been easy to improve upon many of the Vesalian figures but that he had desisted from altering them extensively to avoid suspicion of envy or maliciousness. Yet he did audaciously change several figures, especially the skeletons, and in at least two points he corrected the Vesalian anatomy. His eye-muscle figures are a great improvement on those of Vesalius as is the representation of the muscles of nose and larynx. There is no doubt that Valverde had a large vogue as the many editions of his *Anatomia* clearly indicate; it is something of an irony that he too was plagiarized, by Christopher Plantin, the famous Belgian printer (see VI.D.43).

Copies: Waller; Cushing; DSG; NNC⁄M; ICJ; DLC; MiU (Crummer).

Copy used: H.C., "purchased for a song in Madrid, March 31, 1915, while *en route* to Paris with the Harvard Unit"; in original limp vellum binding; sig. P 10 (Tav. 6, Bk. III) missing.

VI.D.—33

VALVERDE, Anatomia, plates — Rome, 1556 [?1586]

Engraved title: Historia / De la composicion del cuerpo humano / [etc., as in preceding].

Collation: Fol. [42] *ll.* [no signatures; all versos blank].

Contents: l. [1]*a* engr. title identical with that of VI.D.32; *l.* [2]*a* engr. portr. of Valverde; *ll.* [3⁄40] plates from VI.D.32; *ll.* [41⁄42] trial engr. proofs.

Note: This is a collection of the original Valverde plates without text evidently issued, as is pointed out by Dr. E. C. Streeter (who discovered this collection in 1923 and presented it to Dr. Cushing), for the use of artists. Since it also contains the signed portrait of Valverde, by Niccolò Beatrici (signed NB) which did not appear until the Italian Giunta edition of 1586 (and later ed. of 1589), it is possible that the collection was not issued until 1586 or later. After the portrait, the plates follow in order (with Latin lettering and Roman numerals as in the Giuntine editions below). This copy, however, lacks the important osteological plates 1 and 2. (Tabula I and Tab. II, libri 1). Fol. [41] is a trial proof of the title⁄page appearing in the Giuntine edition of Venice, 1586, save that there is no printing or device in the central oval. Fol. [42] is an un⁄finished proof of the Tabula Lib. IV, which occurs on page 108 in the Venetian Giuntine ed. of 1586.

This proof was discarded. In redrawing it for the above edition, the two chief figures and cardiac sec⁄tions were all reversed. The proof is just half finished (figura I and figs. VII, VIII, IX, X, XI, XII and XIII are in outline only). It is curious to find that Tabula Lib. IV, when it finally came to be printed in the edition of 1586, was reversed. There is one feature of this series not easily explained if we assume that these plates were issued from the press of Giunta in 1586. How did he get possession of that title⁄page of the first Spanish edition published in Rome, 1556? Did Giunta buy the printing establishment of Niccolò Bevilacqua, the first printer of Valverde, or did he come by the plate through the engraver, N.B.? (*Cf. A Catalogue of Italian engraved title⁄pages in the sixteenth century,* by A. F. Johnson. Suppl. to Bibliogr. Soc. Trans., No. 11, 1936.) *Niccolò Beatrici* is here listed as "of Lorraine, working in Italy, *ca.* 1540⁄65," and it is stated that (1) he en⁄graved the title of Valverde's Spanish edition, Rome, 1556, and also the anatomical plates, a few of which have his initials; and (2) also the plates of the Italian edition, Rome, 1560.

Copy used: Cushing, presented by Dr. E. C. Streeter who had acquired it from Olschki at Rome in 1923.

VI.D.—34

VALVERDE, Anatomia, plates — Rome [n.d.]

Title: Compendio de la anatomia hecho por Joan de Valverde, dirigado al Illustriss. S. don Frai Joan de Toledo, C. de Santiago.

Note: Choulant states that the Valverde plates were sold separately. The title is taken from Turner (402), who had seen a copy in the print room of the Bibliothèque Nationale in Paris.

Copy: Paris (BN); not seen.

VI.D.—35

VALVERDE, Anatomia.   Italian   *Rome (Venice)*, 1559

Engraved title: Anatomia / del corpo humano composta / per M. Giouan Valuerde di Hamusco, / & da luy con molte figure di rame, / et eruditi dis-corsi in luce / mandata. / in Roma per Ant. Salamanca, / et Antonio Lafrerj. / M.D.Lviiij.

Colophon (l. 154b): In Vinegia, appresso Nicolò Beuilacqua Trentino.

Collation: Fol. a⁶, B-C⁶, A⁴, B-Z⁶, AA-CC⁶; [18] 154 *ll.*

Contents: a1a engr. title; a1b blank; a2a-b dedication 'Alla S.C.R. Maesta del Re Filippo' (Philip of Spain), dated Rome, May 20, 1559; a3a-b second dedication to the Cardinal Archbishop of Toledo; a4a To the reader; a4b-a5a table of contents; a5b-c6b index; A1a-A2b prologue; A3a-CC6b (ll. 3-154) text.

Note: This, the first Italian rendering of Valverde, was translated by one Antonio Tabo under Val-verde's supervision. The elaborate title-page was engraved by Niccolo Beatrici. The 42 engraved copperplates of the Spanish edition reappear un-changed and a few small woodcuts are added on the margins of the text. The printer, Nicolò Bevilacqua of Trent, was probably a student of Paolo Manuzio who remained in Venice until 1573 when he was called to Turin by the regent, the Duchess Mar-guerite of France (Fumagalli, *Lexicon typographicum Italiæ*, p. 417). De Feyfer describes the edition of 1560, but had not seen this earlier issue. As with the Spanish edition, the plates are for the most part copies of Vesalius; those that are non-Vesalian are Lib. II, tav. 1 (l. 64), Lib. III, tav. 1-3 (ll. 94-96), and Lib. VI, tav. 1 (l. 133).

Copies: NNNAM; ICU; NNC-M; MiU (Crum-mer); Cushing.

Copy used: H.C., from Davis & Orioli, 1926, priced £8/9/6. J. Halle had a copy in 1928 for RM.200, but this first issue of the Italian translation is obviously very rare.

VI.D.—36

VALVERDE, Anatomia.   Italian   *Rome (Venice)*, 1560

Engraved title: [Identical with preceding, except for re-engraved date M.D.LX.]

Collation and contents: Identical with the preceding; plates are all from the same cuts.

Copies: Waller; MH-M; PPCP; NNNAM; ICU; Trent; DSG; NNC-M; ICJ; MdBJ-W; CaTAM;

IEN-M; MiU (Crummer); CU-M; Cushing.

Copy used: H.C., purchased February 12, 1913, from Quaritch for £9.

VI.D.—37

VALVERDE, Anatomia.   Italian   *Venice,* 1586

Engraved title: La / Anatomia / del corpo umano / composta da / M. Giovanni Valverde: / Nuouamente Ristampata: / E con l'aggiunta di / alcune Tauoli / Ampliata / [below] In Vinetia nella Stamperia de Givnti M.D.L.XXXVI.

Colophon (l. 154b): In Vinegia, appresso i Gionti.

Collation: Fol. a⁶, B-C⁶, A⁴, B-O⁶, OO⁴, P-Z⁶, AA-CC⁶; [18], 154 *ll.*; 4 inserted *ll.* of muscle figs. after *l.* 82.

Contents: a1a title; a1b blank; a2a dedication to Philip; a2b engr. portrait of Valverde by Beatrici;

a3a-b dedication to the Cardinal Archbishop of Toledo; a4a to the readers. [Remaining contents as in 1559-60 edition, save for the extra quire (OO) of four leaves of muscle men between *ll.* 82 and 83 (O6b and P1a).]

Note: Save for minor changes in the first gathering

and the inserted muscle men, it is a page-for-page reprint, with type newly reset, of the 1559-60 edition. The engraved title is new, and there are minor changes in the wording of the title itself. The portrait (but not the engraved title-page) and many of the plates are signed NB and are therefore attributed to Beatrici.

Copies: Waller; CaMM-Os; MH; MH-M; PPCP; NNNAM; CSmH; DSG; CSt-L; MdBM; ICJ; MiU (Crummer); Cushing.

Copy used: H.C. (lacking portrait). Dr. Cushing had notations of four other copies sold in 1926-27 at prices ranging from £4/10/- to £8/8/-.

VI.D.—38

VALVERDE, Anatomia.   Latin   *Venice,* 1589

Engraved title: Anatome / Corporis Humani, / Avctore / Joanne Valverdo: / Nunc primùm à Michaele Colum- / bo Latine reddita, / et Additis nouis ali- / quot tabulis exornata. / [at foot] / Venetiis; studio, et industria Ivntarvm M.D.L.XXXIX / Cum Licentia Et Priuilegiis.

Colophon (Ee8a): Venetiis, Apvd Ivntas. / M D LXXXVIII.

Collation: Fol. a-c⁶, A-Z⁶, Aa-Dd⁶, Ee⁸; [18] *ll.,* 339 pp. [wrongly numbered 340].

Contents: a1a engr. title; a1b blank; a2 dedication of Colombo to Duke of Savoy; a3 table of contents; a4a-c2b index; c3a-5a preface; c5b Valverde to the reader; c6a blank; c6b engr. portr. of Valverde signed NB; A1a-Ee8a text; Ee8b blank.

Note: The date on the title (1589) differs from that in the colophon (1588); careful examination of the engraved date in the H.C. copy suggests that it had been changed to M.D.L.XXX*IX* from M.D.L. XXX*VIII*; it is possible therefore that copies exist

with the 1588 title. This is the first Latin translation of Valverde. It contains the new muscle men (pp. 171-177) which first appeared in the Italian edition of 1586. The same copperplates were used as in the 1586 edition with line enclosures; impressions of the muscle men, curiously enough, seem fresher and clearer in this than in the earlier edition.

Copies: Waller; Cushing; DSG; NBMS; NNC-M; MiU (Pilcher).

Copy used: H.C., from Gilhofer and Ranschburg in 1928 for Frs. 250 (a second interleaved copy lacking portrait and muscle men was given to Dr. Fred T. Murphy).

VI.D.—39

VALVERDE, Anatomia.   Italian   *Venice,* 1606

Engraved title: Anotomia / del corpo / hvmano / Di Giouanni Valuerde: / Co' Discorsi del Medesimo, / Nouamente Ristampata / E con l' aggiunta d' / alcune Tauole / Ampliata / [at foot] / In Vinetia nella Stamperia de Givnti M D C V I.

Colophon (CC6b): In Venetia, Appresso i Giunti. / [rule] / M D C V I.

Collation: Fol. a⁶, B-C⁶, A⁴, B-O⁶, OO⁴, P-Z⁶, AA-CC⁶; [18], 154 *ll.;* 4 inserted *ll.* of muscle figures after *l.* 82.

Contents: a1a title; a1b blank; a2a Valverde's 1559 dedication to King Philip of Spain; a2b engr. portr. of Valverde; a3 dedication to the Cardinal Arch-bishop of Toledo; a4a Valverde to the reader; a4b-a5a contents; a5b-c6b index; A1a-A2b prologue; A3a-CC6b (*ll.* 3-154) text.

Note: In this edition the 1589 title-page is re-engraved and reversed; the portrait is signed (NB); the four additional muscle figures (001-4) occur between *ll.* 82 and 83. The type has been reset but the foliation follows that of the 1559 and 1586 Italian editions exactly, *i.e.,* 154 leaves. The plates also have line enclosures. There is a printer's device with the Giunta colophon added to the last page.

Copies: DSG; NNC-M; Cushing.

Copy used: H.C., bought from Olschki in 1927.

VI.D.—40

VALVERDE, Anatomia.   Italian   *Venice, 1608*

Engraved title: [Identical with preceding except for date M D C V III.].

Colophon, collation and contents: Identical with VI.D. 39.

Note: A reprint of VI.D.39, with redated title; setting of type unchanged, but many of the plates have been re-engraved (and reversed).

Copies: NNNAM; NNC-M; MdBJ-W; Cushing.

Copy used: H.C., bought from Rappaport, Rome, 1925, for Lire 300.

VI.D.—41

VALVERDE, Anatomia.   Latin   *Venice, 1607*

Engraved title in vignette: Anatome / Corporis Humani, / Avctore / Joanne Valverdo: / Nunc primùm à Michaele Colum-/bo Latine reddita, / et Additis nouis aliquot tabulis exornata. / [at foot] / Venetiis; studio, et industria Ivntarvm M.D.CVII. / Cum Licentia Et Priuilegiis.

Colophon: Venetiis, Apvd Ivntas. / M D C VII.

Collation: Fol. a-c⁶, A-Z⁶, Aa-Dd⁶, Ee⁸; [18] *ll.,* 339 pp. [wrongly numbered 340].

Contents: Identical with the Latin ed. of 1589, but the type has been reset.

Note: Title-page identical with that of 1589 edition except that the old date MDLXXXIX has been scratched and the new one engraved over it. The portrait is re-engraved; also the four muscle plates,

which are reversed from the 1589 edition. The copperplates are otherwise the same as in the 1589 Latin and 1606 Italian editions. The title-page would suggest that this edition was published before the 1606 edition, but other reasons would seem to me to outweigh this assumption. [H.C.]

Copies: Waller; Cushing; PPCP; DSG; NNC-M.

Copy used: H.C.

VI.D.—42

VALVERDE, Anatomia.   Italian   *Venice, 1682*

Engraved title: Anotomia / del corpo / hvmano / Di Giouanni Valuerde: / Co' Discorsi del Medesimo, / Nouamente Ristampata / E con l' aggiunta d' / alcune Tauole / ampliata / [at foot] / In Venetia Appresso Nicolò Pezzana M.DC.LXXXII.

Colophon: none.

Collation: Fol. a⁶, b⁸, A-Z⁶, Aa-Cc⁶; foliated, [14], 152 *ll.*

Contents: a1a title; a1b blank; a2a Valverde to the reader; a2b-3a contents; a3b-b6a index; b6b-8a prologue; b8b portr.; A1a-Cc6b (*ll.* 1-152) text.

Note: This is a reprint, with type reset, of the Giunta edition of 1606-08, with the only change the

printer's name. The new printer has followed the 1606-1608 Italian edition but has used the re-engraved portrait from the Latin edition of 1607 and also the re-engraved four added muscle plates. [H.C.]

Copies: NNNAM; DSG; MdBJ-W; MBM; Cushing; Fulton; van Wagenen.

Copy used: H.C., bought from L'Art Ancien, 1921, for 45 Swiss frs.

VALVERDE, Vivæ imagines   *Antwerp,* 1566

Title within engraved border: Vivæ / imagines / partivm / corporis / hvmani / æreis formis / expressæ. / [ornament] / Antverpiæ. / Ex officina Christo- / phori Plantini. / M. D. LXVI.

Colophon: none.

Collation: 4°. A-S⁴, T⁵, a-f⁴; [8], 9-153 pp., [24] *ll.*

Contents: A1a (p. 1) title; A1b blank; A2a-3b Plantin's dedication to the Antwerp Senate; A4a Plantin's explanatory note to medical students; A4b- T5a text and figures; T5b blank; a1a-f2a text of Vesalius' *Epitome;* f2b Grévin's table differentiating the parts of the body; f3a imperial privilege dated Vienna, February 21, 1565; f3b privilege of the king of Spain dated Brussels, January 28, 1565, and errata; f4 blank [H.C. copy has blank gathering of four leaves after f4].

Note: This consists of the 42 Valverde plates re- engraved on copper, several being reversed, *e.g.,* plates 3 and 4 of book VI which place the spleen and the aorta on the right. The explanatory text is drawn from Wechel's 1564 edition of Grévin's *Anatome* which in turn is based on Geminus (and hence on Vesalius' *Epitome*). At the end on special signatures and unnumbered pages is the full but unillustrated text of Vesalius' *Epitome* in the original Latin. So in the *Vivæ imagines* we have the complete text and letterpress of Vesalius' *Epitome* with the Valverde plates re-engraved (see Turner [402]).

This book has been described in great detail by Vander Haeghen in his *Bibliotheca Belgica* (37). He states that M. Rooses, Conservator of the Plantin Museum, informed him that the title-page was de- signed by Lambert van Noort and engraved by one Pierre Huys, the one receiving 3.10 florins for his services, the other 11 florins, on February 5, 1566. The plates, as distinct from the engraved title, were engraved jointly by Pierre and François Huys. Three of them were completed prior to 1562; these ap- peared in the Plantin sale and were bought by one Silvius who returned them to the Maison Plantin in 1564 (see Rooses' *Christophe Plantin,* Antwerp, 1882, pp. 51 *et seq.*). The 39 others were executed between 1564 and 1565 at a cost of 11 florins apiece. The collaboration of François Huys is evident from the following passage in a Plantin ledger: "Anatomes figuræ 1564, 18 avril à 11 decembre. Pour 22 planches taillées en cuivre à Pierre Huys et François Huys, lib. 40-6-8." The edition of 1566 was limited to 600 copies. Pierre Huys had engraved the plates at a cost of 22 florins per 100. He also did those for the Dutch edition of 1568 which ran to 450 copies. Vander Haeghen also gives details concerning the indices of the *Vivæ imagines* which are translated directly from the Italian edition of 1559, and he gives a long list of index entries proving the source.

Copies: London (BM); Louvain; Waller; Cush- ing; Fulton; CaMM-Os; NNNAM; NNC-M; CU-M.

Copies used: H.C. and J.F.F. The H.C. copy was sold by Davis and Orioli in 1926 for £32/10/- to Voynich who passed it on to Dr. Cushing for $200. J.F.F. copy from Tregaskis in 1935 for £2/15/-. Both are perfect.

VI.D.—44

VALVERDE, Vivæ imagines   Dutch   *Antwerp,* 1568

Title within engraved border: Anatomie, / Oft / Levende / beelden vande deelen / des menschelicken / lichæms: / Met de verclaringhe van / dien, inde Neder- duyt- / sche spræcke. / [fleuron] / T'Antwerpen, / By Christoffel Plantijn. / M. D. Lxviij.

Colophon: None.

Collation: Fol. *⁴, A⁸, 8 *ll.* (1 blank), B-F⁴, 16 *ll.,* G-I⁴, 6 *ll.,* K⁴, 2 *ll.* (1 blank), L-M⁴, 4 *ll.* (1 blank), N⁶, O⁴, 6 *ll.* (1 blank), P-Q⁴, 4 *ll.* R-Y⁴ Z⁶; [4] *ll.,* 198 (erroneously paged 196) pp., 1 *l.,* 42 pl. with 3 blank *ll.*

Contents: *1a title; *1b blank; *2a-4a Plantin's French dedication to Gérard Grammay; *4b Plantin to Dutch medical students; A1a-Q4a text with 42 figures inserted in groups as indicated in collation; R1a-Z5b (pp. 141-198) Dutch text of Vesalius' *Epitome*; Z6a Grévin's table; Z6b blank.

Note: This is the Dutch translation of the 1566 *Vivæ imagines* including the text of Vesalius' *Epitome* here first rendered into Dutch. The engraved title and plates are the same as in the 1566 edition save that the plates have had engraved numerical indications added, i.e., *Tabula I Libri I, Tabula II*, etc. The French preface is set up in an unusual *civilité* type face with flowing capitals and Greek e's. Vander Haeghen states (37: V103, 2) that 450 copies of this translation were printed (see note to next entry).

Plantin paid Jean Thorius 35 florins for translating the explanation of the figures into Dutch (March 17, 1566). One Martin Everaert translated the rest of the text (principally the *Epitome*) and received 24 florins for this service (May 12, 1566).

Copies: Louvain; Waller; Cushing; DSG; NNC-M; MdBJ-W.

Copy used: H.C. (2 copies): (i) Bound with David van Mauden's *Bedieninghe der Anatomien,* published by Plantin in 1583, bought from Hertzberger, Amsterdam, for 180 guilders; (ii) Smaller copy, bought from Burgersdijk and Niermans, Leyden, in 1911 for 35 fl.

VI.D.—45

VALVERDE, Vivæ imagines   *Antwerp, 1579* [?1572]

Title within engraved border: Vivæ / imagines / partivm / corporis / hvmani / æreis formis / expressæ. / [ornament] / Antverpiæ. / Ex officina Christo- / phori Plantini. / M. D. LXXII.

Colophon (V4a): Antveriæ excvdebat / Christophorvs Plantinvs, / Architypographvs regivs, / XVI. Kal. Maii Anno Domini / M. D. LXXIX.

Collation: 4°. A⁴, B⁶, 8 *ll.* (1 blank), C-E⁴, F⁶, 16 *ll.*, G⁴, H⁶, 6 *ll.*, I⁴, 1 *l.*, K⁴, L⁴, 3 *ll.*, M-N⁴, 6 *ll.* (1 blank), O⁶, 4 *ll.*, P-V⁴; [8], 9-171 pp., [2] *ll.* + 42 pl., 2 blank *ll.*

Contents: A1a engr. title; A1b blank; A2a-3b dedication; A4a Plantin to medical students; A4b-O6b (pp. [8]-128) text with 42 figs. inserted on separate leaves as indicated in collation; P1a-V2a (pp. 129-171) text of Vesalius' *Epitome*; V2b Grévin's table; V3a privilege; V3b second privilege (undated); V4a colophon; V4b blank.

Note: This is a shabby, patched-up piece of bookmaking well beneath the standards of Christopher Plantin. The colophon is dated 1579, the title 1572; the engr. title-border is identical with that of the 1566 edition and the 42 plates are also those of the original edition but are much deteriorated (having also been used in the Dutch translation of 1568) and have had the figure numbers (and book) inartistically engraved upon them, as in the Dutch edition. The text has been reset throughout and groups of figures are pitchforked hither and yon into the text as

inserted leaves independent of signatures (see collation). The result is unwieldy hodge-podge, nightmarish to a bibliographer.

Copies: Louvain; Waller; Cushing; Fulton; ICU; NNNAM; DSG; van Wagenen; NBMS; NNC-M; MBM; IEN-M; LNHT; MiU (Crummer).

Copies used: H.C., from Sir William Osler, who wrote in it characteristically as follows: "Oct. 18th, 1910. Dear C. On Friday Oct. 14th I had Maggs Bros. catalogue in which I saw this interesting Vesal item for which I posted an order at once. At the same time I asked them to let me know if you had ordered it, but I thought by this time your 16th century Vesal-wants had been filled. This morning word came from Maggs Bros. that you had cabled to send the Plantin Vesal, and asking what reply they should make. I said 'say sold'! I know how mad you will feel next week when you hear from them. I only hope this may come on the same day to console you. The MS. is Gemini's preface to the first edition of his Vesal piracy. Sincerely yours, Wm. Osler." The Geminus preface mentioned in Sir William's letter refers to four pages of MS. bound in this copy.

J.F.F. copy lacks title; has all plates bound in between pp. 116 and 117.

VI.D.—46

VALVERDE, Vivæ imagines   Dutch   *Amsterdam, 1647*

Engraved title: A. Vesalii en Valuerda / Anatomie / ofte / Afbeeldinghe / van de deelen des / menschelicken lichæms, / en derselver verclaringe. / Met / Een Aenwysinghe om / het selve te ontleden / volgens de leringe / Galleni, Vesalii, Fallopii / en Arantii. / 'T Amstelredam. / By / Cornelis Danckertz, / inde Calver straet in de / Danckbaerheyt / M. DC. XLVII.

Second printed title: A. Vesalii en Valuerda / Anatomie, / Ofte / Afbeeldinghe van de / Deelen des menschelijcken lichæms, / en derselver Verklaringhe. Met / Een aenwijsinghe om het selve te ontleden, / volgens de leeringe / Galleni, Vesalii, Fallopii / en Arantii. / [device] / t'Amstelredam, / [rule] / By Cornelis Danckertz, in de Kalver-straet, inde / Danckbaerheyt, M. DC. XLVII.

Colophon: none.

Collation: Fol. [*]², A⁸, B-M⁴, N⁶, O-Y⁴, Z⁶; [2] ll., 196 pp., 1 l., 42 pl. scattered through text without signatures or pagination.

Contents: [*]1a engr. title; [*]1b blank; [*]2a printed title; [*]2b Danckertz' 'Voor-reden aen den Leser'; A1a-Q4a text; Q4b blank; R1a-Z5b text of Vesalius' *Epitome*; Z6a Grévin's table; Z6b blank; 42 inserted plates scattered through text.

Note: This is a reprint of the 1568 Dutch Plantin edition with newly engraved plates and first title; the latter has an Adam-and-Eve *motif* as have had all the earlier Plantin editions; now, however, sur-mounted by a vignette of Vesalius in place of the coat of arms of Philip II, King of Spain. Cornelius Danckertz, the editor, had brought out the previous year (*i.e.,* 1646) at Amsterdam a new edition of David van Mauden's *Bedieninghe der Anatomien* to which he had appended the text and figures of the present volume (*i.e.,* pp. 1-196, 1 l.). Danckertz' note to the reader in the present volume is illumi-nating. Thus he says: "I published these plates of pictures by Vesalius and Valverde with great difficulty and expense, and cut them in copper and divided them for simplification in seven books; they are chiefly copied from Vesalius but many things have been changed in them and many have been added."

Copies: Louvain; Waller; Cushing; DSG; NB-MS; MdBJ-W; MiU (Pilcher).

Copy used: H.C., from Menno Hertzberger, Am-sterdam, for 5 guilders in 1925. Dr. Cushing also possessed a copy of the Danckertz' van Mauden of 1646 which he had obtained from Burgersdijk and Niermans, Leyden, in 1914, for 20 florins.

~ CHAPTER VII ~

THE CHINA-ROOT EPISTLE
AND THE AFTERMATH OF THE *FABRICA*

BEFORE LEAVING Basel one of Vesalius' last recorded acts was to stand as
godfather for one of Robert Winter's children, a ceremony which Oporinus, being a relative, doubtless attended. We may assume that he had
enjoyed himself greatly during his seven months' sojourn in Switzerland, where
he had found time for things other than proof reading. The Rector had seen to it
that he was given a complimentary matriculation which made it possible for
him to make dissections, and thus it came about that Basel for the first time in its
history had conducted a public "anatomy." This was on the body of a decapi-
tated malefactor named Jacob Karrar, concerning whose articulated skeleton
we have already heard (see *Apologia*) and portions of which are still preserved at
Basel in the Vesalianum.

Basel was then a place of great literary activity and most of the printers were,
like Oporinus, at the same time scholars whose companionship he enjoyed and
in whose gardens after working hours there was certain to be heard stimulating
talk. Felix Platter, who was destined to be the spiritual successor of Vesalius at
Basel, even though Caspar Bauhin was the first officially appointed professor of
anatomy, tells in his diary (321) of having seen the celebrated Vesalius as a child
in the shop of his father, Thomas, the printer. Thomas Plater (or Platter) was
but one of the many interrelated printers then active in Basel, like Jerome
Froben, Johann Herwagen (whose widow Oporinus married) and Heinrich
Petri, to mention but a few. Nor did Vesalius forget them in later years, for we
find him in 1555 securing a printer's privilege for Herwagen, as well as the title
of Imperial Notary for his nephew; and a year later he persuaded the Emperor to
grant Petri a title of nobility.

Life even in this quiet city on the Rhine where Erasmus lived and died had
its uncertainties in those troubled days. It was indeed at about this time, as we
learn from his biographer, Andreas Jociscus (216), that Oporinus was in trouble
over the publication of Bibliander's Latin translation of the Koran. In this very
year of 1543, he was finally allowed to print it, though he had been temporarily
imprisoned for having entertained even the thought of putting his imprint on so

154

infamous a book. It is said that the mediation not only of the towns of Strassburg and Zurich (where Bibliander was professor of theology) but finally of Luther was required before the Basel authorities allowed the book to be issued, even in Latin. Had he undertaken to issue it in the vernacular, as he planned to do, the final resting place of Oporinus would scarcely have been in the Basel cathedral along with Œcolampadius, the founder of the Reformed Church.

In the preceding February the Emperor had made a deal with Henry VIII promising to support his somewhat obscure claim for the French crown provided he would take part in a joint invasion of France. Before such a campaign could be undertaken, it was necessary that the rebellious Protestant prince, William, Duke of Cleves, a traditional ally of France though overlord in one of Charles's own dominions, should be brought to heel. So after making a hurried trip from Spain to Italy, the Emperor gathered a small force and with surprising energy and speed overcame the prince's resistance and restored to the Netherlands and the Catholic Church a large, previously hostile territory.

It is natural to assume that before returning to resume his work in Italy, Vesalius would have taken advantage of the subsequent lull in the incessant military campaigns to make at least a flying visit from Basel to Brussels to see his parents, very possibly carrying with him the presentation copies of the *Fabrica* and *Epitome* for the Emperor and Prince Philip. It has been surmised also that the position of body-physician to the Emperor may have been offered him at this time, an offer which may have favourably affected his suit for the hand of Anna van Hamme of Brussels, whom he subsequently married and who in due course bore him a daughter. If such conjectures have any basis, this must have been a pleasant interlude—all the more so in view of what was to confront him on his return to Padua, supposedly on the opening of the winter session. For at this time he encountered most unfavourable repercussions to his epochal publications which by this time were in the hands of his all-but-forgotten and long-since-forgiven opponents. He had now been absent from his post the better part of a year and to return to it merely to resume his former tasks must have been irksome—the more so as he was obliged to face the inevitable mixture of applause and criticism, both equally distasteful to the writer even of a work less momentous than his. As a mother is conscious of mental and physical let-down after parturition, an athlete after a crucial race, a soldier after an armistice, so an author usually feels after the labour of conscientiously seeing a volume through the press—anything to escape from the possibility of starting in immediately on another baby, marathon, battle or book!

In his case there was little applause to be heard and it must have been highly dispiriting to find that the intrigues against him, already evident before his departure, had increased rather than lessened. Even his former assistant, Realdus Columbus, who had been acting for him during his absence, had joined the ranks of his opponents and had belittled before the students the supposed reforms of the professorial absentee. His chagrin and disgust at the accumulating storm of abuse let loose at him by the firmly entrenched Galenists appear finally to have broken down his resistance and convinced him that the only thing to do was to relinquish his post, change his place of residence and perhaps even his form of occupation. Late in December of 1543 he appears to have held a public anatomy on a female subject—the last dissection he was to make before the Paduan students. And it was soon after this, in a moment of despondency, in order completely to cut himself off from the past, that he made a sacrificial pyre of his accumulated documents. This impulsive act he came later to regret as can be learned from almost the last page of the China-root Epistle written some two years later in which he feelingly says:

"As to my notes, which had grown into a huge volume, they were all destroyed by me; and on the same day there similarly perished the whole of my paraphrase of the ten books of Rhazes to King Almansor, composed by me with far more care than the *Paraphrasis* which I published on the ninth book. With these also went the books of some author or other [Servetus?] on the formulæ and preparation of medicines, to which I had added much matter of my own that I judged to be not without utility; and the same fate overtook all the books of Galen which I had used in learning anatomy, and which I had liberally disfigured in the usual fashion. I was on the point of leaving Italy and going to Court; those physicians of whom you know had given the Emperor and the nobles a most unfavourable report of my books and of all that is pub-lished nowadays for the promotion of study; I therefore burnt all these works mentioned, thinking at the same time it would be an easy matter to abstain from writing for the future. I have since repented more than once of my impatience, and regretted that I did not take the advice of the friends who were then with me."

Soon after this lamentable act, he left Padua to pay a promised visit in Bologna and later to fulfil an engagement at Pisa. In company with Petrus Tronus, professor of surgery at Pavia, he proceeded to Bologna on the invitation of his friend, Professor Andreas Albius, whose guest he had been in the winter of 1539-40. On that occasion, as may be recalled, he had prepared and articulated for comparative purposes a human and a simian skeleton. The surgeon, Bartholomæus Maggius, at the time of this second visit was in process of anato-mizing a body, and on the request of the students Vesalius took over the thoracic part of the dissection in order to demonstrate his views concerning the venous system and its relation to liver and heart. And the story has come down to us that the resulting discussion was prolonged until so late at night it had to be broken off because of the excessive cold (345, p. 188).

After several days in Bologna, he crossed the Etruscan Appenines into Tuscany and made his way to Pisa where he had been specially invited by the Duke of Tuscany to visit the university on whose newly rehabilitated medical faculty the aged Franciscus Pontremulus and the peregrinating (Pavia, Pisa, Padua, Bologna and again Pisa) Matthæus Curtius* had already briefly served. The Duke and his advisers were evidently looking for a permanent appointee for the chair of anatomy; this post, as a matter of fact, Columbus soon accepted. Vesalius had been asked to come to Pisa, therefore, merely as a guest lecturer to carry out the "function of a Public Anatomy," doubtless with the hope that he might agree to remain. The public anatomy, an annual function to which all citizens were invited, was usually held in the early spring at carnival time when all other lectures were discontinued.

Documentary evidence of this sojourn in Pisa has been unearthed by Pro-fessor Andrea Corsini (86) in a series of letters addressed to Pier Francesco Riccio, one of the Duke's confidential secretaries in Florence. They indicate that as soon as Vesalius arrived on January 22, 1544, the Duke sent a special courier to the hospital of Santa Maria Nuova in Florence for two cadavers, male and female, which were to be sent secretly by boat down the Arno to Pisa. Unfortu-nately only one body arrived—that of a nun who had succumbed to thoracic disease ("pleuritis"?); and after the customary demonstrations covering a period of three weeks, an articulated skeleton was prepared. Attending these exercises there is said to have been a large gathering, and from the letters one gets even such details as the attendance of the Duke in person; also the humorous note of an accident that befell one of the court surgeons, who in his eagerness to watch the proceedings, fell off a bench seriously damaging himself. It is made clear also that while in Pisa, Vesalius was called upon to perform an autopsy on the body of an aged lawyer from Siena who had succumbed to an obscure malady, which

* Curtius who died in 1542 had been on good terms with Vesalius until they had a falling out over the venesection controversy. He is best known for his admirable commentary on the Anatomy of Mundinus (Pavia, 1550; Lyon, 1551). The Lyon edition, curiously enough, was edited by Jean Canappe, who in laudatory terms dedicated it to Vesalius with a rebuke to those who denied his great service to anatomy.

goes to show what had long been apparent, that his interests were not restricted to normal anatomy but in the footsteps of Benivieni covered pathological anatomy as well. All of this must have carried him well into February, and when finally Duke Cosimo made him the flattering offer of a permanent position with an annual salary of 600 crowns, Vesalius was obliged to express his regrets on the grounds that he had already been appointed physician at the Imperial Court. Thus came to an actual close what he had described in his letter to Oporinus written little more than a year previously as "that glorious period of undisturbed labour among the gifted scholars of divine Italy."

At about the time when this Pisan episode was drawing to its close in February, 1544, Charles V was attending in person the third Diet held at Spires in Bavaria, where the Reformers originally came by the name of Protestants. There, after branding Francis as an enemy to Christendom for egging on the Turks, Charles secured the military support of the Lutheran Princes with the promise—be it said to the great irritation of the Pope—of soon calling a general council. Acting promptly, he retook Luxemburg and with 50,000 troops started on the invasion which, to the terror of all France, took him down the Marne Valley almost within sight of Paris.

How Vesalius, whom we left in Pisa on the seacoast of Tuscany, managed to catch up with the invading army is not entirely clear. We first authentically hear from him at the siege of St. Dizier on the Marne where the army on July 13th had been joined by the Emperor and where in one of his energetic moods he was directing operations in the trenches and personally carrying out dangerous reconnaissance. It was only two days later, on July 15th by his own account, that Vesalius was called upon to care for René de Chalon, Prince of Orange, who had received what proved to be a fatal gunshot wound of the right shoulder; also on July 24th at the capture of Vitry, the Seigneur d'Aluhin was wounded and died a week later. From St. Dizier and Vitry, Charles had moved on down the valley of the Marne to the south of St. Mihiel and the Argonne, enveloping on his way Bar le Duc, Châlons, Château Thierry, Soissons and probably Meaux—names which became all too familiar to every American doughboy four centuries later—and from Meaux his advance cavalry had made raids almost up to the walls of Paris. Indeed he might well enough have taken Paris and dictated a victor's terms to Francis had the co-operating English army under Henry VIII done its part instead of dallying interminably over the siege of Boulogne. As things stood, the army of the Emperor was not only far from its base but so woefully short of provisions that a truce was sought, and finally on

September 18, 1544, at Crépy-en-Valois terms of peace were agreed upon. It was stipulated that Charles should cede to France the Duchy of Milan; that Savoy was to be given back to its rightful Duke; and that King and Emperor would join in a concerted suppression of heresy.

It was in this campaign, the last of the many conducted by the two life-long rivals against each other, that Vesalius found himself plunged into the unfamiliar business of caring for gunshot wounds, just as many another inexperienced anatomist-surgeon has been plunged at not infrequent intervals ever since, and in the identical terrain—the cockpit of Europe. But it was not with military surgery that he was to be chiefly occupied, but rather the care of the Emperor's health and that of his household; and whether he remained with Charles at Crépy until the treaty was signed, and then returned with him and his entourage to Brussels, is nowhere clearly stated. It is known, however, that in addition to the increasingly difficult problem of the Emperor's health, the several hundred persons constituting the Court soon came under his personal care.

Charles himself, who was now 44 years of age, had for the past ten years and more suffered from attacks of arthritic gout which of late had become increasingly severe. He was also the victim of asthmatic seizures and frequent intestinal disturbances attributed to irregular meals and an uncontrolled appetite. Not only did he disregard the advice of his medical attendants concerning these disorders, but he used a great variety of quack preparations and often accepted the advice of foreign doctors and lay meddlers in preference to that of his professional appointees, much as self-willed people of all times have been accustomed to do. He nevertheless had many admirable qualities among which were generosity and tolerance; and the fact that his body physician could write the above frank statements concerning his health and habits, even in a letter to a brother who soon had the letter published, seemed to have no ill effect on their mutual regard for one another.

From the publication of the *Fabrica* almost to the present day the intimate pursuit of descriptive and topographical anatomy has constituted the high road for entry into the practice of surgery, and not only have surgically inclined graduates usually sought places as prosectors in dissecting rooms, but in many schools until recent times professorships of anatomy and surgery have often been combined. It bespeaks the enlightened attitude of the Court that Vesalius, who was largely responsible for this trend, should have been appointed, soon after he turned thirty, to serve as the Emperor's physician for which responsible post his qualifications might appear to have been slender.

To be sure, he was only second in rank to the aged Cornelius von Baersdorp, under whom there had been several Spanish doctors, few of them distinguished; but even in his youthful *Paraphrasis* Vesalius had insisted that the healing art was the primary goal of medicine and the chief purpose of anatomy in his opinion was to provide a proper foundation for its pursuit. Without anatomical knowledge, how could one understand the causes and recognize the seats of organic diseases? Vesalius indeed had always been so greatly interested in this approach to disease that in every book of the *Fabrica* one may find observations not only on comparative but on pathological anatomy as well.

At the Court he was to have an opportunity to test the value for medical practice of an anatomical background such as his; at the same time he was by no means unfamiliar with the precepts of the medical therapeutics of the day. Among the documents Vesalius committed to the flames before his final departure from Padua in December, 1543, was a treatise on the use of drugs which may have been an expansion of the booklet on syrups composed by Servetus. That slender work by Michael Villanovanus had been printed at Paris in 1537 by Simon de Colines; and since Servetus had been his fellow prosector under Guenther the year before, Vesalius must certainly have known of the work during its preparation and the copy which he appears to have been amplifying was conceivably forwarded to him at Louvain.

While Charles V was so busily holding together his empire in Europe, it must not be forgotten that what was known as "New Spain" comprised an even larger domain in the New World, from which all manner of novel plants, some with unique therapeutic properties and wholly unknown to the ancient Greek and Latin authors, were being shipped to Spain along with plunder of other sorts. One can imagine the enthusiasm of the European doctor-botanists over these new plants, some of which doubtless contained medicinal properties of great therapeutic value yet to be discovered. There were cloves and rhubarb, ginger and cinnamon, not to mention bitumen, amber oil and other strange gums and balsams. Tobacco, to be sure, was not yet introduced and a decade passed before Jean Nicot studied its therapeutic effects of which high hopes were for a time entertained. But already decoctions of guaiac wood (*lignum sanctum*) from Santo Domingo, and of a form of *smilax*,* misleadingly called "China

* Prof. J. B. de C. M. Saunders, whose scholarly translation of the China-root Epistle is presently to be published, comments as follows on the botanical position of China root: "Sarsaparilla was not the China root. Vesalius clearly distinguishes between them, devoting a special section of the letter on the China root to a consideration of sarsaparilla. The China root is *Smilax China* (Linné), although no doubt the roots of other members of the family occurring in India were substituted, *e.g., S. lanceifolia, S. glabra, S. ovalifolia.* The

root"—were being warmly recommended for a great variety of ailments. It was even hoped they might serve to check the ravages of that rapidly spreading afflic-tion known as *Morbus Gallicus*—"French pox" to the vulgar—a disorder which Monardes of Seville was fully convinced had also been transported from the West Indies in Spanish bottoms along with loot of less undesirable kinds. New drugs are all too often hopefully looked upon as possible cure-alls and naturally enough Charles was persuaded to take a course of "Spartaparilla," as Vesalius spelled it, to see what effect it might have on his arthritic gout. Vesalius' experi-ences with the sarsaparilla decoction are told, along with many other things, in the extraordinary China-root Epistle, which is the chief source of our knowledge of many episodes such as the burning of his documents and the information concerning his medical forebears which have been already quoted. In 1546, after the return to Brussels following the Peace of Crépy, Vesalius, as already men-tioned, married Anna van Hamme, the daughter of a local patrician family; in the letter he makes an indirect allusion to the married state, in which such engrossing toil as that in which he had formerly been engaged would scarcely have been possible. Though the Emperor early in the year had suffered a particu-larly severe attack of gout affecting his left shoulder and ankle, he none the less was present at a meeting of the Diet at Worms; and later on, after a journey through Belgium, he attended the long postponed Council of Trent held in accordance with the agreement reached with Francis at Crépy. Then on Janu-ary 2, 1546, he set out to attend the Diet at Regensburg on the Danube. After opening at Utrecht the Congress of the Order of the Golden Fleece, he pro-ceeded on his way through Nimwegen, at which place Vesalius was obliged to remain in order to look after the Venetian ambassador, Bernardo Navagero, who had been taken seriously ill.

It is an ill wind that blows no good. Nimwegen happens to be in the Duchy of Cleves not far from Wesel, the ancestral home of Vesalius' forebears, which he took the opportunity to visit; and the incident led him to give Roelants the details which have already been quoted concerning his family history. How much of the long letter was composed at Nimwegen during his enforced month's sojourn there, and how much of it later on after he had rejoined Charles who had reached Regensburg on April 11th, is perhaps unimportant. But the

Smilax China was very much later referred to as the Chinese sarsaparilla and employed for similar purposes with the official sarsaparilla, *Smilax medica* or *S. officinalis* and perhaps *S. ornata*. Vesalius names Portugal as the source of the sarsaparilla which he describes and mentions its Spanish name, but is in error when he says that it came from India. His description leaves no doubt as to its nature."—Ed.

contents of the letter dated Ratispona [Regensburg], June 13, 1546, are of the greatest possible biographical and of no little bibliographical importance.

It was in the nature of a reply to some questions his old friend, Joachim Roelants, the city physician of Mechlin, had asked on a variety of subjects, such as his experience at court with decoctions of the new China root, to which he replied that compared with guaiacum its therapeutic value had been greatly exaggerated. Roelants was also concerned over the advisability of having his son continue with the study of medicine in Paris under Sylvius, who lost no opportunity of disparaging before the students Vesalius' contributions to anatomy.

"When your son left to study at Paris [Vesalius replies] I commended him in letters to Vassæus, Fernelius, Oliverius and some others whom I respect greatly for their scholarship; and as you know I took particular pains in commending him to Sylvius. In this letter, aside from recommending your son, I mentioned our common studies and added that if any comments in my books on anatomy had displeased him, I hoped he would tell me what they were. For I thought it concerned him, too, if I published anything, since he had established among his colleagues such a high reputation in anatomy, and since I had begun studying medicine with him."

To this Sylvius had replied at length saying that he was still convinced Galen did not recount anything incorrectly and that he could only keep Vesalius as a friend provided he would make a complete retraction of his criticisms which were probably due to his youth and too long association with the Italians. In answer Vesalius said, in effect, that he yielded to no one in devotion and reverence to Galen, but a great number of scholars and philosophers who had attended his dissections had learned to trust their own eyes rather than Galen's writings and had come round to his point of view. Nor had age altered his opinions, for he was only too well aware that his youth to which Sylvius objected was already gone:

"Many persons [he says] are hostile to me because in my writings I seem to hold in contempt the authority of Galen, the prince of physicians and preceptor of us all, because I do not agree indiscriminately with all his opinions, and especially because I have demonstrated that some errors are discernible in his books. Surely scant justice to me and to our studies and indeed to our times! . . . I would rather have counted in this class any one than Jacobus Sylvius, an ornament to the physicians of our age; but, from the letter sent by your son, in which he disclosed that he had read my books, he proved very decidedly that he *does* belong in this group. So now you can easily deduce what ground I covered in my letter to him which I sent on to you from Nimwegen so that your son could deliver it to Sylvius."

The bulk of this remarkable epistle is thus given over to a full discussion of the exchange of letters with Sylvius into which the names of Vesalius' more active opponents, like Dryander, Fuchs, Cornarius, and even Joannes Guinterius were incidentally drawn. After concluding the letter, he adds for Roelants' benefit as a sort of appendix an Italian version of a brief regimen to be followed when using the decoction of China root, the source and authorship of which was unknown to Vesalius and has proved baffling to others. Copies of the long epistle appear to have been circulated by Roelants, one of which must have been sent to Franciscus Vesalius in Ferrara, who doubtless secured his brother Andreas' permission to have it printed by Oporinus with a dedication to Cosimo dei Medici who is cordially mentioned in the text.

VII.— 1

CHINA-ROOT EPISTLE   Ed. princeps.   *Basel,* 1546

Title (Fig. 82): Andreæ Ve / salii Brvxellensis, me / dici Cæsarei epistola, ratio- / nem modum*que* propinandi radicis Chynæ decocti, / quo nuper inuictissimus Carolvs V. Imperator / usus est, pertractans: & præter alia quædam, episto- / læ cuiusdam ad Iacobum Syluium sententiam recen- / sens, ueritatis ac potissimum humanæ fabricæ studi- / osis perutilem: quum quî hactenus in illa ni- / mium Galeno creditum sit, facile / commonstret. / Accessit quo*que* locuples rerum & uerborum in / hac ipsa epistola memorabili- / um, Index. / Cum gratia & priuilegio Imperiali / ad quinquennium. / Basileæ.

Colophon: Basileæ, ex offici- / na Ioannis Opori- / ni, anno salvtis / humanæ MDXLVI. Mense / octobri.

Collation: Sm. fol. A-Z⁴, Aa-Cc⁴, Dd⁶; 204 pp., [8] *ll.*

Contents: A1a title; A1b blank; A2a-B1a dedication to Duke Cosimo dei Medici by Franciscus Vesalius, dated erroneously MDLXVI for MDXLVI; B1b portrait woodcut from *Fabrica* with chipped left upper corner; B2a-Bb4a text: letter to Roelants begins with woodcut initial T and ends with place (*Ratisponæ*), date (June 13 [*Idibus*], 1546) and sub-scription (*Tibi addictiss. Andreas Vesalius*); Bb4b-Cc1a *Italicum scriptum,* introduction by Vesalius to: Cc1a-Cc2b *Regimento per pigliar l'aqua de la radice de Chyna*

—a description in Italian of the pharmaceutical properties and preparations of the China root; Cc3a-Dd4b index in 2 cols.; Dd5a errata; Dd5b colophon; Dd6a blank; Dd6b printer's device.

Note: Text is printed in roman type; dedication, marginal notes, *Regimento* and index in italic type. Type page, measuring 19 by 10.2 cm. excluding head lines and catchwords, has 35 lines of roman, 31 lines of italic type. Initial letters are from *Fabrica* woodblocks. Errors in page numbering are 7 for 9, 196 for 195, 404 for 204.

Copies: London (BM); Louvain; Munich; DSG; CaMM-Os; Cushing; NNNAM; NNC-M; MdBJ-W; MiU (Crummer); CU-M.

Copy used: H.C., bought in 1911 at Van den Corput sale (Item No. 45), Amsterdam, for 200 florins. Contains Van den Corput's *Ex Libris* with letters from Vander Haeghen, the Dutch bibliographer of Ghent, inserted. Copy measures 28.8 by 19.3 cm. I have records of only one larger copy: namely, the Osler one, formerly in the possession of Sir Mitchell Banks of Liverpool, which measures 29.2 by 19.1 cm.

VII.—2

CHINA-ROOT EPISTLE   2nd ed.   *Venice* [1546?]

Title (Fig. 83): Andreæ Vesalii / Brvxellensis, medici Cæsarei / Epistola, rationem modumque propinandi radicis / Chymæ [*sic*] decocti, . . . / [printer's device] / Venetiis.

Collation: 8°. A-N⁸, O⁴; 100, [8] *ll.*

Contents: A1a title; A1b blank; A2a-5a dedication to Duke Cosimo correctly dated; A5b-N3b text of letter to Roelants; N4a *Italicum scriptum*; N4b-5b *Regimento* etc. in Italian; N6a-O4a index; O4b blank.

Note: The British Museum lists this edition as of 1546, but this is probably based on the dated preface.

The printer's device on the title-page has not been identified; it is closely similar to that of Comin de Trino.

Copies: London (BM); Louvain; London (RCS); Cushing; MdBJ-W.

Copy used: H.C., bought from Eckstein & Widenmann, Berlin, 1906, for M.100. Bound in contemporary limp vellum; measures 15.5 by 10.5 cm.

VII.—3

CHINA-ROOT EPISTLE   3rd ed.   *Lyon*, 1547

Title (Fig. 84): Radicis / Chynæ / vsvs, / Andrea / Vesalio / Avthore. / * / [Printer's mark] / Lvgdvni, / Sub Scuto Coloniensi, / [rule] 1547.

Colophon: Lugduni, / Excudebat Ioannes / Frellonius, / [rule] / 1547.

Collation: 16°. A-V⁸, X⁴; 290 pp., [19] *ll.*

Contents: A1a title; A1b blank; A2a-5a dedication to Duke Cosimo; A5b blank; A6a-S6b epistle to Roelants; S7a *Italicum scriptum*; S7b-T1b *Regime pour prendre l'eaue de la racine appellée chyna*; T2a-X4a index; X4b colophon.

Note: There is no indication who was responsible for bringing out this pocket edition nor who made the French translation of the *Regimento*. The edition is less attractively printed than many of Frellon's 16mos, and was probably turned out hastily. Errors of pagination include 115 for 116.

Copies: London (BM); Louvain; Cushing; DSG; CaMM-Os; PPCP; NNNAM [2 copies]; MiU (Pilcher); Belt.

Copy used: H.C., bought of Gustav Fock, Leipzig, Feb. 1907, for M.30. Bound in paper boards with leather back (contemporary?); measures 12 by 7.4 cm.

De Feyfer under his VII.4 cites a reissue of VII.3 above as "idem. Basileæ 1566.—In 4°," which would properly be a fourth edition were the citation correct. He mentions an example (with a question mark) as in the possession of the University Library at Utrecht; but as no such edition has been identified, I strongly suspect it to be a ghost due to a faulty interpretation of the erroneous date printed in VII.1 (the Basel *ed. princeps*) at the end of the preface by Franciscus Vesalius. [The edition is listed in the *Catalogue d'une collection . . . exposée au VIᵉ Congrès International d'Histoire de la Médecine* (Amsterdam), 1927, p. 55.—Ed.]

For de Feyfer's VII.4, however, a worthy substitute may be presented in the shape of a German edition apparently unknown to him. Written by Walter Ryff, of whom we have already heard over-much in other connections, it was printed in 1548 at Würzburg by Hans Myller under the Emperor's privilege. It nowhere mentions the name of Vesalius other than the allusion to *"ein anderer Medicus, ein trefflich gelert man,"* but it appears to be a free translation of the first portion of the Epistle to Roelants, and at the end occurs the Regimen now for the first time translated into German.

VII.—4

CHINA-ROOT EPISTLE   Ryff trans.   *Würzburg,* 1548

Title: Kurtzer ausszug vnd / Summarischer bericht der Natur, / eygenschafft vnd wunderbarlichen wirckung, sampt rech- / tem eygentlichen gebrauch, der frembden, new erfund- / nen Medicin, der Wurtzel China genant . . . Aus Latinischer vnd Tuscanischer sprach transsferirt Durch / D. Gvalthervm H. Rivivm / Medicum & Chirurgum. &c. / Würtzburg. M. D. xlviii. (*cf.* Fig. 85).

Head-title of Regimen (f2a): Copia oder abschrifft des kurtzen berichts, / der newerfundnen Cur, der frem- / den Wurtzel Chi- / na, wie solche inn Tuscanischer sprach, Kay: / Mayestat zugeschickt worden, auffs / new Transsferirt durch / D. Gualtherum H. Riuium Medicum / & Chirurgum &c.

Colophon: Zu Würtzburg Truckts Hans Myller. / Mit Römischer Kay: May: Priuilegio. / Anno Dñi M.D. XLVIII.

Collation: 4°. a-f⁴; [24] ll.

Contents: a1a title; a1b blank; a2a-b2a dedication by Ryff to Michael, Abbot of the Cloister of St. Stephen in Würzburg, dated 1 January 1548; b2b-f1b German text of *Epistola*; f2a-4a text of *Regimen*; f4b blank.

Note: A free rendering of VII.1 with many inter-polations by the translator. Vesalius is not quoted by name but is referred to (b3b) as *"ein anderer Medicus ein trefflich gelert man."* The "cure" of the Emperor Charles and several of his suite is added to the text, but the biographical material relating to Vesalius is omitted.

Copy used: H.C., bought of Taeuber & Weil, Munich, November 1928, for M.250; measures 19.5 by 14 cm.

In the same manner as used by Ryff, the first portion of the Epistle to Roe-lants which deals with the China-root question [B2a-E4a in VII.1], as well as the subjoined *Italicum scriptum* next appear in the first volume of the works deal-ing with the *Morbus Gallicus* [syphilis] assembled from many sources by Aloysius Luisinus of Udine and first printed in a large folio volume (*Tomus prior*) at Venice in 1566 by Zeletti, to be followed a year later by an equally large volume (*Tomus posterior*). These copiously indexed volumes which contain the chief contemporary source material concerning syphilis were reprinted in 1599 and again in 1728 at Leyden under the auspices of Boerhaave with an altered title, *viz., Aphrodisiacus, sive de lue venerea.*

Since these partial reprints of the Epistle have been slighted by de Feyfer, they will be cited here since they also perpetuate the unidentified *Italicum scriptum* now for the first time printed in Latin.

VII.—5

CHINA-ROOT EPISTLE   Luisinus ed.   *Venice,* 1566

Title: De / morbo gallico / omnia qvæ extant / apvd omnes medicos / cvivscvnqve nationis, / Qui vel integris libris, vel quoquo alio modo huius affectus cura- tionem / methodicè aut empiricè tradiderunt . . . In quo de Ligno Indico, Salsa Perillia, Radice Chynæ, Argento uiuo, / cæterisque rebus omnibus ad huius luis profligationem inuen- / tis, diffusissima tractatio habetur. . . . Tomvs prior. / [Printer's device] / Venetiis, apud Iordanum Zilettum, 1566.

Collation: Fol. *⁴, A-Z⁶, Aa-Zz⁶, Aaa-Ooo⁶, Ppp⁸, a⁶, b⁸; [4] *ll.,* 736 pp., [14] *ll.*

Contents: *1a title; *1b blank; *2a-b dedication to Nicolaus Massa; *3a printer to reader; *3b-4a alpha- betical author index; *4b blank. There follow 55 works of 40 different authors. The first portion of the China-root Epistle (*i.e.,* to line 6 of p. 39 [E4a] in VII.1) followed by the *Italicum scriptum,* which has here been translated into Latin (*De modo propinandæ chynæ*) appears on pp. 504-514 (Tt6b-Vu5b) under the following subtitle:

De radice Chynæ, Andreæ Vesalii/ ad Ioachimvm Roelants, Epistola./ In qua inserta sunt & de Sparta Parilla sub finem nonnulla./ Eivsdem scriptvm de ipsamet Chyna,/ Italicum ad Ioachimum missum, sed nuper Latinum accuratè factum.

Note: The section taken from the Epistle goes only as far as line 6 of page 39 (sig. E4a) in the 1546 edition. A few paragraphs of the Epistle were trans- lated into English in Daniel Turner's *Aphrodisiacus, Containing a summary of the ancient writers on the venereal disease.* London, 1736, pp. 144-146. The text was evidently drawn from Ziletti's edition of 1566.

Copies: MH; NNNAM; MdBM; NBMS; IEN- M; ICJ. Cushing; Fulton.

Copy used: H.C., bought of C. E. Rappaport, Rome, November 1936, $105. Chorinski copy with bookplate and characteristic binding, sold (item 244) at sale on June 16, 1930, for M.80. Measures 30.9 by 20.7 cm.

VII.—6

CHINA-ROOT EPISTLE   2nd Luisinus ed.   *Venice,* 1599

Title: Aphrodisiacus / sive / de lve venerea; / in duo volumina bipartitus. / Con- tinens omnia quæcunque hactenus / de hac re sunt ab omnibus Medicis conscripta. / Ubi de ligno Indico, salsa perillia, / radice Chynæ, Argento vivo, cæterisque rebus omnibus ad hujus luis / profligationem inventis, dif- fusissima tractatio habetur. / . . . Volumen primum. / [Printer's device] / Venetiis, M D XCIX. / Apud Baretium Baretium, & Sociis [*sic*]. / Cvm privilegiis.

Collation and *Contents:* As in VII.5.

Note: Although we have not had opportunity per- sonally to examine a copy of this edition, Mr. Heneage Wynne-Finch of London informed us that

the text is identical with that of the 1566 edition, which would place the China-root Epistle on pp. 504-514.

Copy: Mr. Heneage Wynne-Finch.

VII.—7

CHINA-ROOT EPISTLE   3rd Luisinus ed.   *Leyden,* 1728

Title: Aphrodisiacus, / sive / de lue venerea; / in duos tomos bipartitus, / Continens omnia quæcumque hactenus de hac re sunt ab / omnibus Medicis conscripta. / Ubi de Ligno Indico, Salsa Perilla, Radice Chynæ, . . . Editio longè emendatior, & ab innumeris mendis repurgata. / Tomus primus. / [Engraved printer's device] / Lugduni Batavorum, / Apud / Johan. Arnold. Langerak, / et / Johan. & Herm. Verbeek, / Bibliop. / MDCCXXVIII.

Collation: Fol. [*]², †-†††††², *¹, **², A-Y⁴,Z⁴+¹, Aa-Zz⁴, Aaa⁴, Bbb²; Vol. II. [*]², Ccc², Ddd-Zzz⁴, Aaaa-Rrrr⁴, Ssss-Zzzz²; [15] *ll.,* [345] *ll.* numbered by columns 1-1366, [10] *ll.*

Contents: [*]1a half-title; [*]1b blank; [*]2a title; [*]2b blank; †1a-*1b Boerhaave's preface; **1 dedication to Nicolaus Massa; **2 author index; A1a-Ssss2a text; Ssss2b-Zzzz2a subject index; Zzzz2b blank. The same portion of the China-root Epistle

followed by the *Italicum scriptum* as found in VII.5 appears herein in cols. 585-598 (Oo3a-Pp2a) with the same title.

Copies: London (BM); DSG; NNNAM; CSt-L; MdBM; ICJ; MdBJ-W; MBM; Cushing; Fulton; CtY.

Copy used: H.C., bought of C. E. Rappaport, Rome, February 1937, for $39. Measures 39.7 by 24.6 cm.

There were also two other translations, one a fragmentary rendering in Spanish and the other a full and scholarly Dutch edition published in Amsterdam in 1915 and intended for the 1914 celebration. The Saunders translation into English mentioned above had not appeared at the time this bibliography was passing through press (October 1943).—Ed.

VII.—8

CHINA-ROOT EPISTLE   Spanish fragment   *Madrid,* 1821

Head-title: Carta / de Andres Vesalio, / natural de Bruselas, / Médico de Cámara, / en que trata de la dosis y método de administrar / el cocimiento de la raiz de China, de que aca- / ba de hacer uso el muy invicto emperador Cárlos V, y en la que, entre otras cosas, da / su dictámen acerca de una carta escrita á Ja- / cobo Silvio, utílisima á los fisicos y anató- / micos, demostrando en ella con claridad que / se ha dado demasiado crédito hasta aqui á / Galeno.

In: Memoria / sobre / las virtudes y usos de la raiz de Purhampuy / ó China Peruana, / por Don Hipólito Ruiz / . . . / ilustrada y aumentada / por el licenciado Don Antonio Ruiz / . . . / Madrid, / Imprenta de don José del Collado. / 1821.

Collation: 4°. 1-12⁴; [1-7], 8-96 pp.

Contents: p. [1] title; p. [2] blank; pp. [3-5] prologue; p. [6] blank; pp. [7]-37 'Elogio histórico de Don Hipolito Ruiz Lopez'; p. 38 blank; pp. 39-68 'Memoria sobre la planta llamada Purhampuy ó China Peruviana por Don Hipólito Ruiz'; pp. 69-

96 'Carta de Andres Vesalio.'

Note: This Spanish fragment of the China-root Epistle contains merely the first part of the letter to Roelants (from p. 11 to p. 34, line 24 of VII.1). It does not include the dedication by Franciscus Vesalius to Duke Cosimo dei Medici, nor, unfortunately, the *Italicum scriptum.* The translator has in many instances used footnotes to indicate the original marginal notes, and has also added one or two notes of his own commenting on the text.

Copy used: Arnold Arboretum, Harvard University.

VII.—9

CHINA-ROOT EPISTLE   Dutch translation.   *Amsterdam, 1915*

Title in woodcut border: Opuscula selecta / Neerlandicorum / de arte medica / Fasciculus Tertius / quem / Curatores Miscellaneorum / quæ vocantur / Ned- erlandsch Tijdschrift / voor Geneeskunde / collegerunt et ediderunt / Am- stelodami / apud F. van Rossen / MCMXV. [in shield] Andreæ Vesalii / Epistola / de / radicis Chynæ / decocto.

Title of Vol. III: Brief van Andreas Vesalius van Brussel, keizerlijk arts, / behelzende de aanwending van het decoct van Chynawortel, / dat onlangs is gebruikt door den onoverwinnelijken keizer / Karel V en onder meer bevattende den inhoud van zeke- ren / brief aan Jacobus Sylvius, van groot nut voor hen, die / de waarheid en in het bijzonder den bouw van den mensch / wenschen te kennen, daar hij duidelijk aantoont, dat ten deze / tot dusver te veel vertrouwen is geschonken aan Galenus / [ornament] / Naar de eerste Latijnsche uitgave te Bazel 1546 bij / Joannes Oporinus vertaald onder toezicht / van Dr. H. Pinkhof, met een inleiding van / Prof. Dr. E. C. van Leersum en door hen beiden / van aanteeken- ingen voorzien. / Uitgevers en Drukkersmaatschap- pij F. van Rossen, Amsterdam—1915.

Collation: 8°. [*]⁴, 1-3⁸, 4⁶, 1-13⁸, 14⁴; [4] *ll.*, LIX, 214 pp., 1 *l.*

Contents: [*]1-2a blank; [*]2b woodcut portrait; [*]3a title of *Opuscula*; [*]3b blank; [*]4a half-title, *De Arte Medica. III*; [*]4b blank; p. I title in Dutch; p. II blank; pp. III-IV preface by G. van Rijnberk; pp. V-XXXV introduction (plate of *Smilax China* from Burman's *Actuarium* inserted be- tween XXX and XXXI), and pp. XXXVI-LIX biographical notes by E. C. van Leersum; pp. 1-190 letter to Roelants in Dutch; p. 191 explanation to Roelants; pp. 192-194 regimen in Dutch (*Voor- schrift voor het innemen van afkooksel van chynawortel*); pp. 195-214 index to this vol. and also to corres- ponding pp. in original edition; last, unnumbered leaf errata.

Copy used: H.C.

We now come to a separate consideration of the anonymous *Italicum scriptum* added to the Epistle as an appendix of four pages which begins with a prefatory note in Latin by Vesalius as follows:

"It happened more than once, most learned Joachim, when speaking in my letters to you of the manner of administering and preparing a decoction of the China-root, that I mentioned a certain Italian work, which has been sent also to various (physicians) in our court; I now give it also to you in transcription, so that you may know what we have on hand regarding this new and already celebrated remedy. Although I would rather have translated it into Latin, for the sake of (our) friends, I send it to you in Italian, just as I have received it, as I know that you are not ignorant of this language; also in order that you might weigh more exactly and accurately the mind of the author—whosoever this empiricist may be—and that you might judge that I have satisfied your desire (for information). I can hardly have any doubt that it was translated from Span- ish, since we have on hand also a Spanish prescription, together with the method of decocting and preparing the worthless Sparta parilla. However, the Spanish description is much shorter than the Italian, rather mutilated, and in some places violates the rules of art."

It will have been gathered from the citations of the preceding eight items under Section VII that the appended script was looked upon as important, for it was included in all reissues of the Epistle. In VII.2, it again appears in Italian; in VII.3, it has been translated into French; in VII.4, it appears in German; in VII.5, it is turned for the first time from Italian into Latin; and in VII.8, it appears in Dutch. Thus Vesalius' appendix to the Epistle has been printed in five languages, whereas the Epistle itself up to the present time has appeared only in Latin and Dutch.

While the mysterious source of the anonymous Regimen remains unknown, a French rendering was printed in 1545, the year before the Epistle to Roelants was written. It appears in an anonymous translation into French, supposedly by Jean Breche of Tours, of Galen's three books on the compounding of drugs. This slender volume (*Les troys premiers livres,* etc., see Fig. 86) was printed at Tours in 1545 by Jehan Rousset, who states in a note to the reader that a local apothecary, Thibault Lesplegny, happened in while the book was in press and when he saw that there were to be several blank pages at the end of the Galenic text, to fill them up he offered to supply the little treatise *"De la nature, vertu et faculte de la racine du Boys nouullement inuenté, appellé L'esquine: & comme il en fault vser"* which he had received from a friend.

Fortunately Rousset did not omit the subscription which contains the name of the author, Thomas Maglit of Antwerp, to whom Vesalius was possibly indebted:

"Les choses dessusdictes ont esté approuuées, & experimentées par plusieurs. Et mesmement par Thomas Maglit, qui a escript la presente ordonnance, en L'an 1539, au moys de Septembre en la ville d'Antuers, l'ayant euë de son maistre Ruys Fernandes, qui par la grande vertu de ceste eauë dessusdicte en vsant d'icelle par quarante iours, & selon la methode & ordre deuant dicte a esté guary sain & nect d'ung mal qu'il auoit a vne iambe, ou estoient plusieurs perïuys & fistules par l'espace de sept ans apres auoir vsé de tous les remeddes q̄ on a peu trouuer par toute l'Italie, & qui ny ont de rien seruy ne proffité."

From this statement Thomas Maglit, of whom nothing else is known, appears either to have been the author of the tract or to have obtained it perhaps from the same Italian (Spanish?) source that Vesalius did. At all events, Rousset's French imprint precedes by a year the Italian text printed by Oporinus for Vesalius. And if credence may be given to the statement that it was written as an official ordinance of Antwerp, it appears that even before 1539 the China root had been utilized in Italy, or in those sections of it under Spanish control.

FIGURE EIGHTY-ONE

Engraved title-page of the 1559 English Geminus with portrait of Queen Elizabeth.

ANDREAE VE
SALII BRVXELLENSIS, ME
DICI CAESAREI EPISTOLA, RATIO
nem modumq propinandi radicis Chynæ decocti,
quo nuper inuictiſſimus CAROLVS V. Imperator
uſus eſt, pertractans: & præter alia quædam, epiſto
læ cuiuſdam ad Iacobum Syluium ſententiam recen
ſens, ueritatis ac potiſſimum humanæ fabricæ ſtudi
oſis perutilem: quum qui hactenus in illa ni
mium Galeno creditum ſit, facile
commonſtret.

Acceſſit quoq locuples rerum & uerborum in
hac ipſa epiſtola memorabili
um, Index.

Cum gratia & priuilegio Imperiali
ad quinquennium.

B A S I L E Æ.

FIGURE EIGHTY-TWO

Title-page of the first edition of the China-root Epistle, issued by Robert Winter of Basel in 1546.

ANDREAE VESALII

BRVXELLENSIS, MEDICI CAESAREI
Epiſtola , rationem modumq; propinandi radicis
Chymæ decoſti, quo nuper inuictiſſimus
CAROLVS V. Imperator
uſus eſt , pertractans :

ET PRAETER ALIA QVAEDAM,
Epiſtolæ cuiuſdam ad Iacobum Syluium ſententiã
recenſens, veritatis ac potiſſimum humanæ
fabricæ ſtudioſis perutilem:quum qui
haĉtenus in illa nimiũ Galeno
creditum ſit , facile
commonſtret.

Acceſſit quoq; locuples rerum & verborum
in hac ipſa Epiſtola memorabilium , Index .

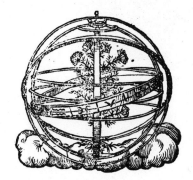

VENETIIS

FIGURE EIGHTY-THREE
Title-page of the rare second edition of the China-root Epistle issued at Venice, probably in 1546.

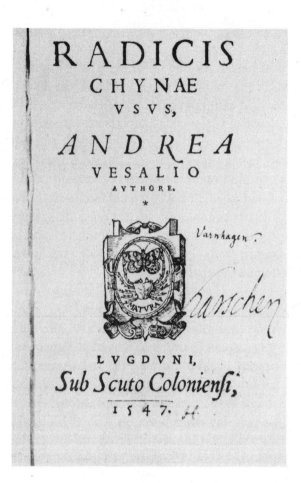

FIGURE EIGHTY-FOUR

The Frellon edition of the China-root Epistle issued in 1547.

❧ CHAPTER VIII ❧

THE 'CONSILIA'*

IN THE autobiographical note at the end of his reply to Fallopius (see Chapter IX) Vesalius states that as physician to Charles V he had followed the Emperor in his travels and campaigns. After his energetic campaign against Francis I ending in the Peace of Crépy, the Emperor had slumped into a period of indecision and irresolution attributable, no doubt, to his ill health. While the Protestant movement had been gaining strength, he had procrastinated over the summoning of a general council, which aroused the suspicions of both Protestants and Pope. The Council of Trent had been a miserable failure and Charles had reluctantly decided that if a civil war against the Smalkaldic League was inevitable, Regensburg on the upper Danube in Southern Bavaria, where he might receive military support from Spain, Italy, or both, was the only possible place from which to launch a campaign.

So with a triple purpose—military, political and religious—he summoned the Diet to meet in distant Regensburg near the terminus of the old *Limes Germanicus*; and to convince the Protestants of his peaceful intentions he had set out from Brussels with only a small guard. He arrived at Regensburg on April 10th, and by June 7th a treaty had been drawn up and signed with the Pope, who promised military aid for a period of six months, and with Duke William of Bavaria, who agreed to allow the passage of troops through his domain.

On June 13, 1546, the very day when Vesalius sent off his letter to Roelants, the Lutheran princes renounced the Council of Trent and demanded of Charles that a national council be summoned. This demand the Emperor flatly refused. If the princes of the Smalkaldic League could not agree on a compromise to settle their religious differences, he would be reluctantly obliged to take matters in his own hands and dissolve the Diet. This could have no other meaning than that the war which Luther had predicted on his deathbed was inevitable, and that Charles had succeeded in covering a religious war with a political cloak. He thereby divided his quarrelsome opponents within the League so that much of the recruiting in his behalf actually came from certain Protestant princes. Had

* The first part of this chapter had been drafted by Dr. Cushing, and it has been completed by Dr. Arturo Castiglioni. The bibliographical descriptions at the end were compiled by the editor. The date in the heading of each *consilium* is that of the MS. consultation, the dates of publication being given in the descriptions of the editions.

they combined, they might easily have overcome his small force and taken him prisoner. To gain time for Spanish and Italian reinforcements to reach him from Italy he moved to Landshut, made a night march on Ingolstadt where he encamped, and by the end of August the two armies faced each other. As in every campaign, Charles promptly recovered his energy and high spirits. Meanwhile the Count of Buren, one of the ablest commanders of his time, had marched from the Netherlands in the Emperor's support and on September 3rd the Army of the League withdrew leaving him in control of the Upper Danube.

During that winter of 1546-47 when the Emperor remained on Württemberg soil, Vesalius appears to have been in constant attendance. They were evidently at Heilbronn on the Neckar until January 18th and on the next day at Esslingen near Tübingen where occurred the following episode quoted by Roth on the authority of Martin Crusius (96; see also 1). Leonard Fuchs who at the time held the chair of anatomy at Tübingen happened on that particular day to criticise something in Vesalius' Anatomy before his students, and after the lecture a stranger came forward and asked politely, "Why have you thus censured me, have I ever offended you?" When Fuchs replied, "Are you really Vesalius?" and received an affirmative answer, friendly greetings and an invitation to dinner promptly followed [see VI.D.14 and 15].

The winter's inaction appeared to have a bad effect on the Emperor's health and at the end of February while at Ulm he had a severe attack of gout which forced him to remain at Nördlingen for the better part of March. Prior to this unfortunate episode, Vesalius early in the month had left to pay a visit at Basel. While there he kept in correspondence with the court and in one of the letters from Ulrich Zasius (376) to Boniface Amerbach still preserved at Basel Zasius says: "If our Dr. Andreas Vesalius is still there, give him the enclosed letters and tell him that from Nördlingen we are going to Nürnberg and then straight to Saxony. Let him therefore not delay his return, for otherwise it will neither be safe nor convenient to reach the Court in such a short time." Thus ordered to terminate his visit, he appears to have rejoined Charles on March 24th at Nürnberg. At about this time, the papal contingent of Charles' army, promised for only six months, was withdrawn and the Pope, using an outbreak of the plague as an excuse, had moved the Council from Trent to Bologna. Whereupon Charles took command of the army in person and with his diminishing forces made his way north and invaded Saxony which had been occupied by John Frederick. The Emperor must have felt that if he was to strike at all it was now or never, and in the early morning of April 24th, his Spanish troops crossed the river near Mühlberg, put the Saxon cavalry to rout, and took their leader, the Elector John Frederick, prisoner, the Emperor, in spite of his gout, having spent the day in the saddle personally urging on his victorious troops.

Subsequently a Diet was summoned to meet at Augsburg, where Charles arrived July 23, 1547, and where he remained until August of the next year. We first hear of Vesalius being in attendance when on November 13th he was called upon to incise the foot of the Cardinal of Trent; and there are many other stories of his operations at this period, not always successful as the Spanish surgeon Daza takes pains to point out. Nevertheless he had come to occupy an enviable position at Court; and it was at about this time that he was asked to suggest someone to act as personal physician to the King of Denmark and, as Cardan states in his autobiography, he recommended Jerome Cardan of Milan. It was not until October 1, 1548, that the Court after nearly three years' absence returned to Brussels where later in the year Vesalius was called upon to care for that valiant soldier, Count Maximilian of Buren, who had returned from England with a severe anginoid infection of the throat (53). It was a hopeless condition and Vesalius, to the astonishment of the Court, predicted the exact day of his death, the autopsy showing an extensive mediastinal abscess.

* * * *

It was customary at this time for doctors to write to other physicians seeking advice, either on request of the patient himself or in response to the wishes of relatives or the physician in charge of the case. Very often, as in the case of Vesalius, the reports concerned patients whom the consultant had not examined personally. We possess a great literature of such *"consilia"* as they were called, *i.e.,* written consultations—which were often printed many years after they were written, without the knowledge of the author, or after his death, so that their authenticity cannot be stated. They are sometimes published in collections containing writings by different consultants, and at that time they played the rôle that clinical reports play in the medical literature of today. Until the end of the Renaissance, these *consilia* were almost the only accounts that have come down to us of individual clinical cases. Only six of Vesalius' *consilia* have been preserved; but it is quite likely that he often gave such consultations. The six that have been preserved probably owe their existence to accident and to the fact that they concerned well-known personalities. No doubt many others dealing with less important personages existed but were lost or not thought worthy of publication. Five of the six *consilia* were published after Vesalius' death.

The first Vesalian *consilium* (see VIII.A) is dated from Padua, 3 May 1542,*
and is directed to Wolfgang Herwart of Augsburg, a patrician who had asked
Vesalius' advice. It concerned a young man 27 years old who was troubled with
partial loss of vision. Vesalius stated that vision had been lost in one eye and
was very weak in the other. He studied the possible origin of the disease and
gave his opinion concerning cause and treatment, following closely the usual
concept and doctrines of Galenic medicine of his time and quoting Galen, and
also Joannes Manardus the famous clinician of Ferrara, and adding some specu-
lation about the possible influence of different foods on the disease. Part of the
prescription, such as the blood of an old pigeon which was to be instilled in the
eye, harks back to the fantastic polypharmacy of the day. The direction concerning the use of different balsams and ointments brings out nothing original, and
is likewise in keeping with the pharmacology of the time. Supposing that the
visual disturbance was due to a cataract, Vesalius declared himself ready to
perform an operation if a skilled specialist should not be available.

The short *consilium* for Marcus Pfister (see VIII.B) dated from Brussels,
6 November 1553, exists only in a manuscript copy in the University Library of
Basel. Pfister was probably a patrician of Augsburg for whom Montanus had
given a *consilium* in 1550, published in his *Consultationes medicæ*. It is a brief letter
which concerns the possibility of using China-root to improve Pfister's health.
However, there is no hint on a diagnosis of the disease. It seems clear that this is
the case of which Montanus speaks. In this *consilium* Vesalius quotes the China-
root Epistle saying that he had there explained sufficiently the way to use it and
the favourable result he had observed.

The third of the *consilia* (see VIII.C) concerns an important personality,
Don Carlos of Aragon, Duke of Terranova, a kinsman of the royal house of
Spain. Giovanni Filippo Ingrassia, a famous anatomist and clinician, who was
at this time "protomedicus" (chief of the health department) of Sicily, had been
called to cure the patient who at a tournament at Palermo had received a broken
fifth rib and a penetrating wound of the left chest which left a suppurating fistula
of the thorax. Ingrassia wrote to the brother of the patient, Don José of Aragon,
on his request, an extensive report about the case; this was shown to Vesalius,
who was asked to express his opinion and addressed his letter to Ingrassia as the
physician in charge. Ingrassia opposed operative intervention. Vesalius, however, said that his experience would lead him to favour an operation in such

* Place of publication of the various *consilia* and other bibliographical details are given at the end of
the chapter.

cases and that he would advise operation for the Duke. He related in his letter the classic operation for empyema which, according to a quotation of Marcellus Donatus (Bk. III, Chap. 9), had been described first by Valescus in 1418; but Vesalius was probably the first who often practised it personally. Other surgeons were not so favourably disposed to this operation, such as the Spanish surgeon, Dionisio Daza Chacon, who frequently criticised Vesalius as an operator and had attended an operation for empyema by Vesalius at Augsburg in 1547. He stated that the loss of blood had been very conspicuous, but that no pus had come out of the pleural cavity. The patient died some days later. The description of the operation on animals as given by Vesalius in the *Fabrica* (1543, Bk. VII, Ch. 19) offers clear proof that he was well acquainted with the dangers of the operation and with the possibility of injury to the intercostal vessels. Vesalius had written: "But in order that this may be more plainly seen, I free more rib bones from their cartilages, opening this side of the thorax as much as possible, in order that, through the membranes that partition the thorax, the other lung, which, in the as yet uninjured cavity of the thorax, is moving nicely with the thorax, may conveniently present itself to view; and then, those membranes also being pierced, the lung on this side may also be seen to collapse and fall in, in consequence of the perforation. Then, on the other side also, in one cut with a sharp knife I free the rib bones from the cartilages, and I cut away the diaphragm from the cartilages and breast-bone, to enable that bone, together with the cartilages, when the membranes that partition the thorax have been torn apart, to be bent up and back towards the neck, and the envelope of the heart to be brought into view." [See VI.A.7, p. 95]

In the *consilium* to Ingrassia, Vesalius gives a clear description of the opera-tion. He says that he is accustomed to intervene as soon as the patient complains of pain in the region of the diaphragm and when dyspnœa appears. On the upper edge of the tenth rib he advises that an incision be made down to the bone, cautiously opening the thoracic cavity and exploring with the finger. After the issue of blood and pus he usually puts a unguent in the wound. He asserts that this incision cannot hurt any important part, neither the diaphragm nor the vessels lying at the lower edge of the ninth rib. The lung is also not in danger because it is small and flaccid on account of the air which has penetrated it. In certain rare cases in which there is adherence of the lung to the pleura, he separates it from the diaphragm and pleura with the finger. It is remarkable to see how well Vesalius explained the fact that the seat of the external wound did not correspond to the seat of the empyema in this case. He observes that the lifting movement of the left shoulder which occurs in jousting may have caused a temporary displacement of the relative position of arm and chest. He quotes four cases in which he had recently performed this same operation in Madrid, three times in consequence of penetrating wounds and once in a case of spontaneous empyema. Only one case of the first group ended fatally; the three others recovered. In one case where the scapula was perforated by the weapon, an abscess formed behind it; this had been successfully operated upon by another approach.

Roth (345) observes correctly that if this *consilium* of Vesalius is compared with the others, and especially with that of Eustachius about the same case, one can surely assert that Vesalius was a most expert surgeon, and the only one who had opportunity to practise this operation and to speak authoritatively on the basis of the results of his own wide experience. At the beginning of the *consilium* he writes that it is quite possible that the illustrious patient may have recovered before the arrival of his letter, and then his advice is useless; however, if the condition should be worse and the symptoms more alarming, the operation is advisable. In this *consilium* Vesalius quotes Avicenna and other classical authors, but evidently he gives the greatest importance to his own experience and to the cases which he had seen, especially the case of the Marquis of Velena who had previously been operated upon unsuccessfully by another surgeon, establishing a permanent fistula as a result. Later, he was operated upon by Vesalius and recovered perfectly. The letter is written to Ingrassia whom Vesalius knew well and with whom he was on most cordial terms, and it is interesting to note that the advice is not given to the parents or relatives of the patient (who had requested it) but is very correctly sent to the physician direct.

In a volume in which he published some little treatises concerning purgative remedies, blood-letting and several other questions, Ingrassia included his full description of the illness in the case of the Duke of Terranova. He himself was not favourable to the operation. In his book which contains the opinions of Roman physicians, among them Eustachius, with exhaustive quotations of all medical classics and gives an interesting picture of medicine of the time, we find an exhaustive description of the case and a long discussion of problems which really have nothing to do with an empyema or with a lesion of the thorax. Bartholomæus Eustachius, whom we may judge to have been an excellent anatomist (but a poor surgeon), advised against operation, and suggested treatment of the patient with laxatives, quoting two cases which had recovered following such a régime. From the answer to Vesalius written by

Ingrassia, we learn that the Duke of Terranova had recovered perfectly without operation before Vesalius' *consilium* was received.

The fourth *consilium* (D, see below) addressed to Pieter van Foreest (better known as Forestus), a Dutch physician and consultant of the Republic of Delft, concerned a young man whose name is not quoted. It is a case of nosebleed which was referred by his physician to Vesalius who evidently had never seen the patient. In this case the young man had a grave debility following the loss of blood. The advice of Vesalius concerned only the use of some oils and unguents and a very substantial nutrition and relaxation. He approved of the treatment administered by his physician. It is interesting that in the book of Forestus, after the *consilium* of Vesalius, one finds the *opinio auctoris,* the judgment of the author Forestus himself; but he does not add much beyond stating his approval of the purgatives, and advising the use of decoction of guaiac and the application of some external ointments.

The *consilium* (without date; E, see below), published in Garetius' *De arthritidis præservatione et curatione . . . consilia* in 1592, is addressed to I. D. Pratensis (Louis de Flandre, Seigneur de Praet, minister of Charles V). In this *consilium* are collected some passages of different letters of Vesalius to the same man. It is difficult, however, to pass judgment on the cases and the course of the diseases, since we do not know at what time the different letters were written. These passages appear to be accounts of operations performed by Vesalius in one or more cases of abscess. In the first he describes an incision in the foot of Granvellanus (Cardinal Granvelle, whose physician Vesalius had been) who had an ulcer and symptoms of an extensive inflammation; in the second, an incision in the arm at the inner edge of the deltoid muscle; in the third excerpt he discusses in what cases the operation should be preferred to cauterization. In the other short excerpts we find some hints about the use of different ointments and oils for the treatment of ulcerations.

The *consilium* (F, see below) published in the book of Lorenz Scholz (Frankfurt, 1598) is without date,* and we do not know for whom it was written. It seems to be rather an impersonal letter of advice about the treatment of epilepsy and tinnitus. The therapeutic advice of Vesalius corresponds to the usual medicine of the time and after a long discussion, theoretical and vague, on the origin and causes of epilepsy, and a description of the epileptic aura, the advice to use with success the decoction of guaiac wood in order to avoid the effects of the pernicious humours appears as a consequence of the general favour which

* Roth (345, p. 240) says it may have been written in 1546.

guaiac, like many other remedies imported from the New World, enjoyed at this time. Guaiac was considered the ideal remedy to purge the obnoxious humours of the body and was accepted as one of the most efficacious remedies against syphilis. What success could have been observed with the use of guaiac in epilepsy is highly problematical. In the same letter Vesalius speaks of the possibility of curing epilepsy by making a fontanel in the left leg in a case in which he supposed that the disease had its origin from an ulceration there. We would call this today a kind of shock therapy. But he does not seem to be too confident of success. The explanation of ringing in the ears as a consequence of abundance of humours in the brain and its treatment with various remedies is based on contemporary therapeutics.

VIII.A

CONSILIUM IN MONTANUS   *Padua,* 3 May 1542

Heading: Pro visv partim depravato, partim abolito, D. Andreæ Vuesalij [*sic*] Consilium, ad Vuolfgangum Heruuart Augustanum scriptum.

VIII.A.—1   *Basel,* 1572

In: Consvltationes / Medicæ / Ioannis Baptistæ Montani./ Antea qvidem/ Ioannis Cratonis Vratislaviensis/ Medici Cæsarei opera atque studio/ correctæ, emendatæ,/ adauctæ:/ Nvnc vero/ Et nouorum Consiliorum Appendice, & necessarijs/ veterum Additionibvs locupletatæ./ [woodcut portrait of Montanus]/ Cum Gratia & Priuilegio S. Cæsareæ Maiesta-/ tis peculiari ad annos sex./ M. D. LXXII.

Colophon (cols. 1023-1024): Basileæ,/ per Henricvm Petri, et Petrvm Pernam, Anno M. D. LXV.

Collation: Fol. [9] *ll.,* [256] *ll.* (1024 cols.), [35] *ll.* (138 cols.), 3 *ll.*

Note: This, the earliest of the Vesalian *consilia,* dated from Padua, May 3, 1542, occurs in cols. 129-138 (wrongly numb. 137) of the Appendix, and is fully described in the text above. In a note to the reader immediately above the heading, the printer states that when he discovered the *consilium* among the writings of Montanus, he wished to communicate it to students. Montanus was born at Verona in 1498 and had flourished at Padua as professor of medicine until his death in 1551. The *Consultationes* were brought out posthumously by Johann Crato of Vienna as a handsome folio which passed through at least two editions, both of which contained the Vesalian *consilium* in the Appendix. As with all the *consilia,* the full text has been reprinted by Roth (345).

The Vesalian *consilium* does not occur in Montanus' *Consultationum medicinalium centuria prima* of 1554, 1556 or 1557. In view of the date of the colophon (1565), it is probable that an earlier edition exists. So far, none has been traced.

Copy used: H.C., a gift from H. M. Evans, February 16, 1930.

VIII.A.—2   [*Basel*] 1583

In: Consvltationes / medicæ / Ioannis Baptistæ Montani/ Veronensis/ Olim quidem Ioannis Cratonis Vratislauiensis/ Medici Cæsarei opera atque studio / correctæ, ampliatæque: / Nvnc verò / Post secundæ Editionis Appendicem & Additiones.../ Cum Priuilegio Cæsareo, ad annos sex./ M D XXCIII.

Colophon: none.

Collation: [10] *ll.,* [256] *ll.* (1120 cols.), [14] *ll.,* [35] *ll.* (140 cols.), 1 *l.*

Note: This is virtually a page-for-page (1120 cols. instead of 1124) reprint of the 1572 edition with type entirely reset. The Vesalian *consilium* occurs in cols. 129-135 of the Appendix.

Copy used: H.C., bought for $50 from Voynich; bears the autograph of William Ernest Scheffer (1590-1665).

VIII.A.—3   *Berlin,* 1892

In: Roth (345): pp. 388-396.

Kurtzer außzug vnd

Summarischer bericht der Natur/

eygenschafft vñ wunderbarlichen wirckung/sampt rech=
tem eygentlichen gebrauch/der frembden/new erfund=
nen Medicin/der Wurtzel China genant/ein nützliche/
krefftige Artzney / für vilfeltige schwere/innerliche vnd
eusserliche leipliche gebrechen/ so auch zum theil für vn=
heylbar geachtet werden / inn sonderheit aber für aller
handt Flüß/vnd mancherley schedliche gebrechen
daruon verursacht/eusserlicher vnnd inner=
licher glyder/Als Podagram/ Zipper=
le/ Lemnuß/Lungen sucht/Leber
vnd Miltz sucht/vñ dergleichen
vil andere schwere zufel
vnd gebrechen.

Solcher maß vnd gestalt geordnet vnnd ge=
stellet/wie dise new erfundne Artzney nechst verschiener Jar /von
Römischre Kayf. Mayest.selbst aigner person gebraucht/
nützlich vnd heylsam befunden worden.

Zu sonderlicher tröstlicher hilff deren / so
mit mancherley langwirigen Kranckheiten vnd leip=
lichen gebrechen beladen seindt.

Aus Latinischer vnd Tuscanischer sprach transfferirt. Durch

D. GVALTHERVM H. RIVIVM
Medicum & Chirurgum.&c.

Würtzburg.   M. D. xlviij.

FIGURE EIGHTY-FIVE

Title-page of Ryff's fragmentary translation of the China-root Epistle.

LES TROYS
PREMIERS LIVRES
DE CLAVDE GALIEN
DE LA COMPOSITION
DES MEDICAMENS
EN GENERAL.

❧ Redigez en Epitome, ou abregé du Grec en langage Françoys, au proffit & commodité de touts Chirurgiens, & Apothicaires.

❧ Brief traicté des Poids & mesures pour l'intelligence dudict œuure.

❧ Aultre petit traicté du Boys de L'esquine, & la maniere d'en preparer le breuaige, & d'user d'iceluy.

IMPRIME A TOVRS,
PAR IEHAN
ROVSSET.

M. D. XLV.

FIGURE EIGHTY-SIX

Title-page of tract containing Rousset's regimen for China-root, 1545.

VIII.—B

CONSILIUM FOR PFISTER [*?Brussels*] 6 Nov. 1553

Heading [from Montanus]: De debilitate ventriculo, pro M. Pfister Augustano.

Note: An early manuscript copy of this brief consultation, dated 6 Nov. 1553, when Vesalius was
probably in Brussels, is in the Huber Collection at
the University Library in Basel (Roth, [345], p.
238, footnote 6). This manuscript has been transcribed in full by Roth (p. 397), and Montanus
describes the case in a separate *consilium* in his *Consultationes* of 1572 (VIII.A.1; *consilium* No. 197,
cols. 483-486) and of 1583 (VIII.A.2, cols. 487-
490). The patient probably was one Marcus Pfister,
in 1548 Mayor of Augsburg, who died in 1561.

VIII.B—1 *Berlin,* 1892
In: Roth (345): p. 397.

VIII.—C

CONSILIUM TO INGRASSIA *Madrid,* 1562

Heading: Pro Magni, et illvstr. Terrænovæ Ducis fistula, ex leui axilla in thoracis
concauum peruia, & aliis grauibus non paucis affectibus, ob puris supra
septum transuersum coaceruationem, & ineptam per fistulam expurga-
tionem, subinde prouenientibus.

VIII.C.—1 *Venice,* 1568

In: Ioannis Philippi Ingrassiæ/.../ Qvæstio De
purgatione per medicamentum, atque obiter etiam/
De sanguinis missione, An Sexta morbi die fieri
possint. . . . / Venetiis sumptibus Angeli Patessij
Bibliopolæ Neapolitani./ M D LXVIII. Cum Il-
lustrissimi Senatus Veneti Priuilegijs.

Collation: 4°. 4 *ll.*, 68 pp.; 101 pp.; 1 *l.*, 112 pp.;
50 pp., 1 *l.*

Note: In addition to the "consilium pro fistula"
(pp. 92-98), this volume contains the letter (pp. 99-
101) of Ingrassia to Vesalius, dated Palermo, 1563.
The Vesalian *consilium* is dated at the end: "Madriti,
feriis Nataliciis. 1562." For particulars of Ingrassia,
see text above.

Copy used: H.C., obtained from Voynich for $50.
Lier offered a copy in 1929 for Swiss frs. 200. Evidently a very rare book.

VIII.C.—2 *Berlin,* 1892
In: Roth (345): pp. 398-405.

VIII.—D

CONSILIUM TO FORESTUS n.p. [*c.* 1556]

Heading: Consilium Vesalij, medici Imperatoris excellentissimi [on a case of
epistaxis].

VIII.D.—1 *Leyden,* 1590

In: Observationvm/ et cvrationvm/ medicinalivm/
libri tres:/ Nempe Octavvs De exterioribus vitiis &/
morbis cutaneis Capitis: Nonvs De variis/ Capitis
doloribus: Decimvs De vniuersis/ ac cerebri & men-
ingum eiusdem Symptoma-/tis ac morbis./.../
D. Petro Foresto Alcmariano / . . . Auctore. /
Lvgdvni Batavorvm,/ Ex Officina Plantiniana,/
Apud Franciscum Raphelengium,/ M. D. XC.

Collation: 8°. [12] *ll.*, 90 pp., 2 *ll.*; 323 pp., [9] *ll.*;
919 pp., [3] *ll.*

Note: The Preface is dated 'Ex Lycæo Batauiensi
Lugoduno [*sic*] Anno M. D. XC,' so this is evidently the first edition. There are three separate
paginations for books 8, 9 and 10 (Bks. 1-7 by
Forestus had been issued previously), the bulk of the
text being taken up with Bk. 10 on diseases of the
head (pp. 1-919) in which Vesalius' *consilium* on a

case of epistaxis occurs on pp. 694-696 with comments on pp. 696-700.

Pieter van Foreest (1522-1597) of Alkmaar was an encyclopædic Dutch physician whose five-year sojourn in Italy as a student had coincided with that of Vesalius to whom he had attached himself for several years at Padua. Foreest had wide interests, among others botany, and he brought back from Italy to Holland a large number of medicinal plants. His voluminous *Observationes et Curationes* series which he began to publish at Leyden in 1588 had extended at the time of his death to some 32 books. He usually issued three or four books at a time. On van Foreest's tomb in the church at Alkmaar is the following apt chronogram of the year of his death, 1597:

> eVICtVs fato CVbat haC sVb
> MoLe forestVs: hIppoCrates
> bataVIs sI fVIt, ILLe fVIt.

Copy used: H.C., from Taeuber & Weil, 1928, for RM. 120.

VIII.D.—2   *Frankfurt,* 1602

In: Observationum et curationum medicinalium, sive Medicinæ Theoricæ et Practicæ. Libri XXVIII. Francofurti, e Paltheniana officina, 1602.

Note: This large folio contains the first 28 books of van Foreest's series. The Vesalian *consilium* is in Bk. X, obs. 97. In addition to appearing here, Vesalius' *consilium* also is reprinted in van Foreest's *Opera omnia*, of which there were many editions, the first being published at Frankfurt in 1619 [5 pts., 1 vol., 1609-1614]; also Frankfurt, 1623 and 1634, Rouen, 1653, and Frankfurt, 1660.

Copy (not seen): DSG.

VIII.D.—3   *Berlin,* 1892

In: Roth (345): pp. 405-406.

VIII.D.—4   Latin & Dutch   *Amsterdam,* 1935

In: Opuscula selecta Neerlandicorum de arte medica. Fasciculus 13, quem curatores miscellaneorum quæ vocantur Nederlandsch Tijdschrift voor Geneeskunde collegerunt et ediderunt. Amstelodami, 1935.

Note: In this volume of *Consultationes medicæ,* edited by M. A. van Andel, the "Consilium Vesalii ad Petrum Forestum" occupies pp. 9-15, with translation into Dutch, biographical note in English, and portraits of Vesalius and Forestus.

Copy used: J.F.F.

VIII.—E

CONSILIUM IN GARETIUS   *Augsburg* [n.d.]

Heading: Ex literis Andreæ Vesalii ad I. D. Pratensem [De arthritide consilia quædam].

VIII.E.—1   *Frankfurt,* 1592

In: De Arthritidis/ Præserva-/ tione et Cvratione,/ clarorvm Doctissimo-/ rvmqve nostræ ætatis/ medicorum,/ Consilia./ . . ./ Opera et stvdio/ Henrici Garetii Lovani-/ ensis, . . ./ Francofvrti/ Apud Ioannem Wechelum & Petrum/ Fischerum consortes,/ M D XCII.

Collation: 8°. [8] *ll.,* 128 pp.

Note: The extracts from the various Vesalian letters are found on pp. 122-125; unfortunately they are all

undated. Henri Garet (d. 1602), a native of Louvain, received his medical degree from Padua in 1558 after which he returned to the Low Countries and practised for many years in Brussels. The above compilation on gout is his only published work.

Copy used: H.C., from Taeuber and Weil, 1928, RM. 126.

VIII.E.—2   *Berlin,* 1892

In: Roth (345): pp. 406-409.

VIII.—F

CONSILIUM IN SCHOLTZ   n.p., n.d.

Heading: In epilepsia, deque Ligni Guaiaci vsu in hac affectione: Item, de Tinnitu aurium, D. Andreæ Vesalii.

VIII.F.—1 *Frankfurt,* 1598

In: Consiliorvm / Medicina⸣ / livm, / conscri⸣ / ptorvm / à / Præstantiss. atque Exercitatiss. nostro⸣ rum / temporum Medicis, / Liber Singvlaris. / . . . / Nunc primum studio & opera / Lavrentii Scholzii à Rosenaw Med. Vratisl. / hoc modo in lucem editus. / [device] / Francofvrti ad Mœnvm, apvd / Andreæ Wecheli Hæredes, . . . / M. D. IIC.

Collation: Fol. [34] *ll.,* 1164 cols., [9] *ll.*

Note: The Vesalian *consilia* (Nos. 40 and 41) are found in cols. 109⸣119. Lorenz Scholtz von Rosenau (1552⸣1599), Silesian botanist and physician, flour⸣ ished after Vesalius had died. He does not record to whom the two *consilia* were addressed. Roth believes them to have been written prior to 1546.

Copy used: H.C., bought from Taeuber & Weil, November 22, 1928, for RM. 165.

VIII.F.—2 *Hanau,* 1610

In: Consiliorvm / medicina⸣ / livm, conscri⸣ / ptorvm / . . . / Liber singvlaris / . . . / Hanoviæ / Typis Wechelianis apud hære⸣ / des Ioannis Aubrii. / [rule] / M DC. X. / Cum priuilegio Cæsa. Maiest. ad annos Decem.

Collation: identical with VIII.F.1.

Note: The book has been reset throughout with minor variations in typography, printer's ornaments, etc., and the errata on Ddd5a of the 1598 ed. have been omitted. The long *consilium* (No. 40) occurs as in VIII.F.1 in cols. 109⸣117; the short one (No. 41) in cols. 117⸣119.

Copies used: Bodleian (examined by Dr. Cushing in 1913); DSG.

VIII.F.—3 *Berlin,* 1892

In: Roth (345): pp. 409⸣419.

CHAPTER IX

FALLOPIUS AND VESALIUS

By Arturo Castiglioni, M.D.

GABRIELE FALLOPPIO* was born in 1523 at Modena, the son of Gironi⁄mo Falloppio and Caterina de' Bergomozzi. He began to be interested very early in anatomy and in December 1544, before entering the medical school, had dissected at the College of Surgeons in Modena the corpse of a criminal who had been hanged. It appears that he began to practise surgery as a young man, but in 1545 he went to Ferrara where he was enrolled in the medical school. He stayed there until 1548, and performed dissections for the students. In 1548 the Duke of Florence, Cosimo I dei Medici, called him to teach anatomy in Pisa, giving him the chair that had been previously (1544) offered to Vesalius. He stayed in Pisa until 1551 and in September of that year he was appointed professor of anatomy, surgery and botany at the University of Padua. The chair of anatomy there had been vacant after the resignation of Realdus Columbus in 1545 and since then only obscure teachers had per⁄formed occasional dissections. The chair of botany was also vacant after the death of Francesco Bonafede.†

Fallopius was a diligent teacher, and he dissected frequently in the first years of his teaching. Later he was often ill, very likely with tuberculosis, and from the Acts of the German Nation‡ in Padua we know that he often missed the dissections. He was well known as a practitioner and people came from all parts

* The name was written in different forms: Falloppio, Fallopio, Falloppia, or Faloppio. The original form seems to have been Falloppia; Latin, Fallopius or Falloppius. The most usual Italian spelling is Falloppio. The origin of the name is illustrated by the coat of arms of the family which belonged to the nobility and it shows three *falloppe* (singular *falloppa*), which is the Italian term for a silk cocoon not perfected by the silkworm which has died inside it. In common language it means a mistake or a failure.

† The man who recommended Fallopius to the Venetian Senate was Augustinus Gadaldinus, a very learned man who had revised the edition of the works of Galen printed by the Giuntas (see Chapter V). We know that Gadaldinus was also a good friend of Vesalius, and we find his name in the printer's preface to the *Examen* of Vesalius.

‡ The *Acta Nationis Germanicæ* were for about two centuries a very diligent and exact register of the students enrolled in the German nation (not only Germans, but also Flemish, Poles and other *Transalpini*), with data about their native country, heir studies and very important notices about their life after leaving Padua. They contain also a valuable chronicle of the events of the University, and especially of the school of medicine and the teaching of anatomy, which often gave opportunity for discussions and intervention of the students with the Venetian authorities.

of Italy and from abroad in order to consult him. He was a physician and good friend of the Duchess Eleonora d'Este and of the Gonzagas, Dukes of Mantua.

In 1562, having restored the fame of the anatomical school of Padua, and being generally considered as the outstanding anatomist of his time, Fallopius died from pleurisy after a long illness. The only book unquestionably written by him is the *Observationes anatomicæ*, published in Venice in 1561 by M. A. Ulmus and dedicated, not to a prince or an influential personality as was the custom of the times, but to his friend Petrus Manna of Cremona, physician to Francesco Sforza II, Duke of Milan*. In the preface he tells that he had written the book four years earlier, on the insistence of Manna who, however, had died before its publication. The preface and dedication are very different from the verbose writings of the time. In simple language, without flattery and without exaggeration, the author states the purposes of his book. From the beginning he feels the necessity of defining his position in relation to Vesalius, justifying with candid modesty his disagreement with some of Vesalius' observations.† Thus in his preface he writes:

To Petrus Manna, physician from Cremona

"Long before writing these observations to you, most learned Manna, I determined that I never would commit to the press anything concerning an anatomical subject. This resolution of mine was caused to no small extent by my reading of that extraordinarily complete anatomical treatise of Andreas Vesalius in which, it seemed to me, nothing pertaining to a thoroughly adequate account of anything concerning the number, the measure or the consistence, kind or use of the parts, and a more true history of the human body, could be desired. . . . Hence I concluded that this divine monument of Vesalius would endure forever, and would never disappear from the mind or from the memory of posterity: and that I, or anyone else, would labour in vain, in endeavouring again to attack this thoroughly and completely administered

* The authenticity of numerous works published under the name of Fallopius, among which the *De morbo gallico* (Padua, apud L. Bertellium, 1564; 2nd ed., Venice, F. Laurentinus, 1565) was the best known, was early put in doubt by contemporaneous writers. The *Lectiones de partibus similaribus,* edited by Volcher Coiter, his most famous pupil (Nürnberg, T. Gerlach, 1575), is probably a collection of class notes. The *Opera generalia omnia* (published in 1584 by Wechel at Frankfurt, then in 1606 at Venice) is also a collection of pupils' notes. *De humani corporis anatome compendium* (Padua, apud P. Meietum, 1585) was judged by Haller the work of an *"ignarus discipulus."*

† The supposition that Fallopius had been a pupil of Vesalius is not correct. He had come to Ferrara in 1545 and to Padua later, in any case after Vesalius had left Italy. He clearly stated that he was a pupil of Vesalius in the same sense that Vesalius was a disciple of Galen, "not in the schools listening to his voice, but in the library . . . having read his writings diligently and having given them thorough consideration."

province . . . I persisted in this opinion for many years . . . until, as I gradually became more experienced in this anatomical art, and was made bolder by the authority of Vesalius himself . . . I attempted to judge whether Galen or Vesalius came nearer to the truth . . . In their most important arguments I do not deny that I observed one fact: namely, that the finest anatomist, Andreas Vesalius, as a great warrior, aroused, so to speak, by the ardour of victory and moved by its force, frequently undertakes something which neither contributes to his own glory nor satisfies the greatest dukes and emperors; in that he some-times seizes upon the words rather than the ideas of Galen, or sometimes refuses to excuse, as he should, any corrupted word, and that he often carps at and accuses Galen in a manner unbefitting an anatomist, a philosopher and so pre-eminent a physician. Nevertheless (I say) in making this judgment . . . I came to concur in the opinion of the divine Vesalius in regard to the greatest part of their contrary ideas, and I now persist in this conviction.

"In the public schools of Pisa and of Padua, where so many very famous philosophers and physicians teach and where the divine talents of many students are cultivated, I always took the side of Vesalius rather than that of Galen, and I never discovered any educated or experienced man who reproached me for this stand. To be sure (lest you deny this fact), many are found who, because of the education of our finest youth, defend Galen's part and very frequently dispute with me; but I never have discovered one of them who in the end, when his reason was almost confuted, was unwilling to confess the truth, and so did not relinquish Galen's beliefs and accede to Vesalius. However (I say), after making this decision, as my reasoning became stronger I began to ask, in regard to this art in which Hippocrates first erred, and after him Aristotle, Erasistratus, Mari-nus and Herophilus, and finally Galen, whether Vesalius alone, since he never is caught napping, surpassed not only these divine writers but Homer himself who sometimes nods (as the adage goes): or whether, on the other hand, in that anatomical volume of his, there is anything that he overlooked, related with insufficient clarity or with some error, or recounted in a way that is at variance with the actual account of the parts of the human body.

"I sweated a great deal over this undertaking for many reasons: first, because I had attempted a task very difficult in itself; second, because having sworn allegiance to the words of the master, and setting such store by his authority, I dared not overstep the barriers which he had imposed on the art; third, and most serious, because I greatly feared public censure and already seemed to hear the critics snarling at my ears. Nevertheless, I finally succeeded in overcoming all of these obstacles. I conquered the difficulty of the task with the greatest zeal and labour in countless vigils; and I assuaged my reverence for the Master, and my fear of him, by his own example. For as Vesalius himself became a disciple of Galen, not in the schools listening to his voice but in the library (because Vesalius was an absolute glutton with regard to all of Galen's writings), he was not deterred by the authority of his preceptor, but added to the art a great many things that the latter had omitted. So it is with me in the school of Vesalius because, having read his writings diligently and having given them thorough consideration, I too have attempted to aid the art. Finally . . . I have recognized clearly that these critics are to be feared no more than futile and empty shadows which, dissolving by themselves, disappear in smoke; for particularly in these controversies, there can be no other judge than man himself, and those parts which constitute the organ of the human mind. Clinging to and resting on these fundamentals, I have found certain facts, not a great many, by which this art of ours, so to speak, can be adorned with new discoveries, and can be increased a little, if pride is set aside. You must excuse me for the brevity of this book, but I am preparing a very complete work in which I shall deal with the most minute things which are connected with this art. It will be illustrated with a great number of figures concerning the anatomy of men and apes, so that Galen's assertions may be easily verified."

Fallopius' *Observationes* was considered by some as a sharp criticism and an attack on Vesalius' *Fabrica*. This judgment is surely not wholly correct; we may say that it is the first book written by a great anatomist and a diligent observer who declared himself openly to be an admirer of Vesalius, calling him "the prince of anatomists, an admirable physician, and a divine teacher," amplifying or respectfully correcting some of his assertions. Fallopius was evidently animated chiefly by the desire to publish his own discoveries and personal observations. He was ill, had to miss dissections frequently, and he was trying to protect himself against plagiarism which at this time was very common. This small book is the only document we possess of the activity of the man who may be considered as the real and dignified follower of Vesalius' teaching and who, because of illness, did not live to complete the great work on anatomy which he had projected.

It is true, as Roth observes, that Fallopius emphasized the importance of Berengarius as the reformer of anatomy; and this opinion, which cannot be considered essentially wrong, was generally accepted in Italy at that time. However, Roth's remark that the "apparently innocent statement of Fallopius which is hidden among flattery has damaged the estimation of Vesalius up to the present time" is certainly exaggerated, and we believe rather that it was Fallopius' judgment which actually enforced the authority of Vesalius. Fallopius was con-sidered by all anatomists as a great scholar of utmost diligence and honesty. If we compare the dignified and respectful tone of his observations on Vesalius with the form in which other anatomists of the time criticised one another, and Vesalius himself gave expression to his disagreement, we must recognize that modesty was one of Fallopius' characteristics. He recognized and asserted the great work done by Vesalius. He attributed to Canano the discovery of the valves of the veins, to Ingrassia the discovery of the stirrup (bone of the ear) and of the *musculus palmaris brevis*. His criticism of Vesalius was dictated in the first place by his wish to defend his own work and to show how important were his contributions to the art.

The most important disclosures of Fallopius lay in his description of the formation and growth of the bones, the discovery of the Fallopian hiatus (the opening in the petrosal bone of the greater superficial petrosal nerve), the liga-mentum teres of the uterus, and the Fallopian tubes. The description of the origin of nerves which sometimes pass together through the same cranial foramen (*Obs., ll.* 137a-138a)* may also be mentioned; the descriptions of the third nerve (*l.* 144a), the trigeminus (*ll.* 148a-152b), and of the hypoglossus (*l.* 154a), are definite improvements on those of Vesalius. The demonstration of the eye muscles and their function extends and corrects the description of Vesalius. His account of the vessels of the penis (*ll.* 190a-192b) corrects the inexactness of Vesalius' description. The anatomy of the female genital organs for the first time was expounded in a clear and correct manner, including the clitoris (*l.* 193a) and its analogy to the penis and also the hymen; and in thus correcting Vesalius (*l.* 193b) it is clear that Fallopius was right. The presence of allantois in the human fœtus was denied by Fallopius (*l.* 207a) against the assertion of Vesalius (*Fabrica*, p. 541). The ligamentum teres is correctly described by Fallopius who insisted that it was not a muscle, as Vesalius had asserted (*l.* 195a). We quote some other important observations of Fallopius. He maintained, for example (*ll.* 177b-178b), contrary to Vesalius (*Fabrica*, p. 509), that the biliary ducts do not open into the stomach and that the vena cava does not originate in the heart (*Fabrica*, pp. 275 [for 375] and 589) but in the liver (Fallopius, *ll.* 117a).

---

* All text citations, unless otherwise indicated, are from Fallopius' *Observationes anatomicæ*, Venice, M. A. Ulmus, 1561 (Fig. 87).

We may now quote several passages of Fallopius which gave rise to the controversy with Vesalius: the first concerns the discovery of the ossicles (*l. 25a et seq.*); the second deals with the discovery of the *musculus levator palpebræ superioris* (*l. 64b et seq.*); and the third has to do with the muscles of the throat (*l. 76a et seq.*). It was this last and the passage about Galen in the Preface which caused Vesalius to be accused of having used a faulty translation of Galen.

"These (ossicles) were unknown to the ancient anatomists (if we can trust their writings), and the first to discover them was Jacobus Carpensis [Berengarius] who beyond all doubt was also the first to reinstate the anatomical art which Vesalius later perfected. In the *Isagoge anatomica* and in the extensive commentaries on the anatomy of Mundinus, Carpensis made clear mention of the two ossicles. The divine Vesalius later elaborated this account and described them both very accurately; he called the one which comes first the *malleolus* and the other the *incus*, from their similarity to these objects. The third ossicle (if we are unwilling to defraud anyone of due praise) was discovered by Joannes Philippus ab Ingrassia, a Sicilian philosopher and a very learned physician, while he was publicly teaching anatomy in the Neapolitan school, and was engaged in both theoretical and practical medicine (as they say). It is evident from his published writings that this man is so skilled in all branches of our art that he can justly be considered and called a most consummate physician, as indeed he is.

"This is the way in which the third ossicle later became known: In the year of our Lord 1548, when I first began to practise at Pisa, no mention of this bone had been made either by Vesalius, who had taught anatomy at Pisa long before, or by Columbus, your fellow citizen,* who had taught the same subject there in the preceding year. At the time when I was engaged in this work, there came to me a certain student of mine, a very learned young man who (if I remember rightly) had received his doctor's degree with honours and was very distinguished, and who was related by marriage to Ingrassia (I absolutely cannot recall his name now). He advised me that Joannes Philippus had discovered a third ossicle in the tympanum and, because of its form, had given it the name of *stapes*. Incited by this to a more zealous application, I was happy to discover this ossicle and I immediately proclaimed it publicly to everybody, to their great admiration. Furthermore, I told about it in a letter to Bartholomæus Madius of sacred memory, a most learned and celebrated physician, and I also wrote about

* Realdus Columbus, like Petrus Manna, had been born in Cremona.—Ed.

it to certain friends in Rome. They wrote back that they had not heard anything about it from Columbus, who had lectured on anatomy a short while before, nor from anyone else; for aside from those mentioned previously, at that time in Italy there was no one else capable of teaching anatomy skilfully, with the single exception of Joannes Baptista Cannanus [*sic*], a most celebrated physician and anatomist. This is the true account of the way in which the discovery was made known. And although I sometimes have said that this discovery was my own, and others have asserted that it was theirs, nevertheless the glorious God knows that the discoverer was Ingrassia."

*   *   *   *

"This passage [in Oribasius] injected suspicion into my mind, and made me so diligent that I finally discovered the truth—but see the way in which it happened. In the year 1553 after the birth of Christ, on December 29th, while I was completely occupied with public anatomy here at Padua, the head of a seal, purchased at the fish market, was sent to me by Matthias Guttich, a German physician practising medicine in a very admirable manner at Venice (he is a man not only learned in the philosophical and medical disciplines and in knowledge of Latin, Greek and Hebrew, but he also surpasses anyone I have yet known in excellence at penetrating the quintessence of drugs by the power of fire, a process which is called sublimation). The seal's head was delivered by Rubertus Phinch, who was at that time my student and, so to speak, my most loving son . . . and is now physician to the Queen of Poland.

"After I had received it, I began to dissect the head, and in dissecting I observed that this animal moves each eyelid and completely uncovers the eye . . . Made more skilled by this example, I discovered a small muscle in the human eye . . . which, raising the eyelid, uncovers the eye . . . I took the greatest delight in showing this muscle at a public anatomy. And I glory in the fact that I am the first in Italy to loosen the knot of Oribasius. For in reading the anatomical work of Valverde which has recently been printed in Spanish at Rome, I find no mention of this muscle which I have made known; and by this proof I am persuaded to believe the word of the Roman anatomists . . . that this muscle has been overlooked to this day."

*   *   *   *

"Vesalius passed over the muscles of the throat with some negligence (for all of us cannot do all things). Those who have come after him, and who either have read or should have read the book of Galen and Oribasius *De dissectione musculorum* have forgotten these muscles of the throat just as if they did not exist, or at least as if Galen had completely failed to point them out. For the work of Vesalius was published before my fellow citizen, Augustinus Gadaldinus, a most learned physician, published his own Latin translation of Galen's little book *De dissectione musculorum*. Therefore, while all the anatomists who have written since the publication of Vesalius' work deserve to be censured on this account, Vesalius himself must be freed from blame in this respect."

Fallopius' *Observationes* ends with a most graceful reference to Vesalius (*ll. 221b-222b*):

"Thus, my most learned father [Petrus Manna], I have now concluded my enumeration of what, without any guidance and with no small labour, I have discovered in anatomy . . . I profoundly hope that my words will offend no one into whose hands this little book of mine may come, since I have written in it nothing capable of injuring other anatomists if they are willing to appraise my work justly and equitably . . . But if, not purposely, but rather unwittingly or unintentionally, I have inflicted a wound on the divine Vesalius, or on any other anatomist, I beg them to accept from me as an antidote the fact that I erred through imprudence; or, if I have related anything true, I accredit it all principally to Vesalius himself, because he paved the way that made possible for me the further progress which I certainly never could have achieved without his aid."

Vesalius' answer to this book (which had been sent to him from Padua through Ægidius Hertogh, a Flemish physician and pupil of Fallopius) bears evidence of his having appreciated and been flattered to see that his school in Padua, "the most praiseworthy in the whole world," was now guided by Fallopius. I believe that the preface is of first importance because it indicates that Vesalius did not regard Fallopius' book as a personal attack. On the contrary, he really considered it as an appendix to the *Fabrica*. We know that Vesalius would not have failed to give a sharp answer if he had been hurt by Fallopius' book.

Vesalius' reply to Fallopius is essentially weak since he did not have recourse to a dissecting table. Fallopius' book was an anatomical work written cautiously and was based on first-hand observation. Vesalius was at a disadvantage, and his reply came from the armchair. Roth, his indulgent biographer, acknowledged that "Vesalius did not follow his own precept of exact observation on the cadaver and, having confidence in his knowledge, underestimated his adversary." He denied the existence of the arteries of the penis and, what seems unbelievable, rejected the existence of the clitoris and its homology with the penis, preferring to accept the mistaken description of Galen rather than recognize his error. In the same way he insisted on the existence of the seventh muscle of the eye. He recognized, however, that his own description of the so-called fourth form of the skull was imaginary. He defended his assertion that the os sacrum is formed by six vertebræ but recognized the absence of the allantois in the human embryo, asserting that his error was caused by a statement of Sylvius which he had mistakenly accepted.

We do not know whether Vesalius had intended to publish his answer at the time he wrote it.* Judging from the preface of the printer, it may be supposed that he had decided to do it only after repeated requests. He had probably considered the possibility of again obtaining the chair at Padua, and this may have been the reason why his friends insisted on the publication of the answer, and why he emphasized in many passages the importance of Padua and its school. The printer explains things as follows:

The Printer to the Reader

"Before Andreas Vesalius recently left here for Jerusalem, he was greeted in my bookshop by Augustinus Gadaldinus, Andrea Marinus, and some other prominent physicians who had met there by chance. They asked him particularly whether anything had been done about his *Anatomicarum Gabrielis Falloppii observationum examen*; for he had told them that, as he had been informed by Alexandrus Baranzonus, it had been given to some Venetian ambassador, who would see that it reached Padua. Vesalius said that his *Examen* had, in fact, been given to that outstanding ornament of the Venetian Senate, the most renowned Paulus Teupulus [Tiepolo] when he left the court of King Philip. However, because of the civil wars in France and also because of the lack of a trireme, Teupulus was compelled to remain in Catalonia for many months and to come here later than he intended; but during this time, Fallopius (as they knew) had died. For this reason, Teupulus still kept the *Examen,* which could easily be obtained from him. Consequently, since some of those present greatly desired a copy, they all considered it wisest to give me the *Examen* as soon as it was received from Paulus Teupulus and to have me share it with everybody after it was printed. By using it, you will learn the amount of decoration and increase

---

* The fact that in the preface Vesalius calls his letter to Fallopius *familiaris* (intimate or personal) and that he leaves it to him to decide whether he would like to bring it to the attention of his readers so that they might compare Vesalius' own assertions with Fallopius' observations, seems to me to prove that originally the letter was considered by Vesalius as a private one.

which accrues to anatomical investigation from this writing which was com⸗ posed earlier but was long suppressed; and you will readily find out how, through a friendly comparison of the studies of those investigating this field, anatomy still can be augmented daily. Venice, 24 May, 1564."

Vesalius' introductory comments are significant:

Andreas Vesalius to Gabriel Falloppius

"It is now three days, my dearest Falloppius, since I received your anatomical observations through the kindness of Ægidius Dux,* a physician from Brussels. You can gather how greatly they pleased me, both because they were produced by you, who are considered most proficient in performing dissections on bodies, as well as in the different branches of medicine; and also because they came from that Paduan school, the most praiseworthy in the whole world where, for nearly six years, I held the same office that you now fill in it.

"You are aware of how, particularly in that place, it was my custom to increase the knowledge of the human structure; and you realize, too, that this structure is so remarkable and varied that it always presents something new to the investigator and shows distinctly some of its previously unobserved parts, together with their formerly unknown functions and uses; consequently, you certainly should not be astonished at the eagerness and joy with which I em⸗ braced your lucubrations. For I believed that I could expect only the very greatest and most noteworthy augmentation and adornment of this discipline of ours from your indefatigable zeal, which has caused you to employ the utmost diligence and all your energy in practising anatomy ever since its renaissance. Hence, neglecting everything else, I devoured all of your observations and devoted myself entirely to this unexpected reading. That this perusal has com⸗ pletely fulfilled my greatest expectation, and should thoroughly and deservedly satisfy the zeal that I myself have expended in investigating the mysteries of nature, will be evident to you from this intimate letter in which I intend to examine in a friendly manner what you have at last published. In this way you will, so to speak, again weigh your convictions in the balance and will observe many points, through the exposition of which you may instruct your disciples. Moreover, if perhaps it seems wise to you to share this writing with those who have read your observations, you will cause these people to discuss the latter more attentively and to provide themselves with a more substantial knowledge of the art. It might almost be called an appendix to my *De humani corporis fabrica*.

* Latin form of the name *Hertogh.*—Ed.

"Thus I particularly commend your purpose of offering your opinions in published books (on whatever occasion you finally may do this) for the use of all men in common. Moreover, I sincerely hope that you may long maintain this purpose in that sweet leisure of letters which is yours, and in that throng of most learned men whose studies are dear to their hearts and with whom you can daily compare the concepts of your mind. For I feel that the ornaments of our art originate in that arena from which, as a young man, I was diverted to the mechanical practice of medicine, to numerous wars and to continuous travels; and I see the accomplishment of those things whose blameless foundations I laid, in accordance with my ability and as my age and judgment then permitted. Therefore continue to embellish our common school, whose memory is always most dear to me, with the fruits of your talent and industry; and, if you are willing, weigh these remarks of mine one by one with those in the open book of your observations." [IX.1, pp. 1-2]

In answer to Fallopius' comment on the structure of the inner ear, Vesalius offers the following:

"But in your observations you say that I overlooked a certain ossicle of that organ. While I was cleaning a skull in order to prepare a skeleton, an ossicle from the ear accidentally fell down on me; I opened the auditory organ in the unprepared skull, and besides that ossicle I found a second one and I described the matter as it then appeared to me. But after I had heard that a third ossicle also had been observed, I too found it later; and perceiving that it was very small, I praised the work of the observer, Ingrassia of Sicily, and I gladly accepted the comparison of it with the stirrup of the Neapolitan horsemen. For it seems to be exceedingly similar to a stirrup and to that instrument for melting silver and gold coins which receives its name from a stirrup." [IX.1, p. 24]

The only point to which Vesalius replied in a rather irritated tone was the very mild accusation of Fallopius that he might not have correctly understood Galen; but this point also is more an answer to other critics than to Fallopius. In fact, he says: "I do not want to say how shamefully many people have behaved (and still behave) who, changing in one way or another certain words of Galen, try to prove sometimes that his judgment was in agreement with mine and with the verity of human anatomy, and sometimes in agreement with them." The only serious reproach which he makes is that Fallopius had omitted to observe the great importance of Vesalius' discoveries in the anatomy of the heart, emphasizing some errors of little consequence. But we could easily answer that Fallopius had accepted in general and with enthusiasm Vesalius' teaching, and he believed it important to accentuate his own original contribution to this problem.

Valverde, whom Fallopius had treated with a certain respect, was considered an enemy by Vesalius, which accounts for the vehemence with which he attacks him:

"Are you, pray, so greatly influenced by the authority of Valverde (who never employed a hand in dissection, who knows nothing of medicine or the primary disciplines, and who made a Spanish translation in connection with this art of ours only for dishonourable profit, and has left our common school) ... that you dispute with him as if he had actually ever bestowed earnest work on the art? The ridiculous example cited by him, or rather by his preceptor, Columbus (who, as many people know, studied anatomy under me without any books or commentaries) ... which you believe strengthens your convictions, in reality proves that your opinion is false." [IX.1, pp. 72-73]

* * * *

"I willingly confess that in dissections of healthy women I have observed nothing corresponding to what you have found outside the peritoneum, although I have dissected the abdominal muscles in several women, and especially in the one which first fell to my lot for anatomy at Paris. She was hanged by a noose, and had a most attractive figure. Her body exhibited (as I learned at the time) a notably fleshy likeness to the vessels carrying semen from the testes [*i.e.,* ovaries] into the uterus; consequently, as I still was a tyro in dissection and completely lacked the guidance of a preceptor, I wrote that I then believed those vessels were the cornua of the uterus." [IX.1, p. 145]

* * * *

"Thus I have now come to the end of your observations, which have brought me more than a little pleasure and the delightful and joyous memory of that very pleasant life which was mine while I was working on anatomy in Italy, the true nurse of genius. You will conclude that I have returned, with little benefit to you, what you communicated to me to my great profit; and I sincerely desire that, as you successively excel and surpass yourself in eliciting the mysteries of nature, you will inform me of anything new which may present itself hereafter. Meanwhile, although no opportunity to undertake a dissection can occur here (where I cannot conveniently obtain even a skull), I still promise myself that on some future favourable occasion I shall examine thoroughly that true book of ours, the human body of man himself. Moreover, I shall in turn impart to you, in order to complete the art, any additional aspects worthy of considera-tion which he will exhibit, by virtue of his own great abundance and of the singular skill of his creator. Madrid, from the Royal Court, 27 December, 1561." [IX.1, p. 171]

The two books had a strange fate, connected with the fate of their authors. Gabriel Fallopius, who was preparing a complete textbook of anatomy, and who tried to give notice in his little book of his most important discoveries and to declare that he considered himself as a true pupil and follower of Vesalius, died as a young man in 1562, one year after the publication of his book and with no knowledge of Vesalius' reaction. The most important part of the diligent work of this great anatomist, who surely would have been able to maintain and increase the fame of the Paduan school, is confined to this little book. Andreas Vesalius, who must have been glad to see his chair occupied by a man whose diligence and knowledge he freely and sincerely acknowledged, wrote him a letter which probably was not intended for publication; for had he so intended, he would have sent the text to his publisher without waiting to know whether Fallopius had received it. Only after three years, when he came to Venice on the way to Palestine, did Vesalius learn of Fallopius' death. He had not known before that Paolo Tiepolo, the ambassador of Venice to Philip II, to whom he had consigned his letter, had been compelled to remain in Spain for many months, and had been unable to carry out his commission; and when he finally arrived in Venice, Fallopius had died. The fact itself that Vesalius did not have another copy of this letter and that it was necessary to ask Tiepolo for it gives added evidence that he did not intend to publish it.

Vesalius, however, was not able to see his last work in print because he had died alone and unknown in Zante before the publication of the book. Fallopius' book had been his last message and his open acknowledgment of Vesalius' work; Vesalius' answer had been the final proof of his deep attachment to Padua and to his school, and of his ever-present longing to return to his anatomical studies.

GABRIELIS FALLOPPII
MEDICI MVTINENSIS
OBSERVATIONES
Anatomicæ.

AD PETRVM MANNAM
medicum Cremonenſem.

Cum Priuilegio Summi Pontificis,
Regis Philippi, Senatusǿue
Veneti.

VENETIIS.
Apud Marcum Antonium Vlmum
M D LXI.

FIGURE EIGHTY-SEVEN

Title-page of Fallopius' *Observationes anatomicæ* issued in 1561 which pleased Vesalius and resulted in the *Examen* on Fallopius, Vesalius' final publication (see Fig. 88).

ANDREAE
VESALII,
ANATOMICARVM
GABRIELIS FALLOPPII
OBSERVATIONVM
EXAMEN.

CVM PRIVILEGIO.

VENETIIS,
Apud Franciscum de Franciscis, Senensem.
M D LXIIII.

FIGURE EIGHTY-EIGHT

Title-page of Dr. Cushing's copy of Vesalius' *Examen* on Fallopius, 1564, carrying
the autograph of Caspar Bauhin, dated Padua, 1577.

ANDREÆ
VESALII
ANATOMICA-
RVM GABRIELIS
FALLOPII OBSER-
uationum Exa-
men.

MAGNI, HVMANI CORPORIS
Fabricæ, Operis Appendix.

IESSENII
Curâ in publicum reducta.

HANOVIÆ
Typis Wechelianis àpud Claudium Mar-
nium & heredes Ioan. Aubrii.
M. DC. IX.

FIGURE EIGHTY-NINE

Title-page of the rare second edition, 1609, of Vesalius' letter to Fallopius.

IX.—1

COMMENT ON FALLOPIUS
Venice, 1564

Title (Fig. 88): Andreæ / Vesalii, / anatomicarvm / Gabrielis Falloppii / obser- vationvm / examen. / Cvm privilegio. / [Printer's device] / Venetiis, / Apud Franciscum de Franciscis, Senensem. / M D LXIIII.

Collation: 4°. †², A-X⁴, Y²; [2] *ll.,* 171 pp.

Contents: † 1a title; † 1b blank; † 2a-b the typographer to the reader (explaining the circumstances under which he is publishing the book), dated 24 May 1564; A1a-Y2a text, dated (on last page) Madrid, from the Royal Court, 27 December 1561.

Copies: Louvain; Budapest; London (BM); Cush- ing; PPCP; DSG; CSt-L; MnU; MiU (Crum- mer).

Copy used: H.C., purchased from Ludwig Rosen- thal, Munich, in June 1907 for M.18. Caspar Bauhin's copy ("Caspari Bauhini Basili, 1577. Patavii" on title-page and many of his notes through- out the book); measures 20.5 by 14.8 cm.

IX.—2

COMMENT ON FALLOPIUS
Hanau, 1609

Title (Fig. 89): Andreæ / Vesalii / Anatomica- / rvm Gabrielis / Fallopii obser- / uationum Exa- / men. / Magni, hvmani corporis / Fabricæ, Operis Appen- dix. / Iessenii / Curâ in publicum reducta. [Printer's device (Wechel)] / Hanoviæ / Typis Wechelianis apud Claudium Mar- / nium & heredes Ioan. Aubrii. / [rule] / M. DC. IX.

Collation: 8°. A-Q⁸, R²; 260 pp.

Contents: A1a title; A1b blank; A2a-5a Jessenius' dedication to the Bishop of Halberstadt, Duke of Brunswick and Luneburg, dated Vienna, Austria, calends of February, 1609; A5b-R2b text (same as in IX.1).

Copies: Louvain; Cushing; CaMM-Os; MiU (Pilcher).

Copy used: H.C., bought from C. E. Rappaport, Rome, March 1936, for $78. Measures 16.4 by 10.1 cm.

❧ CHAPTER X ❧

VESALIANA*

THIS section of the bibliography includes all references to general literature cited in the preceding chapters, including a few entries of a purely bibliographical character. The principal entries, however, relate to Vesalius, his copyists and followers and every attempt has been made to ensure its completeness. The compiler first went over a card index which Dr. Cushing had accumulated over a long period of years and examined the reprints and notes which Dr. Cushing had collected in preparation for this chapter. These were then supplemented from the usual bibliographical sources such as *Quarterly Cumulative Index,* and the *Index Catalogue of the Surgeon-General's Office.* It is hardly necessary to add that Roth, de Feyfer and Spielmann have been continuously consulted. During the course of the work it has sometimes seemed that each new reference led on to another; although this is an exaggeration, titles continued to accumulate up to the date of publication.

An attempt has been made to see every work cited, sometimes through microfilm and photostat copies. Those references that it was impossible to obtain are designated by an asterisk in the list below and the location of the reference indicated in parenthesis. Numbers in bold face are used for those items to be found at Yale University, in the original, in microfilm, reprint or photostat. That this chapter has suffered from the lack of the delicate touch of Dr. Cushing's precise hand will be evident to all.

We wish especially to thank Miss Madeleine Brown of the General Library of the Yale School of Medicine for her tireless assistance in running down obscure references and locating items in other libraries. To the Librarians of the General Library and Historical Library of the Yale School of Medicine, Boston Medical Library, New York Academy of Medicine, Army Medical Library, Newberry Library, John Crerar Library, University of Chicago Library, Library of the Catholic University of Washington, Columbia University Library and the Library of the Metropolitan Museum of Art we extend our grateful appreciation for their generous co-operation in lending us books and supplying microfilm and photostats.

* Compiled by Mrs. John P. Peters.

1 ADAM, Melchior. *Vitæ Germanorum medicorum: qui seculo superiori, et quod excurrit, claruerunt: congestæ et an annum usque MDCXX deductæ.* Haidelbergæ, impens. heredum J. Rosæ, 1620. 16 *ll.*, 451 [1] pp. 13 *ll.*
See pp. 129–134, 180.

2 ALBERTI, Salomon. *Historia plerarumque partium humani corporis, membratim scripta, et in usum tyronum retractatius edita.* (Vitæbergæ, exc. Hæredes J. Cratonis, 1585). 8 *ll.*, 121 [2] pp. F.VI.D.1.

3 ALVIN, Frédéric. *Les portraits en médailles des célébrités de la Belgique.* Bruxelles, G. van Oest, 1916. 106 pp.
See p. 85.

4 AMERICAN MEDICAL ASSOCIATION. *Exhibit commemorating the quatercentenary of the birth of Vesalius,* Atlantic City, June 24–26, 1914. n.p.
Arranged by Drs. Harvey Cushing and Edward C. Streeter.

5 ANALYTICAL and critical reviews. I. *Etudes sur Vésale . . .* Par Ad. Burggræve, Gand, 1841. Andreæ Vesalii *Opera omnia anat. et chirurg.* Cura H. Boerhaave et B. S. Albini. Lugd. Batav., 1725. *N. Amer. med.–chirurg. Rev.,* 1861, 5:1–53.
Review.

6 ANDRE Vésale. *Illustrirte Welt,* 1858, 87–88.
With engraving resembling Hamman portrait.

7 ANDRE Vésale. *Messager des Sciences,* 1882, 2.s., *1:* 444.

8 ANDREAS Vesalius. *J. Mo. med. Ass.,* 1915, *12:* 117–131.

9 ANDREAS Vesalius. The father of modern anatomy. *Clin. Med. Surg.,* 1931, 38:233–234. Portr.

10 ANDREAS Vesalius. *New Engl. J. Med.,* 1943, 228:840.

11 ANDREAS, Valerius. *Bibliotheca belgica: in qua Belgicæ seu Germaniæ inferioris provinciæ, urbesque viri item in Belgio vita scriptisque clari, et librorum nomenclatura.* Lovanii, apud H. Hastenium, 1623.
See pp. 147–148.

12 —— *Bibliotheca belgica de Belgis vita scriptisque claris. Præmissa topographica Belgii totius seu Germaniæ inferioris descriptione. Ed. renov. et 3a parte auctior.* Lovanii, J. Zegers, 1643. (16) 900 pp. vign. and engr.
See pp. 58–59.

13 *—— Imagines doctorum virorum e variis gentibus, elogijs brevibus illustratæ.* Antverpiæ, apud D. Martinium, 1611. (BM)

14 ANSON, Barry J. Old and rare books in the Archibald Church Library. The Fabrica of Andreas Vesalius. *Quart. Bull. Nthwest. Univ. med. Sch.,* 1938, 16:221–231.

15 ARBORSELLUS, Simon. Angelo Fortio S.P.D. n.p., n.d. 8 *ll.*
Brief mention of Vesalius as a teacher.

16 ASTRUC, Jean. *Mémoires pour servir à l'histoire de la Faculté de Médecine de Montpellier.* Paris, P. G. Cavelier, 1767. 2 *ll.*, lvi, 432 pp.
Using Astruc as part of his evidence, Roth (no. 343) says: "Nur in der *Chirurgia magna* I.8, p. 59 (no. F.X.2) ist von Vesals Studium in Montpellier die Rede."

17 ATZROTT, Georg. Andreas Vesalius aus Brüssel 1514–65. *Dtsch. med. Wschr.,* 1938, 64:21–23.

18 AUFFRET, C. Coup d'oeil sur l'histoire de l'anatomie, et spécialement sur la vie et les ouvrages des grands anatomistes des XVIe et XVIIe siècles. *Arch. Méd. navale,* 1874, 22:353–379.

19 AVALON, J. André Vésale; à propos de son quatrième centenaire. *France méd.,* 1914, 51:69–73.

20 BAASTRUP, Chr. I. Os vesalianum tarsi and fracture of tuberositas ossis metatarsi V. *Acta radiol., Stockh.,* 1922, 1:334–348, 3 pl.

21 BAIN, E. Un anatomiste au XVIe siècle: André Vésale. *Montpellier méd.,* 1908, 27:121–136; 145–160; 169–179.

22 BAKER, Frank. The two Sylviuses. An historical study. *Johns Hopk. Hosp. Bull.,* 1909, 20:329–339.

23 —— The relation of Vesalius to anatomy and anatomical illustration. *Johns Hopk. Hosp. Bull.,* 1915, 26:120.

24 BALDE, Jakob. *Medicinæ gloria per satyras XXII asserta.* Monachii, Sumptibus I. Wagneri, 1561. 4 *ll.*, 73 pp.
Pp. 41–45: "Satyra XII. Vesalij anatomici prastantissimi [*sic*] laus. Contra Atheos."

25 BALL, James Moores. The anatomical renascence. II. Andreas Vesalius (1514–1564), the greatest of anatomists. *Tri–St. med. J.,* 1897, 4:221–229. Repr. *Magazine Med.,* 1897, 3:9–16; *St. Louis med. J.,* 1897, 72:9–21.
Titles vary slightly.

26 —— *Andreas Vesalius, the reformer of anatomy.* St. Louis, Med. Science Press, 1910. xvii, 149 pp. 2 portr.

Review: The Luther of anatomy. *Brit. med. J.,* 1911, 2:383-384.

27 BALLANTYNE, J. W. The "Byrth of Mankynde" (Its author and editions). *J. Obstet. Gynæc.,* 1906, 10:297-325; 329-368. (Its contents). *Ibid.,* 1907, 12:175-194; 255-274.

28 BARATTE, L. H. André Vésale. *Un. méd.,* 1847, 1:537-538.

29 —— André Vésale. *Arch. hist. litt. N. France Belg.,* 1850, 3.s. 1:492-499.

30 BAUDRIER, H. L. *Bibliographie Lyonnaise,* ixe série. Lyons-Paris, 1912.

Pp. 13-418 biography of Guillaume Roville and list of his productions.

31 BEILIN, Adolph. Andreas Vesalius, 1514-64; father of scientific anatomy. *Hygeia, Chicago,* 1937, 15:739-740.

32 BELLELLI, F. Un cimelio di Andrea Vesalio. *Riforma med.,* 1935, 51:1109-1110.

A note on a humerus prepared by Vesalius and inscription describing it (Museo Anatomico di Napoli); portr. by Titian.

33 BENEDETTI, Alessandro. *De re medica opus . . . De omnium . . . morborum signis, causis, differentijs, indicationibus et remediis . . . lib. XXX. De medici et ægri officio aphorismorum lib. I. De pestilentiæ causis, præservatione et auxiliorum materia lib. I. Humani corporis anatome tractata lib. V. Omnia nunc . . . recognita et castigata* [a Marco Hoppero]. Basileæ, [per H. Petri, 1549]. 14 *ll.,* 623 [1] pp.

"Prefatory dedication of Marcus Hopper to Vesalius, also refers to illustrations in lieu of any attempt to copy them or have others made (see p. 577). The 1539 edition by the same printer has no Vesalian allusions."—H.C.

34 BERENGARIO, Jacopo. *Isagogæ breves, perlucidæ ac uberrimæ in anatomiam humani corporis . . .* [Bononiæ, B. Hectoris, 1523] 80 *ff.*

35 BERNARD, Auguste. *Geofroy Tory, painter and engraver: first royal printer: reformer of orthography and typography under François I. An account of his life and works,* tr. George B. Ives. Cambridge, Riverside Press, 1909. 12 *ll.,* 332 pp., 4 *ll.* [1st French ed. 1857; 2nd ed. 1865.]

Pp. 223-226, an account of C. Estienne's *De dissectione partium corporis humani,* etc. See also p. 134.

36 BIBLIOGRAFIA Vesaliana. *Bibliofilia,* 1915, 16: 443-446.

37 BIBLIOTHECA BELGICA. *Bibliographie générale des Pays Bas,* par le bibliothécaire in chef [F. van der Haeghen] et les conservateurs de la Bibliothèque de l'Université de Gand. Première série. Gand, C. Vyt, 1880-90. 27 vol.

See vol. 25 for complete list of Vesalius' works and Vesaliana.

38 BIZZARRI, Pietro. *Pannonicum bellum, sub Maximiliano II. et Solymano imperatoribus gestum: Cumque Arcis Sigethi expugnatione . . . descriptum. Unà cum Epitome illarum rerum, quæ in Europa insignoriores gestæ sunt: et præsertim de Belgarum motibus, ab anno LXIII, usque ad LXXIII.* Basileæ, per S. Henricpetri (1573). 27 *ll.,* 322 pp., 1 *l.*

"On p. 284 is supposedly the first printed account of the tragic death of Vesalius."—H.C.

39 BLOUNT, Thomas-Pope. *Censura celebriorum authorum; sive tractatus in quo varia virorum doctorum de clarissimis cujusque seculi scriptoribus judicia traduntur . . .* Londini, R. Chiswel, 1690. 4 *ll.,* 746 pp., 3 *ll.*

See pp. 478-479, including verses by J. de Rycke.

40 BLUMENBACH, Johann Friedrich. *Introductio in historiam medicinæ litterariam.* Goettingæ, apud J. C. Dieterich, 1786. xvi, 462 pp.

See pp. 120-121.

41 BOEKE, J. André Vésale comme réformateur de l'anatomie. *Janus,* 1914, 19:508-522.

42 —— Andreas Vesalius als hervormer der ontleedkunde. *Ned. Tijdschr. Geneesk.,* 1915, 1:31-45.

43 —— De platen van de Fabrica van Vesalius. *Ned. Tijdschr. Geneesk.,* 1917, 61:946. Discussie, *Ibid.,* 947.

44 BOERHAAVE, Hermann, and ALBINUS, Bernhard Siegfried. The life and work of Andreas Vesalius, translated from the Latin by Benjamin Farrington. *Trans. roy. Soc. S. Afr.,* 1930, 19:49-78.

45 *BOISSARD, J. J. *Bibliotheca chalcographica illustrium virorum, sculptoribus* J. T. de Bry, S. Furckio et J. Ammonio. Francofurti, 1650-54. 3 vol. (Brunet).

46 *—— *Icones virorum illustr. doctrina et eruditione præstantium cum eorum vitis descriptis: omnia in æs incisa artificiose* per T. de Bry. Francof., 1597-99. 4 pt. (Brunet).

See pt. 3, p. 314.

47 BONAVERA, Domenico. *Notomie di Titiano.* n.p., n.d. 17 *ff.* VI.D.9.

48 BORDEY, Pierre. [Letter to Granvelle about Vesalius' death.] Vol. 8, p. 525 in: *Papiers d'état du Cardinal de Granvelle* (no. 312).

49 *BOREL, Petrus. *Champavert. Contes immoraux* . . . Bruxelles, 1872, xxxvi, 334 pp. (BN)

50 —— Don Andréa Vésalius, l'anatomiste, in his: *Champavert,* vol. 3, pp. 111-142, *Oeuvres complètes,* Paris, 1922.

51 BORGARUCCI, Prospero. *Andreæ Vessalii Chirurgia magna in septem libros digesta.* Venetiis, ex off. Valgrisiana, 1568. 475 [40] pp. (See Appendix, p. 217).

52 BORN, Charles. *Vesalius, reformer and martyr of science; a historical sketch.* Cincinnati, O., The Author, 1907. 2 *ll.,* 227 pp.

53 BRANTÔME, Pierre de Bourdeille, *seigneur de. Memoires contenans les vies des hommes illustres et des grands capitaines estrangers de son temps.* Leyde, J. Sambix, le jeune, 1666.
Vol. 1, p. 269, illness of Le Comte de Buren attended by Vesalius.

54 BRISSOT, Pierre. *Apologetica disceptatio, qua docetur per quæ loca sanguis mitti debeat in viscerum inflammationibus, præsertim in pleuritide.* Parisiis, Ex officina S. Colinæi, 1525. 68 *ll.*

55 BROECK, Edouard vanden. Jetons de présence de la Société de Médecine de Bruxelles. *Rev. Belge Numismat.,* 1900, 56:428-440.
Description and illustrations of the two medallions by Merlen (Spielman, 1, 2), one each in the collection of Mme. Soehne the only ones known.

56 BROECKX, Corneille. *Essai sur l'histoire de la médecine belge, avant le XIXe siècle.* Gand, Leroux, 1837. 2 *ll.,* viii, 322 [2] pp.
Pp. 20-21, Vesalius' family; pp. 56-57, life of Vesalius; pp. 317-318, list of his works; portr.

57 BROEK, A. J. P. van. Iets over de verhouding van de ontleedkunde van Vesalius tot die van Leonardo. *Ned. Tijdschr. Geneesk.,* 1915, 59:74-85.

58 BRUNFELS, Otto. *Herbarum vivæ Eicones ad naturæ imitationem, summa cum diligentia et artificio effigiatæ, una cum effectibus earundem, in gratiam veteris illius, et iamiam renascentis herbariæ medicinæ* . . . Argentorati, apud J. Schottum, 1532. 4 *ll.,* 266 pp., 32 *ll.,* 313 [1] pp., 3 *ll.,* 240 pp., 2 *ll.*

59 BRUSCH, Caspar. *In divorum Caroli V. et Ferdinandi regis fratrum gratiam et honorem schediasmata quædam encomiastica et fatidica.* (Augustæ in Rhætis, Apud P. Ulhardum, 1550). 10 *ll.*

On leaf C3 the poem: "De poculo Cæsareo et vitreo quod Bruschio dedit Andreas Vesalius Medicus Imperatorius."

60 BULLART, Isaac. *Académie des sciences et des arts, contenant les vies, et les éloges historiques des hommes illustres* . . . Amsterdam, D. Elzevier, 1682. 2 vol.
See vol. 2, pp. 86-88, portr.

61 *BURGGRAEVE, A. *Précis de l'histoire de l'anatomie, comprenant l'examen comparatif des ouvrages des principaux anatomistes anciens et modernes.* Gand, 1840. (BNed)

62 —— Etudes sur André Vésale, précédées d'une notice historique sur sa vie et ses écrits. Gand, C. Annoot-Braeckman, 1841. xxxiii, 439 pp. Reprinted in part as vol. 1, of his: *Oeuvres médico-chirurgicales.* Paris, 1862.

63 —— Vésale, vol. 3, pp. 43-65 in: *Les Belges illustres* (Panthéon national). Bruxelles, 1845.

64 —— Eloge de Vésale. *Mém. Acad. R. Méd. Belg.,* 1848, 1:90-101, portr.

65 CABANES, A. Deux consultations de Vésale: Charles-Quint, Henri II. *Gaz. méd. Paris,* 1912, 83:184-185.

65a —— Les légendes sur Vésale. *Chron. méd.,* 1914, 21:265-266.

65b CAIUS, John. *De canibus britannicis, liber unus: De rariorum animalium et stirpium historia, liber unus; De libris propriis, liber unus.* Londini, per G. Seresium, 1570. 1 *l.,* 13 *ff.,* 2 *ll.;* 1 *l.,* 30 *ff.,* 1 *l.;* 1 *l.,* 31 *ff.,* 4 *ll.*
See *f.* 6 of *De libris propriis* for reference to Vesalius; see also no. 159.

66 CANANO, Giovanni Battista. *Musculorum humani corporis picturata dissectio.* [Ferrara, n.p., 1541?] 20 *ll.*
See also Facsimile edition, annotated by Harvey Cushing and Edward C. Streeter. Florence, 1925.

67 *CAPOA, Leonardo di. *Parere divisato in otto ragionamenti, ne' quali partitamente narrandosi l'origine, e'l progresso della medicina* . . . Napoli, A. Bulison, 1681. 3 *ll.,* 658 pp., 11 *ll.*
Del Gaizo (no. 154) quotes *Il Parere,* vol. 1, pp. 35-37, BM also lists 2nd ed. 1689 in 2 pts.; 3d ed. 1714 in 3 vol.

68 CARBONELLI, Giovanni. *Bibliographia medica typographica pedemontana* . . . *sæc. XV & XVI.* Romæ, Fieramosca Centenari, 1914. 4 *ll.,* 436 pp.
P. 290, title-page and collation of POZZI, F. (no. 324).
P. 389, title-page and collation of Epistola docens, 1544 (no. IV.2).

69 CARDANO, Girolamo. *Contradicentium medicorum liber, continens contradictiones centum octo.* Venetiis, apud H. Scotum, 1545. 8 *ll.*, 188 *ff.*, 3 *ll.*

70 —— *Libelli quinque . . . I. De supplemento almanach . . . V. De exemplis centum geniturarum. Additis insuper Tabulis . . . Eiusdem, antea non edita, Aphorismorum astronomicorum segmenta VII.* Norimbergæ, apud J. Petreium, 1547. 4 *ll.*, 309 *ff.*, 1 *l.*
　Horoscope xciii, Vesalius (*f.* 178). Also in his *Opera omnia,* ed. C. Spon, Lyons, J.A.Huguetan, etc., 1663. 10 vol.

71 CARTIER, Alfred. *Bibliographie des éditions des ae Tournes imprimeurs Lyonnais. Mise en ordre avec une introduction et des appendices* par Marius Audin *et une notice biographique* par E. Vial. Paris, Editions des Bibliothèques Nationales de France, 1937-38. 2 vol.
　Paraphrasis (no. I.4) no. 208, p. 318.
　Fabrica (no.VI.A.2) no. 235, p. 339.

72 CASTELLAN, Pierre. *Vitæ illustrium medicorum qui toto orbe, ad hæc usque tempora floruerunt.* Antverpiæ, Apud G. à Tongris, 1618. 255 [1] pp., 4 *ll.*
　See pp. 195-201.

73 CASTIGLIONI, Arturo. *The renaissance of medicine in Italy. Hideyo Noguchi Lecture. Publ. Inst. Hist. Med., Third Series, Volume I.* Baltimore, Johns Hopkins Press, 1934. xiv, 91 pp.

74 —— Andreas Vesalius and the "Fabrica" 1543-1943. *J. Amer. med. Ass.,* 1943, 121:582-584.

75 —— Three pathfinders of science in the Renaissance. *Bull. med. Libr. Ass.,* 1943, 31:203-207.

76 *CATTI, Francesco Antonio. *Anatomes enchiridion, partes corporis humani brevi ordine mire explicens.* Neapoli, M. Cancer, 1552. sign. A-F.　　(BN)
　Contains epigram by Federigo Pizzimenti with mention of Vesalius.

77 CHADWICK, Alice. Vesalius. *Med. Pickw.,* 1915, 1: 137-139, portr.

78 CHAIGNEAU, Gérard. *L'illustration anatomique dans l'oeuvre d'André Vésale.* Angers, 1935. 92 pp. Thèse de Paris.
　Contains list of Vesalius' works.

79 CHOULANT, Ludwig. *Handbuch der Bücherkunde für die ältere Medicin zur Kenntniss der griechischen, lateinischen und arabischen Schriften im ärztlichen Fache und zur bibliographischen Unterscheidung ihrer verschiedenen Ausgaben, Uebersetzungen und Erläuterungen. Zweite durchaus umgearbeitete und stark vermehrte Auflage.* Leipzig, L. Voss, 1841. xxii, 434 [2] pp.

80 —— *Geschichte und Bibliographie der anatomischen Abbildung nach ihrer Beziehung auf anatomische Wissenschaft und bildende Kunst.* Leipzig, R. Weigel, 1852. 8 *ll.*, xvi, 203 pp. Translated and edited by Mortimer Frank, Chicago, 1920.

CLUSIUS, see no. 248.

81 COLLECTION *depuis André Vésal, jusqu'à nos jours des plus belles pieces d'anatomie du corps de l'homme et de la femme. D'après les meilleurs auteurs colorée d'après nature avec l'explication des os, des muscles, des vaisseaux et artere* [sic]. En 4 cahiers de six feuilles chaque. Paris, Mondhare et Jean, 1792. 23 pl.

82 COLUMBUS and Vesalius—the age of discoveries. *J. Amer. med. Ass.,* 1915, 64: 248-249.

83 CONNOR, P. S. Vesalius. An introductory lecture before the class of the Medical College of Ohio. *Clinic, Cincinnati,* 1873, 4: 121-124.

84 CORIAT, Isador H. Vesalius and Louvain. *Bost. med. surg. J.,* 1918, 178:210.

85 *CORRADI, A. *Memorie e documenti per la storia dell'Università di Pavia.* 1878.　　(From no. 344)

86 CORSINI, Andrea. *Andrea Vesalio nello studio di Pisa.* Siena, Tipografico S. Bernardino, 1915. 21 pp.

87 —— Nuovi documenti riguardanti Andrea Vesalio e Realdo Colombo nello studio pisano. *Riv. Stor. crit. Sci. med. nat.,* 1918, 9:507-512.

88 CRATO VON KRAFFTHEIM, Johann. *Consiliorum et epistolarum medicinalium liber tertius; nunc primùm labore L. Scholzio in lucem editus.* Francofurti, apud A. Wecheli hæredes, 1592.
　See pp. 301, 304.

89 *CRŒSELIUS, Joannes. *Elogia in duas divisa partes, quorum prior jam inde Constantino illo Magno, imperatorum, regum, ducum aliorumque insignium Heroum . . . encomia complectitur; posterior eos collaudat, qui eruditionis laude et publicatis literarum monumentis vel olim claruerunt vel etiam clarescunt.* Ingolstadii, 1584.　　(BM)
　See Pt. 2, p. 447.

90 CRUMMER, LeRoy. Early anatomical fugitive sheets. *Ann. med. Hist.,* 1923, 5:189-209.

91 —— Further information on early anatomical fugitive sheets. *Ann. med. Hist.,* 1925, 1:1-5.

92 —— The copper plates in Raynalde and Geminus. *Proc. R. Soc. Med.,* 1926, 20:53-56.

93 —— An original drawing of the title-page of Vesalius' Fabrica. *Ann. med. Hist.,* 1930, 2(n.s.): 20-30.

94 —— A check list of anatomical books illus- trated with cuts with superimposed flaps. *Bull. med. Libr. Ass.,* 1932, *20* (n.s.):131-139.

95 —— and SAUNDERS, J. B. deC. M. The ana- tomical compendium of Loys Vassé (1540) *Ann. med. Hist.,* 1939 (3rd s.) *1*:351-369.

96 *CRUSIUS, Martinus. *Annales Suevici, sive chron- ica rerum gestarum . . . Suevicæ gentis . . . adjunctis cæteræ quoque Germaniæ ac vicinarum provinciarum ad nostra usque tempora memorabilibus rebus . . .* Francofurti, 1595-96.   (BM)
    See pp. 724, 728. There is also a German edition, 1733.

97 CULLEN, George Matheson. Andreas Vesalius. *Dublin J. med. Sci.,* 1894, 97:219-231; 296-307; 403-416; 497-507.
    Contains list of Vesalius' works.

98 —— The passing of Vesalius. *Edinb. med. J.,* 1918, *13*:324-339; II. Madrid to Zante, *Ibid.,* 388-400.

99 —— Vesalius and the Inquisition myth. *Lancet,* 1929, 2:362.

100 CUNEO, Gabriele. *Apologiæ Francisci Putei pro Galeno in anatome, examen.* Venetiis, apud F. de Franciscis, 1564. 125 pp.
    A defense of Vesalius and attributed to him by Cardan, whom Roth shows to have been wrong.

101 CUSHING, Harvey. Portraits of Vesalius. *N. Y. med. J.,* 1915, *101*:489-490.

102 DANIËLS, C. E. Andreas Vesalius. *Onze Kunst voortzetting van de Vlaamsche School,* 1905 (pt. viii):16-21.

103 —— André Vésale. *L'Art flamand holl.,* 1905, 4:16-21.

104 DAREMBERG, C. V. *Histoire des sciences médi- cales, comprenant l'anatomie, la physiologie, la médecine, la chirurgie et les doctrines de pathologie générale.* Paris, J. B. Baillière et fils, 1870. 2 vol.

105 DARRICARRERE, J. Les diagnostics de Vésale. *Chron. méd.,* 1913, *20*:347-348.

106 *DAZA CHACON, Dionisio. *Práctica y teórica de cirujia en romance y en latin, primera y segunda parte.* Valladolid, Herederos de B. de Sanctodomingo, 1595. (BM) Second edition, 1609. Reprinted: *Co- leccion de documentos inéditos para la historia de España,* vol. 18, pp. 537-563.
    See also Vol. 3, pp. 283-305 in: Morejón (no.

294), "Relacion verdadera de la herida de la cabeza del sereníssimo príncipe don Cárlos . . . la cual se acabó en fin de julio del ano de 1563" which is a direct quotation and gives a day by day case history of the illness of Don Carlos with frequent references to Vesalius.

107 DELLEPIANE, L. La nomenclatura muscular en la obra de Andreas Vesalio, "De corporis hu- mani fabrica septem liberi " [*sic*]. *Rev. argent. Hist. Med.,* 1942, 1:85-90.

108 DEMPSTER, Wilfrid T. European anatomy before Vesalius. *Ann. med. Hist.,* 1934, 6:307-319; 448-469.

109 DEUTSCH, Albert. Free minds pay tribute to unshackled science tonight. *PM,* Jan. 13, 1943.

110 DIAGNOSTICS (Les) de Vésale. *Chron. méd.,* 1913, *20*:115-116.

111 DIDOT, Ambroise Firmin. *Essai typographique et bibliographique sur l'histoire de la gravure sur bois.* Paris, 1863. 2 vol.
    Col. 91-96—Oporin et l'oeuvre de Vésale.

112 DOLCE, Lodovico. *Giornale delle historie del mondo, delle cose degne di memoria di giorno in giorno occorse dal principio del mondo sino a' suoi tempi, riveduto da Guglielmo Rinaldi.* Venetia, Al Segno della Sala- mandra, 1572. 54 *ll.* 464 pp.
    Contains an early reference to the death of Ve- salius (p. 376) from a tertian chill at Zante on the way from Jerusalem.

113 DOOLIN, William. In the days of Vesalius. *Irish J. med. Sci.,* 1933, 1:97-110.

114 DOUGLAS, James. *Bibliographiæ anatomicæ speci- men; sive catalogus omnium penè auctorum qui ab Hip- pocrate ad Harvæum rem anatomicam . . . illustrarunt; . . . Editio secunda.* Lugduni Batavorum, Apud G. Langerak, 1734. 12 *ll.,* 264 pp., 6 *ll.*
    See pp. 77-89, list of Vesalius' works.

115 DRINKER, Cecil K. To commemorate our Vesalian assignation, February 18, 1926. Typescript of a lecture presented before the Harvard Medical School.
    Translation of vivisection chapter 19, Book VII, of the *Fabrica.*

116 DRYANDER, Johann. *Anatomia capitis humani . . .* Marpurgi, ex officina E. Cervicorni, 1536. 3 *ll.,* 11 pl.

117 DU LAURENS, André. *Historia anatomica hu- mani corporis et singularum eius partium multis contro-*

___

___

versiis et observationibus novis illustrata. Francofurti, apud M. Beckerum (1600). 12 *ll.*, 442 pp., 14 *ll.* F.VI.D.40.

118 DUMESNIL, R. *Histoire illustrée de la médecine. Editions d'histoire et d'art.* Paris, Librarie Plon (1935). 264 pp.

   Pp. 116-120, portr. frontispiece *Anatomia,* etc.

119 *[DU MONCHAUX, Pierre] *Anecdotes de médecine, ou choix des faits singuliers qui ont rapport à l'anatomie, la pharmacie, l'histoire naturelle, etc., auxquels on a joint des anecdotes concernant les médecines les plus célèbres.* Lille, J. B. Henry, 1766. 2 pties. (CaMM-Os)

   See also *Vaderlandsch Museum,* 1862, 4:368 for a short anecdote from p. 166 of 1762 edition of this.

EBER, Paul. *See* Melancthon, no. 285, dedication.

120 EBSTEIN, Erich. *Ärzte-Briefe aus vier Jahrhunderten.* Berlin, J. Springer, 1920. xii, 204 pp.

   Pp. 2-3, Latin letter of Vesalius to A. P. Gasser, 1557.   (*See* F.IX.8)

121 EDSON, C. E. Andreas Vesalius. *Colo. Med.,* 1915, 12:4-8.

122 EERSEL, C. van. Hôtel de Vesalius à Bruxelles. *Bull. Ann. Acad. Archéol. Belg.,* 1843, 1:190-193.

   Contains a previously unpublished deed bestowing Vesalius' house in 1587 on Pierre Ernest de Mansfelt for his signal services during the troubles of 1587.

123 EMPLACEMENT de la statue de Vésale. Délibération au Conseil Communal de Bruxelles. Séance du 30 Mai. *Gaz. méd. belge,* 1846, 4:119-120.

   A petition by V. Uyterhoeven and J. de Biefve and the resolution of the city council calling for the naming of the square Place Vésale instead of Place des Barricades.

124 [EPITAPH] *Vaderlandsch Museum,* 1862, 4:271.

125 ERRERA, Paul. Art et science chez Léonard de Vinci. *Rev. Univ. Brux.,* 1901, 7:97-124.

126 EUSTACHIUS, Bartholomæus. *Tabulæ anatomicæ ... Præfatione, notisque illustravit, ac ipso suæ bibliothecæ dedicationis die publici juris fecit* Jo. Maria Lancisius. Romæ, Ex Officina F. Gonzagæ, 1714, xliv [ii], 115 *ff.*, 6 *ll.*

   See poem p. xxix by P. M. Pini with mention of "impudens Vessalius."

127 EXHIBITS on Vesalius. *Bull. med. Libr. Ass.,* 1943, 31:275-278.

128 *FACCIOLATI, J. *Fasti Gymnasii patavini.* 3 pt. Patavii, 1757.   (BM)

   See pt. 3, p. 386.

129 FALLOPIUS, Gabriel. *Observationes anatomicæ.* Venetiis, apud M. A. Ulmum, 1561. 8 *ll.*, 222 *ff.*, 1 *l.*

   A full description of this has been given in Chap. IX above.

129a FARRINGTON, Benjamin. Vesalius on the ruin of ancient medicine. *Modern Quarterly,* 1938, 1:23-28.

   See also no. 44.

130 FEYFER, F. M. G. de. Die Schriften des Andreas Vesalius. *Janus,* 1914, 19:435-507, 7 pl., 1 tab.

   This is the only detailed bibliography of Vesalius and has formed the basis for the enumeration adopted in this present work.

131 —— Lijst der Geschriften van Andreas Vesalius met aanteekeningen voorzien. *Ned. Tijdschr. Geneesk.,* 1915, 59:86-113.

132 —— Een onbekend portret van Andreas Vesalius. *Meded. ned. hist. Inst.,* 1926, 6:123-132.

133 —— Een portret van Andreas Vesalius. *Ned. Tijdschr. Geneesk.,* 1932, 76:60-73, 1 pl.

134 —— Jan Steven van Calcar (Joannes Stephanus), 1499-1546. *Ned. Tijdschr. Geneesk.,* 1933, 77: 3562-3579.

135 *FIGUIER, Louis. *Vies des savants illustres depuis l'antiquité jusqu'au dix-neuvième siècle.* Paris, Hachette et Cie., 1876-81. 5 vol   (BN)

   See vol. 3, pp. 283-311.

136 FISCH, Max H. Vesalius and his book. *Bull. med. Libr. Ass.,* 1943, 31:208-221.

137 —— The printer of Vesalius' *Fabrica. Bull. med. Libr. Ass.,* 1943, 31:240-259.

138 FISCHER, Alfons. André Vésale et Ambroise Paré au chevet de Henri II. *Feuill. méd.,* 1933, 2: 181-183.

139 FISHER, George Jackson. Historical and bibliographical notes: A series of sketches of the lives, times and works of the old masters of anatomy and surgery. I. Andreas Vesalius. *Ann. Anat. Surg.,* 1880, 2:34-37.

   On p. 37 a brief list of editions of *De fabrica.*

140 FLETCHER, R. A rare reprint of a rare work of Vesalius. *Trans. Coll. Phys. Philad.,* 1909, 31:340-342.

   (F.II.2.)

141 FOPPENS, Jo. Franciscus. *Bibliotheca belgica sive*

virorum in Belgio vita, scriptisque illustrium, catalogus. Bruxellis, per P. Foppens, 1739. 2 vol.

Vol. 1, pp. 61⁄62, short sketch and list of works, portr. the portraits used in this are also used in LeMire (no. 253) and Bullart (no. 60).

142 FORSTER, A. Einiges über die Beziehungen Vesal's zu Leonardo da Vinci und zu Marc'Antonio della Torre. *Arch. Anat. Physiol., Lpz.*, 1904, *28 (Anat. Abt.)*: 373⁄384.

143 FOSTER, *Sir* Michael. Vesalius: His forerunners and followers, pp. 1⁄24 in his: *Lectures on the history of physiology during the sixteenth, seventeenth and eighteenth centuries.* Cambridge, University Press, 1901.

143a FOUR (The) hundredth anniversary of the greatest medical book. *Texas Rep. Biol. Med.*, 1943, 1:93⁄94.

143b FOURTH centenary of "De Fabrica." *Brit. med. J.*, 1943, 1:791.

144 FRANCIS, Henry S. The woodcut initials of the *Fabrica. Bull. med. Libr. Ass.*, 1943, *31*:228⁄239.

145 FREHER, Paul. *Theatrum virorum eruditione clarorum* . . . Norimbergæ, Impensis J. Hoffmanni, 1688. 2 vol.

Portrait of Vesalius on pl. 56 and life on p. 1254.

146 FRIEDENWALD, Harry. Cardanus horoscope of Vesalius. *Bibliofilia*, 1933, *35*:421⁄430.

Description of horoscope of Vesalius said to be in Cardano's hand under the former's portrait in Dr. Friedenwald's copy of *De fabrica.*

147 FRIES, Lorenz. *Spiegel der Artzny* . . . (Strassburg, J. Grieninger, 1518). 184 *ff.*

148 FUCHS, Leonhard. *De sanandis totius humani corporis* . . . *malis libri V* . . . Venetiis, apud A. Arrivabenum, 1543. 12 *ll.*, 487 pp.

149 —— *New Kreüterbuch in welchem nit allein die gantz histori* . . . *des meysten theyls der Kreüter so in Teütschen unnd andern Landen wachsen* . . . Basell, M. Isingrin, 1543. 16 *ll.*, [854] pp. (*See also no. 190*)

150 *FUCHS, Remaclus. Illustrium medicorum qui superiori sæculo floruerunt ac scripserunt vitæ* . . . Parisiis, apud P. Gromorsum, 1541. Sign. A⁄H.   (BN)
See fol. H7*b.*

151 FÜRER VON HAIMENDORF, Christoph. *Itinerarium Ægypti, Arabiæ, Palæstinæ, Syriæ, aliarumque regionum orientalium* . . . Norimbergæ, ex officina A. Wagenmanni, 1621. [16] 118 [113] pp.
See p. 2. Fürer von Haimendorf mentions stopping at Zante and gives inscription from Vesalius' tomb there.

152 FUTCHER, T. B. Association between famous artists and anatomists. *Johns Hopk. Hosp. Bull.*, 1906, *17*:38⁄39.

153 GACHARD, L. P. *Don Carlos et Philippe II.* Bruxelles, E. Devroye, 1863. 2 vol.
See vol. 1, pp. 75⁄79; 83⁄84; vol. 2, pp. 634⁄635.

154 GAIZO, M. del. Contributo allo studio della vita e delle opere di Andrea Vesalio. *Atti Accad. med. chirg. Napoli*, 1916, *70*:219⁄232.

155 GALEN. *De ossibus.* Ferdinando Balamio interprete. Lugduni, apud Hæredes S. Vincentii, 1535. 43 [1] pp., 2 *ll.*

156 —— *De ossibus ad tyrones, versus quidem à Ferdinando Balamio: erroribus verò quàm plurimis, tum Græcis tum Latinis purgatus, et commentariis illustratus, à Iacobo Sylvio.* Parisiis, apud viduam I. Gazelli, 1549. 62 pp.

157 *—— Liber de ossibus ad tirones, interprete Ferdinando Balamio, enarrationibus illustratus à Ludovico Collado.* Valencia, por Juan Mey, 1555.   (BM)
See Morejón (no. 294), vol. 3, pp. 47⁄54, in which he mentions the defense of Vesalius against Sylvius by the editor Collado.

158 —— *De ossibus græcè et latinè. Accedunt Vesalii, Sylvii, Heneri, Eustachii, ad Galeni doctrinam exercitationes. Ex bibliotheca Joannis van Horne.* Lugduni Batavorum, apud D. vander Boxe, 1665. 6 *ll.*, 276 pp.

159 *—— Libri aliquot Græci partim hactenus non visi, partim à mendis quibus scatebant innumeris ad vetustissimos codices repurgati et integritati suæ restituti, annotationibusque illustrati per Ioannem Caium.* Basil., (apud H. Frobenium et N. Episcopium) 1544. (CaMM⁄Os)
Pp. 281⁄336 Caius' description of help received from Vesalius on Greek mss. See also no. 65b.

160 *GALLE, Philippe. Virorum doctorum de disciplinis effigies xliiii.* Antverpia 1572.   (BM)
See fol. C3. B. A. Montanus epigram.

GALLUS, *see no. 249.*

161 GARRISON, F. H. Anatomical illustrations before and after Vesalius. *N. Y. med. J.*, 1915, *101*:489.

162 —— The personality of Vesalius. *Johns Hopk. Hosp. Bull.*, 1915, *26*:121⁄123.

163 —— In defense of Vesalius. *Bull. Soc. med. Hist. Chicago*, 1916, *4*:47⁄65.

164 —— *The principles of anatomic illustration before*

Vesalius. An inquiry into the rationale of artistic anatomy. New York, P. B. Hoeber, 1926. 58 pp.

164a —— *An introduction to the history of medicine with medical chronology, suggestions for study and bibliographic data.* Fourth edition, revised and enlarged. Philadelphia, W. B. Saunders Co., 1929. 996 pp.

165 GEDENKSCHRIFT *zur Eröffnung des Vesalianum, der neu errichteten Anstalt für Anatomie und Physiologie in Basel. 28. Mai 1885.* Leipzig, Veit u. Comp., 1885. 2 *ll.,* 110 pp.
   See also His, no. 189.

166 GELJL. De echtheid van den Andreas Vesalius uit het Medisch-pharmaceutisch Museum ontkend. *Geneesk. Cour.,* 1905, 59:371-372.

167 GERSDORFF, Hans von. *Feldbüch der Wundartzney.* Strassburg, J. Schott [1517], 4 *ll.,* 95 *ff.*

168 GESNER, Conrad. Andreas Vesalius medicus, pp. 272-273, pt. 3, in: PANTALEON, H., *Teutscher Nation warhafften Helden* ... Basel, L. Ostein, 1578.
   Same portrait used pt. 3, p. 459, for Rheinerus Solenander Clevischer medicus!

169 —— *Bibliotheca universalis, sive catalogus omnium scriptorum locupletissimus, in tribus linguis, Latina, Græca, et Hebraica: extantium et non extantium, veterum et recentiorum in hunc usque diem, doctorum et indoctorum, publicatorum et in bibliothecis latentium.* Tiguri, apud C. Froschouerum, 1542. 17 *ll.,* 631 *ff.*
   See *f.* 42.

170 *GLOIRES* Nationales. *Album biographique de Belges célèbres. Texte par Gachard, De Reiffenberg, A. Baron ... Illustrations par Schubert Devigne, Schaepkens, etc.* Bruxelles [1860]. 461 pp. portr.   (BM)

171 GOETHALS, F. V. *Lectures relatives à l'histoire des sciences, des arts, des lettres, des moeurs et de la politique en Belgique et dans les Pays limitrophes* ... Bruxelles, Chez l'auteur, 1837-38. 4 vol.
   Vol. 2, pp. 112-133. Careful analysis of evidence, with contemporary quotation from L'Ecluse (Clusius) on reasons for Vesalius' voyage to Jerusalem (no. 248).

172 —— *Notice biographique sur André Vésale.* [Brussels, 1841]. 4 pp.

172a GRASSET DE SAINT-SAUVEUR, André. *Voyage historique ... dans les isles et possessions ci-devant venitiennes du Levant ... Zante ...* Paris, Tavernier [1800]. 3 vol.
   See vol. 3 for description of Zante.

173 GREEN, Robert M. Louvain and its university. *Bost. med. surg. J.,* 1914, 171:995-998.

173a *GROSS, Johann Georg. Urbis Basil. epitaphia et inscriptiones omnium templorum, curiæ, academ. et aliar. ædium public., lat. et german. quibus reliquarum orbis urbium monumenta et inscriptiones selectiss ... accesserunt.* Basileæ, sumpt. J. J. Genathii 1622. 502 pp. (BN)

174 *GRUNDHOFF, W. Andr. Vesalii et Theophrasti Paracelsi ... vitæ et merita et scripta.* Berlin thesis, 1860. (From no. 345)

175 GRYLLUS, Laurentius. *De sapore dulci et amaro libri duo. Nunc primùm per Adamum Landauum ... in lucem editi. Accessit in fine Oratio de peregrinatione studij medicinalis ergo suscepta.* Pragæ, apud G. Melantrichum ab Aventino, 1566. 16 *ll.,* 97 *ff.,* 9 *ll.,* 16 *ff.*
   Mention of Vesalius on *f.* 9 of *Oratio.*

176 GUARDIA, J.-M. *La médecine à travers les siècles. Histoire—Philosophie.* Paris, J. B. Ballière et fils, 1865. lx, 804 pp.
   Pp. 234-274, detailed discussion of the illness of Prince Carlos of Spain and Vesalius' part at that time.

177 *GUEVARA, Alfonso Rodriguez de. In pluribus ex iis quibus Galenus impugnatur ab Andrea Vessalio in constructione et usu partium corporis humani, defensio: et nonnullorum quæ in anatome deficere videbantur supplementum.* Coimbra, por J. Barreiro, 1559.
   See Morejón (no. 294), vol. 3, pp. 86-87.

178 *GUILLIAUME, Jules L. A. Vésale, drame.* (From *Bibliotheca belgica,* no. 37.)

179 GURLT, E. *Geschichte der Chirurgie und ihrer Ausübung. Volkschirurgie, Altertum, Mittelalter, Renaissance.* Berlin, A. Hirschwald, 1898. 3 vol.
   Vol. 3, pp. 296-309. Brief list of works and portrait from *De fabrica.*

HAEGHEN, Ferdinand vander. See no. 37.

180 HAESER, H. Geschichte der Medicin und der Krankheiten. *Jber. Leist. ges. Med.,* 1867, 1:351-369.
   See pp. 363-364.

181 HAINES, W. D. Andreas Vesalius. *Trans. West. surg. Ass.,* 1935, 45:304-321.

182 HALLER, A. von. *Bibliotheca anatomica* ... Lugduni Bat., apud Haak et Socc., 1777. 2 vol.
   See vol. 1, pp. 180-187; vol. 2, p. 741.

183 HECKETHORN, Charles William. *The printers of Basle in the XV. and XVI. centuries. Their biographies, printed books and devices.* London, Unwin Brothers, 1897. xvi, 208 pp.

184 HEGER, Paul. Notes sur André Vésale. *Rev. Univ. Brux.*, 1903, *9*:161-200.

185 *HELVETIUS, Johann Friedrich. *Amphitheatrum physiognomiæ medicum. Runder Schauplatz der arzneyischen Gesichtskunst.* Heydelberg, 1660. (BM)

186 —— *Microscopium physiognomiæ medicum, id est, Tractatus de physiognomia . . .* Amstelodami, apud Janssonio-Wæsbergios, 1676. 51 *ll.*, 244 pp., 2 *ll.*
Portrait of Vesalius and text, pp. 143-145.

187 HENERUS, Renatus. *Adversus Jacobi Sylvii depulsionum anatomicorum calumnias, pro Andrea Vesalio apologia: in qua præcipuæ totius negotii anatomici pene controversiæ breviter explicantur . . .* Venetiis, [n. pr.], 1555. 8 *ll.*, 134 pp., 1 *l.*
Poem by Nicolaus Stopius on leaf *b*1.

187a *HENNE, Alexandre. *Histoire du règne de Charles-Quint en Belgique.* Bruxelles, E. Flatau, 1858-60. 10 vol. (DLC)
See vol 5, p. 281; vol. 8, p. 257.

187b *——, and WAUTERS, A. *Histoire de la ville de Bruxelles.* Bruxelles, Perichon, 1845. 3 vol. (DLC)
See vol. 3, p. 396.

188 HEROES of medicine. Andreas Vesalius. *Practitioner*, 1896, *56*:62-65.

189 HIS, Wilhelm. *Beobachtungen des anatomisches Unterrichtes in Basel.* Leipzig, 1885. 39 pp.
Reprinted from *Gedenkschrift*, 1885, no. 165.

190 HIZLER, Georg. *Oratio de vita et morte Leonhardi Fuchsii . . . Carmina etiam doctorum aliquot virorum in eiusdem obitum conscripta.* Tubingæ, 1566. 64 pp.
See p. 24.

191 HOLL, M. Leonardo da Vinci und Vesal. *Arch. Anat. Physiol., Lpz.*, 1905, *29* (Anat. Abt.): 111-140.

192 —— Die Kraniologie Vesals. *Arch. Gesch. Med.*, 1910-11, *4*:431-440.

193 —— Vesals Darstellung der Drüsen des "Stomachus." *Arch. Gesch. Med.*, 1911-12, *5*:401-411.

194 —— Vesals Darstellung des Baues der Niere. *Arch. Gesch. Med.*, 1912-13, *6*:129-148.

195 —— Vesals Anatomie des Gehirns. *Arch. Anat. Physiol., Lpz.*, 1915, *39* (Anat. Abt.):115-192.

196 ——, and SUDHOFF, K. Eine dem Leonardo da Vinci zugeschriebene Skelettzeichnung in den Uffizien zu Florenz. *Arch. Gesch. Med.*, 1914, *7*: 323-334.

197 HOLMGREN, E. Andreas Vesalius. Promotionstal hållet vid medicine doktors-promotionen i Karolinska institutets anatomiska hörsald 30 maj 1912. *Hygeia, Stockh.*, 1912, *74*:625-632.

198 HORNE, Johannes van. Μικροκοσμος seu brevis manuductio ad historiam corporis humani. In gratiam discipulorum secundùm edita. Lugduni Batavorum, J. Chouët, 1662. 3 *ll.*, 142 pp., 8 *ll.* (*See* also no. 158.)
On *l.* 3, "Hoc interea fruere, donec alter prodeat libellus, huic succenturiandus: simulque . . . mea ad singula Epitomes Magni Vesalii capita absolvantur notæ et additamenta, in quibus quæ hic strictim indigitantur, uberrime explicata reperies."

199 —— Andreæ Vesalii et Jacobi Sylvii super libello Galeni de ossibus controversiæ, pp. 117-276 in: GALEN, *De ossibus* (no. 158). F.VI.D.34.

200 HOUDET. [Discours, Sociètè de Gand]. *Messager des Sciences*, 1836, 2.s., *4*:119-123.

201 HUNDT, Magnus. *Antropologium de hominis dignitate natura et proprietatibus de elementis, partibus et membris humani corporis . . .* (Liptzick, per Wolfgangum [Stoeckel], 1501). 119 *ll.*

202 HYDE, Walter Woodburn. Roman Alpine routes. *Mem. Amer. philos. Soc.*, 1935, *2*:1-211.

203 HYMANS, Henri. Jean Etienne de Calcar. *L'Art*, Paris, 1883, *33*:61-65.
Two engravings of Louvre portrait of Vesalius.

203a ILLUSTRIUM *et clarorum virorum epistolæ selectiores, superiore sæculo scriptæ vel a Belgis, vel ad Belgas. Tributæ in centuria duas . . .* Lugduni Bat., apud L. Elzevirium, 1617. (48), 988, (14) pp. (MH)
See Epist. LXXII, pp. 370-385.

204 IMPERIALI, Giovanni. *Musæum historicum et physicum. In primo illustrium literis virorum imagines ad vivum expressæ continentur, additis elogiis eorundem vitas, et mores notantibus. In secundo animorum imagines, sive ingeniorum naturæ, differentiæ, causæ, ac signa physicè perpenduntur.* Venetiis, apud Iuntas, 1640. 8 *ll.*, 122 pp., 1 *l.*, 219 pp., 12 *ll.*
Pt. 1, p. 54, portrait, pp. 55-56, sketch of life of Vesalius and poem to him by G. Ronconi. Motive for his pilgrimage given as a desire to be free of the antagonism of the Galenic School. Further mention of Vesalius in Pt. 2, p. 195.

205 INAUGURATION de la statue de Vésale. *Arch. Méd. belge*, 1847, *24*:121-131.

206 *INGRASSIA, Giovanni Filippo. *Iatrapologia. Liber quo multa adversus barbaros medicos disputantur,* collegijque modus ostenditur, ac multæ quæstiones tam physicæ quam chirurgicæ discutiuntur. Venetiis, I. Gry-phius (1547?) 12 ll., 431 [17] pp.   (CaMM-Os)

207 —— *In Galeni librum de ossibus . . . commentaria. Nunc primum sedulò in lucem edita et aptè naturam imitantibus iconibus insignita . . .* Panormi, ex typ. I. B. Maringhi, 1603. 4 ll., 276 pp., 5 ll.   F.VI.D.35.
  "Contains 3 skeletal figures poorly copied via Valverde and 14 small copperplate illustrations of bones in text."—H.C.

208 —— [Letter to Vesalius], pp. 99-101 in his: *Quæstio de purgatione per medicamentum,* Venetiis, 1568.   F.IX.3.

209 IVINS, William M., Jr. The woodcuts to Vesalius. *Bull. Metropolitan Mus. Art,* 1936, 31:139-142.

210 —— A propos of the Fabrica of Vesalius. *Bull. Hist. Med.,* 1943 (Dec.).

211 JACKSCHATH, E. Die Begründung der modernen Anatomie durch Leonardo da Vinci und die Wiederauffindung zweier Schriften desselben. *Medicinische Blätter,* 1902, 15:770-772. Abstracted, *Verh. Ges. dtsch. Naturf. Ärzt. (Naturwiss. Abt.),* 1902, 116.

212 —— Zu den anatomischen Abbildung des Vesal. *Mitt. Gesch. Med. Naturw.,* 1903, 2:282. Also: *Janus,* 1904, 9:238.

213 JACKSON, Holmes C. Little biographies. IX. Andreas Vesalius. *Albany med. Ann.,* 1906, 27:652-655.

214 JAMES, W. B. Quadricentennial of Vesalius. *N. Y. med. J.,* 1915, 101:487-488.

214a JENNINGS, Oscar. *Early woodcut initials.* London, Methuen and Co., 1908. x, 288 pp.
  See pp. 37-38.

215 *JOBST, Wolfgang. *Chronologia sive temporum supputatio omnium illustrium medicorum tam veterum quam recentiorum.* Francoph. ad Viadrum, J. Eichhorn, 1556. x, 174 pp.   (BN)
  See p. 147.

216 JOCISCUS, Andreas. *Oratio de ortu, vita, et obitu Ioannis Oporini . . . Adiunximus librorum per Ioannem Oporinum excusorum catalogum.* Argentorati, Excudebat T. Rhelius, 1569. 52 ll. Reprinted pp. 601-704 in: *Vitæ selectæ quorundam eruditissimorum ac illustrium virorum.* Breslau, 1711.

217 JOHNSON, Charles B. Andreas Vesalius, founder of modern anatomy. *Illinois med. J.,* 1917, 31:253-260.

218 JONES, Tom. The artists of Vesalius' *Fabrica. Bull. med. Libr. Ass.,* 1943, 31:222-227.

219 KEIBEL, Franz. Eine Bemerkung zu des Andreas Vesalius sechs anatomischen Tafeln vom Jahre 1538, wie sie M. Holl und K. Sudhoff herausgegeben haben. *Z. ges. Anat. I. Z. AnatEntw. Gesch.,* 1922, 63:423-424.

220 KERSCHENSTEINER, Joseph von. *Andreas Vesalius, Bruxellensis,* von M. Roth. *Aerztliche Rundschau,* 1893, 3:405-407.

221 [KEYS, Thomas E.] Osler, and the Six anatomical tables. *Bull. med. Libr. Ass.,* 1943, 31:201-202.

221a KILNER, S. D. Vesalius and Gray on anatomy. *Brit. med. J.,* 1943, 2:56.

222 KINGSLEY, Charles. Andreas Vesalius, pp. 385-411 in his: *Health and education,* London, 1887.

223 KISER, William. The medical library. *J. med. Ass. Ga.,* 1930, 19:330-331.
  On the acquisition of a copy of *De fabrica* by the A. W. Calhoun Library of Emory University.

224 KLEBS, Arnold C. Die Lemgoer Ratsapotheke. Historische Reiseskizze. *Arch. Gesch. Naturw. Tech.,* 1913, 5:102-107. 2 pl.
  With reproduction of bas-relief portrait of Vesalius on façade of Lemgo Ratsapotheke.

225 —— Leonardo da Vinci's scientific research, with particular reference to his investigations of the vascular system. *Bost. med. surg. J.,* 1916, 175:1-7; 45-50.

226 —— Leonardo da Vinci and his anatomical studies. *Bull. Soc. med. Hist., Chicago,* 1916, 4:66-83.
  Discussion of Vesalius on pp. 75 *et seq.*

227 ——, and GARRISON, Fielding H. Leonardo and Vesalius (Holl-Roth controversy). A disputation. *Cleveland med. J.,* 1915, 14:615-617.

228 KLEIJ, J. J. van der. Von wo stammen die Vorfahren von Vesalius her? *Janus,* 1914, 19:523.

229 KLEIN, Gustav. Leonardo da Vinci und Vesals geburtshilflich-anatomische Abbildungen. *Münch. med Wschr.,* 1904, 1:821-822. Reprinted: *Mschr. Geburtsh. Gynäk.,* 1904, 20:866-867.

230 —— Geburtshilfliche und gynäkologisch-anatomische Abbildungen des 15. und 16. Jahrhunderts. (Leonardo da Vinci, Vesal, Roesslin). *Verh. dtsch. Ges. Gynäk.,* 1906, 11:415-420. Abstracted: *Zbl. Gynäkol.,* 1905, 29:845-847; *Mschr. Geburtsh. Gynäk.,* 1905, 22:147-150.

230a —— Ausstellung von Original‑Werken zur Geschichte der anatomischen, besonders der ge‑ burtshilflich‑gynækologischen Abbildung. Aus der Sammlung von G. Klein in München. [1901] 4 *ll.* 2. Verzeichnis, 1902. 4 *ll.*

231 KLUYSKENS, Hippolyte. *Des hommes célèbres dans les sciences et les arts, et des médailles qui consacrent leur souvenir.* Gand, L. Hebbelynck, 1859. 2 vol.
See vol. 2, pp. 572‑578. List of eleven medals in Vesalius' honor, with engraving of the Jouvenal medal (Spielman, no. 9, Kluykens, no. 4).

232 —— Numismatique Vésalienne. *Rev. belge numismatique,* 1874, 5.s. 6:389‑394.

233 KNAPP, George L. Biographical sketches of some of the world's greatest physicians. I. Andreas Vesalius. *J. Homeop.,* 1902‑03, 6:178‑187.
On p. 187 compares Vesalius to Hahnemann.

234 KNAPPERT, L. L'église et la science au temps de Vésale. *Janus,* 1914, 19:420‑434.

235 —— Kerk en wetenschap in Vesalius' dagen. *Ned. Tijdschr. Geneesk.,* 1915, 59:17‑30.

236 KNOX, Robert. *Great artists and great anatomists. A biographical and philosophical study.* London, J. van Voorst, 1852. xii, 213 pp.
Mere passing remark on Vesalius on p. 161.

237 KÖSTER, Karl. *Zur Geschichte der Physiologie des Blutumlaufes insbesondere über die Frage der Durchgängigkeit der Kammerscheidewand bei Andreas Vesalius. Historisch‑kritische Studie.* Inaugural‑Dissertation. Tübingen, H. Laupp, Jr., 1915. 21 pp.

238 KRISTELLER, Paul. Eine Zeichnung von Johann Stephan van Calcar, zum Titelblatte der Anatomie des Andreas Vesalius. *Mitt. Ges. vervielfältigende Kunst,* 1908, pp. 19‑24.

239 LABOULBÈNE, J. J. A. Les anatomistes anciens et la renaissance anatomique au XVIᵉ siècle. V. Vésale. *Un. méd.,* 1887, 3.s. 43:317‑321; 401‑407.

240 LAMBERT, Samuel W. Reading from Andræ Vesalii, "De humani corporis fabrica liber VII; De vivorum sectione nonnulla, caput XIX." *Proc. Charaka Club,* 1935, 8:3‑41.

241 —— The physiology of Vesalius. *Bull. N. Y. Acad. Med.,* 1936, 12:387‑415.

242 —— Description of the vermiform appendix from the "De fabrica" of Vesalius. *Ann. med. Hist.,* 1937, n.s. 9:422‑427.

243 *LANZI, Luigi Antonio. *La storia pittorica della Italia inferiore, o sia delle scuole fiorentina, senese, romana, napolitana, compendiata e ridotta a methodo.* Firenze, A. G. Pagani, 1792. iv, 529 pp.   (BN)

244 LARKEY, Sanford V. The Vesalian compendium of Geminus and Nicholas Udall's translation: Their relation to Vesalius, Caius, Vicary and de Mondeville. *Trans. bibliogr. Soc. Lond.,* 1933, 13:367‑394.

245 ——, and TUM SUDEN, L. Jackson's English translation of Berengarius of Carpi's "Isagogæ breves," 1660 and 1664. *Isis,* 1934, 21:57‑70.

246 LAVATER, J. C. *Essays on physiognomy; for the promotion of the knowledge and the love of mankind . . . translated . . . by T. Holcroft.* London, G. G. J. and J. Robinson, 1789. 3 vol.
Portrait and note on Vesalius, vol. 2, p. 229.

247 LEBOUCQ, G. André Vésale. *Biographie nationale publiée par l'Académie Royale des Sciences, des Lettres et des Beaux Arts de Belgique,* 1937‑38, 26:699‑710, portr.

248 L'ECLUSE, Charles de. A Monsieur le Président de Thou, Vol. 7, Bk. VI, pp. 13‑14 in; DE THOU (no. 389).

249 LECOCQ, Pascal. *Bibliotheca medica. Sive catalogus illorum, qui ex professo artem medicam in hunc usque annum scriptis illustrarunt; nempe quid scripserint, ubi, qua forma, quove tempore scripta excisa, aut manuscripta habeantur . . .* Basileæ per C. Waldkirch, 1590. 16 *ll.,* 457 [1] pp.   (DLC)
See p. 21 *et seq.*

250 LEERSUM, E. C. van. [Review of no. 26.] *Janus,* 1911, 16:363‑364.

251 —— André Vésale. *Janus,* 1914, 19:397‑409.

252 —— Andreas Vesalius. *Ned. Tijdschr. Geneesk.,* 1915, 59:4‑16.

252a —— Opuscula selecta Neerlandicorum De arte medica. *Janus,* 1927, 31:474‑497.
See especially pp. 477‑478.

252b LEJEUNE, Fritz. Zur spanischen Anatomie vor und um Vesal. *Janus,* 1927, 31:413‑422. (See also *Ibid.,* pp. 104‑105.)

253 LE MIRE, Aubert. *Elogia illustrium belgii scriptorum, qui vel Ecclesiam Dei propugnarunt, vel disciplinas illustrarunt.* Antverpiæ, Vid. et Hered. J. Belleri, 1602. 206, 5 *ll.*

254 LEVINSON, Abraham. Medical medallions. *Bull. med. Libr. Ass.,* 1943, 31:5-34.

Medallion of Vesalius on p. 9. Medical Society of Brussels 1804. (Spielman, no. 2.)

255 LINDEN, Johannes Antonides van der. *De scriptis medicis libri duo. Ed. altera, auctior et emendatior.* Amstelredami, apud J Blaev, 1651. 8 *ll.,* 688 pp., 14 *ll.*

See pp. 38-39.

256 LINDLEY, W. Andreas Vesalius. The reformer of anatomy. *S. Calif. Practit.,* 1911, 26:451-453.

257 LINT, J. G. de. Les portraits de Vésale. *Janus,* 1914, 19: 410-419.

258 —— *Catalogus van de tentoonstelling over oude anatomie, te houden te Leiden, Januari 1915, ter gelegenheid van de herdenking van den geboortedag van Andreas Vesalius, mit een bijdrage von* J. Boeke. Gorinchem, T. Horneer, 1914. 48 pp.

259 —— Iets over de portretten van Vesalius. *Ned. Tijdschr. Geneesk.,* 1915, 59:62-73.

260 —— Fugitive anatomical sheets. *Janus,* 1924, 28:78-91, 7 pl.

261 —— *Atlas of the history of medicine. Anatomy. With a foreword by* Charles Singer. New York, P. B. Hoeber, Inc., 1926. 96 pp.

See pp. 41-44. Amsterdam portrait.

262 —— The iconography of Andreas Vesalius [Review of no. 371]. *Janus,* 1926, 30:172-178.

263 —— Some unknown anatomical sheets. *Int. Congr. Hist. Med.,* 1922, 3:91-93, 2 pl.

264 *LIPENIUS, Martin. Bibliotheca realis medica omnium materiarum, rerum, et titulorum in universa medicina occurrentium.* Frankfurt-am-Main, J. Friederic, 1679. 492 pp., 21 *ll.*

Mentions only 1616 edition of *Epitome.*

265 LLORENTE, J. A. *Histoire critique de l'inquisition d'Espagne . . . traduite par* Alexis Pellier. Paris, Treuttel et Wurz, 1817. 4 vol.

Vol. 3, pp. 136-137, description of Don Carlos' illness, May 9, 1652, and operation by "André Basilio . . . médecin du roi . . ." See also Daza Chacon, no. 106.

266 —— *The history of the inquisition of Spain from the time of its establishment to the reign of Ferdinand VII.* London, G. B. Whittaker, 1826. xx, 583 pp.

Description of Don Carlos' illness and operation by Vesalius, pp. 381-382.

267 LOCY, W. A. Anatomical illustration before Vesalius. *J. Morph.,* 1911, 22:945-988.

268 LOW, Frank Norman. The famous Hamman painting of Andreas Vesalius. *Bull. Hist. Med.,* 1942, 12:129-131.

269 *LUTHER, Martin. *Resolutiones disputationum de indulgentiarum virtute ad Leonem X.* Basel, 1518.

Reference furnished by W. M. Voynich, in 1929, to Dr. Cushing.

270 LUTZ, Frank J. Vesalius and the practice of medicine. *J. Mo. med. Ass.,* 1916, 13:72-73.

271 McGILL UNIVERSITY. Montreal. Museum of human anatomy. *Exhibition of the history of anatomical illustration* (edited by John Beattie). Montreal, Renouf, 1930. (ii), 26 pp.

See pp. 6-8; 18-19.

272 McMURRICH, J. Playfair. Leonardo da Vinci and Vesalius: A review. *Med. Libr. hist. J.,* 1906, 4:338-350.

273 MAMLOCK, G. In memoriam Vesalii. Zu seinem 400. Geburtstag. *Dtsch. med. Wschr.,* 1915, 41:21.

274 MANEC, P. J. Vésale, in: *Portraits et histoire des hommes utiles, hommes et femmes de tous pays et de toutes conditions . . . Publiés et propagés par et pour la Société Montyon et Franklin.* Paris, au Bureau de la Société [1833-34].

4 pp. text and engraved portrait (Spielman no. 11).

275 *MANGET, J. J. *Bibliotheca scriptorum medicorum veterum et recentiorum . . . sicque historia medica vere universalis exhibetur.* Genevæ, Perachon et Cramer, 1731. 2 vol.   (DSG)

See vol. 2, pt. 2, p. 502.

276 MANSELL, H. E. Andreas Vesalius. *St. Geo. Hosp. Gaz.,* 1931, 27:[11 pp.].

277 MARTINOTTI, G. *L'insegnamento dell' anatomia in Bologna prima del secolo XIX.* Bologna, Azzoguidi, 1911. 146 pp.

278 —— Prospero Lambertini (Benedetto XIV) e lo studio dell' anatomia in Bologna. *Studi Mem. Storia Univ. Bologna,* 1911, 2:147-178.

279 —— Francesco dal Pozzo e la sua critica di Vesalio. *Mem. R. Accad. Bologna,* 1921-22, 9:31-43.

280 —— Il testamento di M°. Jacopo Barigazzi, o Berengario, da Carpi, lettore di chirurgia nello Studio di Bologna. *Riv. Storia Sci. med. nat.,* 1923, 14:65-73.

281 MARX, K. F. H. Ueber Marc'Antonio della Torre und Leonardo da Vinci, die Begründer der bildlichen Anatomie. *K. Ges. Wissensch. (Abt. math. Cl.) Göttingen,* 1850, 4:131⁄148.

282 MASSA, Niccolò. *Epistolarum medicinalium tomus primus* [*alter*] . . . Venetiis, Ex officina stellæ I. Zilletti, 1558. 2 vol.
See Epistolæ V, VI, Ad Antonium Fracanza⁄num, De re anotomica.

283 MASSON, L. Le mouvement médico⁄historique: Société belge d'histoire de la médecine. *Æsculape,* 1924, 14:218⁄223.
The author describes briefly his search in Zante (Santa Maria delle Grazie) for the exact spot where Vesalius was buried. The church was destroyed by earthquake in 1923 and then rebuilt and its archives were taken at that time to Athens.

284 MEDICI, Michele. *Compendio storico della scuola anatomica di Bologna dal rinascimento delle scienze e delle lettere a tutto il secolo XVIII* . . . Bologna, Tip. Governativa (1857). [6] 430 pp.
See p. 69.

285 MELANCHTHON, Philip. *Liber de anima recognitus.* Lipsiæ, J. Rhamba, 1562. 160 *ll.*
Dedication (*l.* A5*b*) contains poem in praise of Vesalius, quoted from Paul Eber.

286 MENGELINGEN. *Kunst⁄en Letter⁄Blad,* 1841, 2: 92.
Note on vote of Brussels Commission to celebrate the publication of *De fabrica.*

287 MERKEL, Fr. Eröffnungsrede [Zur Ehren von Andreas Vesalius]. *Verh. anat. Ges. Jena.* 1895, 10:2⁄15.

287a MERSSEMAN, J. de. Vésale, vol. 1, pp. 31⁄65 in: *Album biographique des Belges célèbres,* ed. J. A. Chabannes. Bruxelles, 1845.
With Demannez engraving of Titian portrait.

287b METELLUS, J. Arnoldo Birckmanno S.P.D. De morte Andrea Vesalii anno 1565. XV. Kal. Mai, MDLXV, Cologne.
Ms copy on fly⁄leaf of the David Senn copy of *De fabrica,* 1555, in the John Crerar Library, Chicago, Illinois. See also epist. LXXII, p. 372 in no. 203a.

288 MICHEA, C. F. Galérie des célébrités médi⁄cales de la Renaissance. André Vésale. *Ann. Méd. belge,* 1842, 4:177⁄185. *Gaz. méd. Paris,* 1842, 2.s. 10:689⁄695; 721⁄728.

289 MILLOT⁄CARPENTIER, G. Vésale. *Trib. méd. Paris,* 1897, n.s. 29:295⁄298.

MIRÆUS, see no. 253.

290 MOEHSEN, J. K. W. *Verzeichnis einer Samlung von Bildnissen grösstentheils berühmter Aerzte* . . . Berlin, C. F. Himburg, 1771. 6 *ll.,* 240 pp.
List of Vesalius' works on p. 140.

290a MOLANUS, Joannes. *Historiæ Lovaniensium libri XIV, ex codice edidit* . . . P.F.X. de Ram. (Collection de chroniques belges). Bruxellis, M. Hayez, 1861. 2 vol.
See vol. 1, pp. 470⁄471; 559; 560; 570; 572⁄573.

291 MONDINO de' Luzzi. *Matthæi Curtii in Mun⁄dini Anatomen commentarius elegans et doctus.* Lugduni, apud T. Paganum, 1551. 549 pp. 3 *ll.*
Prefatory note by Jean Canappe to Vesalius.

292 MONUMENT (A) to Vesalius. *Lancet,* 1914, 1:1198.

293 MOORE, Norman. 400th anniversary of Vesal⁄ius. *Proc. R. Soc. Med.,* 1914 (Sect. Hist. Med.), 8:27.

294 MOREJÓN, Antonio Hernández. *Historia bibli⁄ográfica de la medicina española; obra póstuma.* Madrid (La Viuda de Jordan e hijos), 1842⁄52. 7 vol.
See Vol. 3, pp. 51⁄52 (Galen, no. 157); pp. 283⁄305 (Daza Chacon, no. 106); pp. 86⁄87 (Guevara, no. 177).

295 [MORLEY, Henry]. Anatomy in long clothes. *Frasers Magazine,* 1853, 48:539⁄550. Reprinted: *Anatomy in long clothes, an essay on Andreas Vesalius.* Chicago, privately printed, 1915. 68 pp. See also Skrainka, P. (no. 364).

296 —— Clement Marot, and other studies. Lon⁄don, Chapman and Hall, 1871. 2 vol.
Vol. 2, pp. 65⁄96, Andreas Vesalius (no. 295 revised).

297 MÜNTZ, Eugène. Une cour de la Haute⁄Italie. II. Ludovic le More et Leonard de Vinci. *Revue des deux Mondes,* 1891, 103:114⁄144.

298 MUMFORD, James G. Andreas Vesalius, pp. 26⁄28 in his: *Surgical memoirs and other essays.* New York, Moffat, Yard and Co., 1908.

299 NAGLER, G. K. *Neues allgemeines Kunstler⁄Lexikon oder Nachrichten.* München, 1835⁄52. 44 vol.
Vol. 2, pp. 281⁄282, notes on Calcar.

300 NEUBURGER, M. Vesal als Gehirnphysiolog. *Med.⁄chir. Zbl.,* 1897, 32:198⁄199.

301 NEWMAN, Sir George. *A century of medicine at Padua.* London, British Periodicals Ltd., 1922. 38 pp.

Discussion of Vesalius, pp. 21-23; portrait.

302 NEW YORK ACADEMY OF MEDICINE. *Quadricentennial of the birth of Vesalius, January 7th, 1915.* 4 pp.

Catalogue of exhibit.

303 NICERON, Jean Pierre. *Mémoires pour servir à l'histoire des hommes illustres dans la république des lettres.* Paris, Briasson, 1725-45. 43 vol. in 44.

Vol. 5, pp. 135-145, life of Vesalius and list of his works.

303a NIEUWENHUIS, G. Einige Anschauungen über die Funktion der Hypophyse. *Janus,* 1931, 35:345-359.

See especially pp. 351-354.

304 NOTITIA *utraque cum orientis tum occidentis ultra Arcadii Honoriique cæsarum tempora . . .* Basileæ, Froben, 1552. 109 *ll.*

Leaf *2 dedication to Vesalius by Gelenius.

305 *NOURRY, C. André Vésale.* Bruxelles, n.d. Portrait.   (BNed)

306 NUIJENS, B. W. Th. Kerk en wetenshap in Vesalius' dagen. *Ned. Tijdschr. Geneesk.,* 1915, 59: 364-367.

307 OLIVARES, S. D. Relación de lo succedido en la enfermedad del Príncipe nuestro señor, vol. 6, pp. 587-607 in *Papiers d'état* (no. 312).

Gachard says this is merely a copy of Daza's account (no. 106) without preamble and conclusions. It is rather an abstract than an exact copy. See also Morejón (no. 294) vol. 3, pp. 130 *et seq.*

308 OLIVER, J. Lure of medical history. Vesalius. *Calif. West. Med.,* 1927, 27:657-659.

309 OLMEDILLA Y PUIG, Joaquín. Andrés Vesalio. Consideraciones biobibliográficas. *Rev. Med. Cirug. práct.,* 1913, 98:249-255; 289-297. Reprinted: Madrid, 1913, 29 pp.

310 OSLER, Sir William. *Evolution of modern medicine.* New Haven, Yale University Press, 1921, xvi, 244 pp.

See pp. 146-163.

310a —— *Bibliotheca Osleriana. A catalogue of books illustrating the history of medicine and science collected, arranged, and annotated and bequeathed to McGill University.* Oxford, Clarendon Press, 1929. xxvi, 786 pp.

311 *PAPADOPOLI, Nicola Comneno. *Historia Gymnasii Patavini post ea quæ hactenus de illo scripta sunt, ad hæc nostra tempora plenius et emendatius deducta. Cum auctario de claris cum professoribus tum alumnis eiusdem.* Venetiis, S. Coleti, 1726. 2 vol. (Vatican)

See Vol. 1, p. 316.

312 PAPIERS *d'état du Cardinal de Granvelle d'après les manuscrits de la Bibliothèque de Besançon publiés sous la direction de Ch. Weiss.* Paris, Imprimerie Royale, 1839-61. 9 vol.

See Vol. 5, p. 282; Vol. 6, pp. 587-607; Vol. 8, p. 525.

313 PAYNE, J. F. On an unpublished English anatomical treatise of the fourteenth century; and its relation to the "anatomy" of Thomas Vicary. *Brit. med. J.,* 1896, 1:200-203.

314 PELTZER, R. A. Der Kistler und Bildhauer Paul Reichel von Schongau der Meister des Tötlein. *Z. Kult. Kunst. Gesch. Schwabens,* 1930, 184-192.

315 PETERS, H. *Der Arzt und die Heilkunst in der deutschen Vergangenheit. Mit 153 Abbildungen und Beilagen nach den Originalen aus dem 15.-18. Jahrhundert.* Leipzig, E. Diederichs, 1900. 136 pp.

Brief mention of Vesalius and portrait from *De fabrica.*

316 —— Die medikohistorische Abteilung des Germanischen Museums in Nürnberg. *Münch. med. Wschr.,* 1904, 2:1701-1702.

317 PETTIGREW, T. J. *Medical portrait gallery. Biographical memoirs of the most celebrated physicians, surgeons, etc., etc., who have contributed to the advancement of medical science.* London, Fisher Son and Co. [1838-40]. 4 vol.

Engraving of Calcar's portrait of Vesalius and 6 pp. of biography in Vol. 2 (item 15).

PHRYESEN, see no. 147.

318 PICHOT, Amédée. Une autopsie. Conte anatomique. *Revue de Paris,* 1832, 35:201-225.

A story of an autopsy in Madrid, with Vesalius as the central figure.

319 PILCHER, L. S. The Vesalian spirit. *Bost. med. surg. J.,* 1914, 171:998-1001. Reprinted: *Bibliofilia,* 1915,16:347-354.

320 PIERSOL, G. A. Andreas Vesalius and his times. *Univ. Penn. Lect.,* 1916, 3:397-416.

PINI, Pietro Matteo. See EUSTACHIUS, no. 126, p. xxxix.

PIZZIMENTI, Federico. See CATTI, no. 76.

321 PLATTER, Thomas. *Thomas und Felix Platter. Zur Sittengeschichte des XVI. Jahrhunderts. Bearbeitet von* Heinrich Boos. Leipzig, S. Hirzel, 1878. xvi, 376 pp.

322 PORTAL, Antoine. *Histoire de l'anatomie et de la chirurgie, contenant l'origine et les progrès de ces sciences; avec un tableau chronologique des principales découvertes, et un catalogue des ouvrages d'anatomie et de chirurgie* . . . Paris, P. Fr. Didot le jeune, 1770-73. 6 vol. in 7.
See Vol. 1, pp. 394-443.

323 POWER, Sir D'Arcy. 'The birth of mankind or the woman's book': A bibliographical study. *Trans. bibliogr. Soc.*, 1927, 8:1-37.

324 POZZI [PUTEUS], Francesco. *Apologia in anatome pro Galeno contra Andream Vessalium.* Venetiis, apud F. de Portonariis, 1562. 30 *ll.*, 184 *ff.*, 4 *ll.*
See F.X.1.

325 QUATERCENTENARY, (The) of Andreas Vesalius. *Bost. med. surg. J.*, 1914, 171:995.

326 RENOUARD, P. *Bibliographie des éditions de Simon de Colines 1520-1546. Avec une notice biographique et 37 reproductions en fac-similé.* Paris, E. Paul, etc., 1894. viii, 518 pp.
Pages 409-410 and 412-413 for citations of Latin and French editions of Estienne and pp. 468-469 for discussion of the books.

327 REUSNER, Nikolaus. *Icones sive imagines virorum literis illustrium . . . Ex secunda recognitione.* Argentorati, curante B. Iobino, 1590. 8 *ll.*, 428 [16] pp.
See pp. 272-274, portrait from *De fabrica.*

328 RICHARDSON, B. W. Vesalius, and the birth of anatomy. *Asclepiad*, 1885, 2:132-156. Portr. Reprinted: pp. 76-94, vol. 1, in his: *Disciples of Æsculapius.* London, Hutchinson and Co., 1900. 2 vol.

329 RICHER, P. Du rôle de l'anatomie dans l'histoire de l'art. *France méd.*, 1903, 50:318-326.
General discussion with mere mention of Vesalius and Calcar on p. 321.

330 RIESMAN, David. *The story of medicine in the middle ages.* New York, P. B. Hoeber, 1935. xii, 402 pp.
Chapter XII on Vesalius, with portrait and title-page from *De fabrica.*

331 RIJNBERK, G. van. Andreas Vesalius, 1514-31 December, 1914. *Ned. Tijdschr. Geneesk.*, 1915, 59:2-3.

332 —— De ontleedkundige afbeelding vóór en in den tijd van Vesalius. *Ned. Tijdschr. Geneesk.*, 1915, 59:45-62.

333 —— Vesalius als proefondervindelijk physioloog. *Ned. Tijdschr. Geneesk.*, 1915, 59:113-130.

334 —— Andreas Vesalius' brief over het afkooksel van den chyna-wortel. *Ned. Tijdschr. Geneesk.*, 1915, 59:717-719.

335 —— Vésale comme physiologiste expérimentateur. *Arch. néerl. Physiol.*, 1917, 1:129-147.

336 ROBERTS, Stewart R. The influence of Vesalius. *J. med. Ass. Ga.*, 1930, 19:324-329.

337 ROBINSON, V. Vesalius and anatomy. *Med. pharm. Crit.*, 1910, 13:311-319.

338 —— Pathfinders in medicine: Vesalius and anatomy. *Med. Rev. of Rev., N.Y.*, 1912, 18:329-334.

339 RÖSSLIN, Eucharius. *Der swangern Frauwen und Hebammen Rosegarten.* (Argentine, M. Flach Jr., 1513) 57 *ll.*

RONCONI, Giulio. See IMPERIALI, G., no. 204, p. 56.

340 ROSENKRANZ, Klaus. Die Initialen in Vesals Anatomie. Ein Beitrag zur Geschichte der anatomischen Abbildung. *Arch. Gesch. Med.*, 1937-38, 30:35-46.

341 ROTH, C., and SCHMIDT, T. P. *Handschriftenproben zur Basler Geistesgeschichte des 15. und 16. Jahrhunderts ausgewählt, transcribiert, übersetzt und erläutert.* Basel, R. Geering, 1926.
Facsimile, transcription and translation of letter of Vesalius to Heinrich Petri (*f.* 22) with short note about Vesalius on preceding unnumbered page.

342 ROTH, Moritz. Andreas Vesalius in Basel. *Beitr. vaterl. Gesch.*, 1885, 12:160-182.

343 —— *Andreas Vesalius Bruxellensis. Rektoratsrede gehalten . . . zu Basel am 26. November 1885.* Basel, B. Schwabe, 1886. 34 pp., 1 *l.*, portr.

344 —— Quellen einer Vesalbiographie. *Verh. naturf. Ges. Basel*, 1889, 8:706-754.

345 —— *Andreas Vesalius Bruxellensis.* Berlin, G. Reimer, 1892. viii, 500 pp., 30 pl.

346 —— Vesalius. *Allgemeine deutsche Biographie*, 1895, 39:639-648.

347 —— Vesaliana. *Virchows Arch.*, 1895, 141:462-478.

348 —— Zwei Originalporträte Vesal's. *KorrespBl. schweiz. Ärz.,* 1905, *35*:681-682.

349 —— Vesal, Estienne, Tizian, Leonardo da Vinci. I. *Arch. Anat. Physiol., Lpz.,* 1905, *29* (Anat. Abt.):79-95; II. 1906, *30*:77-100; [III.] Die Anatomie des Leonardo da Vinci. (Schluss der Aufsätze über Vesal, Estienne, Tizian, Leonardo.) 1907, *31* (Suppl.):1-122.

350 RUCKER, M. Pierce. Andreas Vesalius: A psychogram. *Johns Hopk. Alumni Mag.,* 1927, *16*:29-38.

RYCKE, Justus de, see SWEERTS, no. 384, and BLOUNT, no. 39.

351 ST. LOUIS MEDICAL HISTORY CLUB. Andreas Vesalius. List of books and pamphlets exhibited by members and others at the quatercentenary celebration of the birth of Andreas Vesalius, Dec. 2-24, 1914. *J. Mo. med. Ass.,* 1915, *12*:117-131.

352 SAMBUCUS, Joannes. *Veterum aliquot ac recentium medicorum philosophorumque icones; ex bibliotheca* I. Sambuci; *cum eiusdem ad singulas elogiis.* (Antverpia) Ex officina Plantinana Raphelengii, 1603. 7 *ll.,* 76 *ff.,* 4 *ll.*
References to Vesalius on A4b, *f.* 32, portrait, N4b epitaph, and Latin verses.

353 SANTORIO, Santorio. *Methodi vitandorum errorum omnium qui in arte medica contingunt libri quindecim* . . . Genevæ, apud P. Aubertum, 1631. 8 *ll.,* 605 pp., 25 *ll.,* 108 pp.
See Book III, p. 215. Also edition of Venice 1660, pp. 164-165 in defense and praise of Vesalius.

354 SAUNDERS, John B. de C. M. Vesalius and Don Carlos. A historical footnote, pp. 531-538 in: *Essays in biology in honor of Herbert M. Evans, written by his friends,* Berkeley, Univ. of California Press, 1943.

355 SCHENCK, Joannes à Grafenberg. Παραθήσεων *sive Observationum medicarum, rararum, novarum admirabilium, et monstrosarum volumen, tomis septem de toto homine institutum.* Francofurti, E typ. N. Hoffmani, 1609.
See Book I, p. 17, Book IV, p. 707, Book V, p. 787.

355a SCHMUTZER, Richard. Die Initialen in Vesals Anatomie. *Arch. Gesch. Med.,* 1938, *31*:328-330.

355b —— Die Anatomie der Haustiere in Vesals Fabrica (1543) und Epistola de radice Chyna (1546). *Ergebn. Anat. EntwGesch.,* 1938, *32*: 165-234.

356 SCHOLZ, Lorenz. *Epistolarum philosophicarum: medicinalium, ac chymicarum a summis nostræ ætatis philosophis ac medicis exaratarum, volumen* . . . Francofurti ad Mœnum, apud A. Wecheli hæredes, 1598. 5 *ll.,* 536 col., 6 *ll.*
See Epistolæ 30 and 31.

357 SCHOONEN, Louis. *Hommage à André Vésale.* Ed. de luxe. Bruxelles, D. Raes, 1847. 36 pp.

358 SCHWARZ, I. Ein Konsilium des Andreas Vesalius. *Arch. Gesch. Med.,* 1909-10, *3*:403-407.

359 SEIDEL, Bruno. *Commentarius didascalicus valde eruditus et perspicuus de corpore animato; ac potissimum quidem de corpore et anima hominis. Accommodatus ad faciliorem intelligentiam librorum Aristotelis et interpretum eius, ut et P. Melanchthonis* De anima; *itemque Galeni, Vesalii et aliorum qui de fabrica corporis humani scripserunt. Recognitus a Rod. Goclenio et nunc primum in lucem editus.* Hanoviæ, apud G. Antonium, 1594. 855 pp.
Page 33 *et seq.,* on Vesalius. "Vesalius divina industria ac sagacitate omnium tam antiquorum quam recentiorum studia superavit . . ."

360 *——* Poematum libri septem . . . Basel, 1555.
The short poem mentioning Vesalius on p. 310, is given in full by Roth (no. 345, p. 441).

361 SHUTE, D. Kerfoot. The life and work of Andreas Vesalius. *Old Dom. J. Med. Surg.,* 1910, *10*:195-211.

362 SICURO, Demetrio. Cenni sopra la vita e gli scritti di Andrea Vesalio. *Sperimentale,* 1861, 4 s. *8*:165-183.

363 SIGERIST, H. E. The conflict between the 16th century physicians and antiquity. *Int. Congr. Hist. Med.,* 1922, *3*:250-252.

363a SINGER, Charles. To Vesalius on the fourth centenary of his *De humani corporis fabrica. J. Anat. Lond.,* 1943, *77*:261-265.

364 SKRAINKA, P. Louvain and Andreas Vesalius. *Interst. med. J.,* 1914, *21*:1059-1068.
Editorial including a reprinting from MORLEY, *Anatomy in long clothes* (no. 295).

365 SLEIDANUS, Johannes. *De statu religionis et rei publicæ, Carolo Quinto, cæsare, commentariorum libri xxvj* . . . Argentorati [excudebat I. Rihelius], 5 *ll.,* 408 *ff.,* [11] pp.
See Book xxi, fol. 306.

366 —— *A famous cronicle of oure time called* Sleidanes *Commentaries, concerning the state of religion and com-*

monwealth, during the reign of Emperour Charles the fift . . . *Translated by* Iohn Daus. [London, I. Daie, 1560.] 5 *ll.*, 470 *ff.*, 34 pp.
See Book xxi, fol. 330.

367 *SOLENANDER, Reinert. *Consiliorum medicinalium sectiones quinque, quarum prima . . . a* Joanne Francisco de Gabiano *edita, et cum consiliis* Joannis Montani *in 16 excusa. Reliquæ quatuor auctore jam recens additæ. Ed. secunda.* Hanoviæ, apud C. Marnium et heredes J. Aubrii, 1609. 9 *ll.*, 516 pp., 12 *ll.*
(DSG)

368 SPENCER, Herbert R. *The renaissance of midwifery. Being the Lloyd Roberts Lecture delivered . . . on November 19th, 1924.* London, Harrison and Sons, Ltd. [1924]. 41 pp. See also *Lancet,* 1924, 2:1049-1056; *Brit. med. J.,* 1924, 2:933-937.

369 SPENCER, W. G. The 'Epitome' of Vesalius on vellum in the British Museum Library, pp. 237-244 in: *Essays on the history of medicine presented to Karl Sudhoff on the occasion of his seventieth birthday November 26th, 1923, edited by* Charles Singer and Henry E. Sigerist. Zürich, Seldwyla, 1924.

370 —— Vesalius: His delineation of the framework of the human body in the 'Fabrica' and 'Epitome.' The Fourth Vicary Lecture, 1922. *Brit. J. Surg.,* 1923, 10:382-402.

371 SPIELMANN, M. H. *The iconography of Andreas Vesalius (André Vésale) anatomist and physician 1514-1564. Paintings, pictures, engravings, illustrations, sculpture, medals. With notes critical, literary, and bibliographical.* Wellcome Historical Medical Museum. Research Studies in Medical History No. 3. London, John Bale, Sons and Danielsson, Ltd., 1925, xxviii, 244 pp.

372 *SPIROV, M. [Contribution of Vesalius to anatomy.] *Radyanska meditsina,* 1941, 6:72-73.

373 SPRENGEL, Kurt. *Versuch einer pragmatischen Geschichte der Arzneykunde.* Halle, 1821-28. 5 vol.
See Vol. 3, pp. 52 *et seq.,* portrait.

374 STATUE, (La) Vésale. *Gaz. méd. belge,* 1848, 6:11.

375 STEVENS, Paul de. André Vésale. *La Renaissance belge,* 1847, 9:161-163.
Contains translation of MS attributed to Vesalius, seen by the author in the Escurial, Madrid. Reproduction of Brussels statue.

376 STINTZING, R. *Ulrich Zasius. Ein Beitrag zur Geschichte der Rechtswissenschaft im Zeitalter der Reformation. Mit urkundl. Beilagen.* Basel, Bahnmaier's Verlag, 1857. xx, 387 pp.

377 STIRLING, William. Andrea Vesalius 1514-1564, pp. 2-5 in his: *Some apostles of physiology, being an account of their lives and labours . . .* London, Waterlow and Sons, 1902.

STOPIUS, Nicolaus. See HENERUS, no. 187, p. 245.

378 STREUBER. Neue Beiträge zur Basler Buchdrucker-Geschichte. *Beitr. vaterl. Gesch. Basel,* 1846, 3:65-124.
See especially p. 106.

379 SUDHOFF, Karl. Tradition und Naturbeobachtung in den Illustrationen medizinischer Handschriften und Frühdrucke vornehmlich des 15. Jahrhunderts. *Stud. Gesch. Med.,* 1907, 1:1-92; 23 pl.

380 —— *Ein Beitrag zur Geschichte der Anatomie im Mittelalter speziell der anatomischen Graphik nach Handschriften des 9. bis 15. Jahrhunderts.* Leipzig, J. A. Barth, 1908. viii, 94 pp., 24 pl.

381 —— Die Florentiner Skelettzeichnung des Leonardo da Vinci und die Frage der Beeinflussung Vesals durch Leonardo. *Verh. Ges. dtsch. Naturf.-Ärzt.* (Naturwiss. Abt.), 1910, 88-93.

382 —— Andreas Vesalius zu Ehren zum vierhundertjährigen Gedächtnis seiner Geburt gesprochen. *Verh. Ges. dtsch. Naturf. Ärzt.,* 1920, 162-190.

383 *SUSIO, Giovanni Battista. *Libri tres de venis e directò secandis; in quibus Matthæi Curtij præceptoris sui sententia defenditur, adversus A. Turinum, B. Victorium, V. Trincavellium, et A. Vesalium.* Cremonæ, apud V. Comitem, 1559. (BM)

384 *SWEERTS, F. *Athenæ Belgicæ, sive nomenclator infer. Germaniæ scriptorum, qui disciplinas philologicas, philosophicas, theologicas, juridicas, medicas, et musicas illustrarunt . . .* Antverpiæ, 1628. (BM)
On p. 128, epigram by Juste de Rycke.

385 SYLVIUS, Jacobus. *Væsani cujusdam calumniarum in Hippocratis Galenique rem anatomicam depulsio.* Parrhisiis, apud C. Barbé, vid. I. Gazelli, 1551, 29 *ff.*

386 —— The same. *Denuò per A. Arnaudum castigata.* Basileæ, Ex. Off. J. Derbilley, 1556. 118 pp.

387 TADDEI, A. Local où Vésale faisait à Pise ses demonstrations d'anatomie. *Æsculape,* 1931, 21:244.

388 *TESTA, Antonio Giuseppe. *Delle malattie del cuore, loro cagioni, specie, segni e cura. Nuova ed., riveduta ed aumentata di una appendice per cura di* N. M. Sormani. Milano, Schiepatti, etc., 1831. 2 vol. (DSG)
Quoted by del Gaizo (no. 154) at some length in support of Vesalius' interpretation of the heart.

389 THOU, J. A. de. *Historiarum sui temporis libri CXXXVIII*. Londini, S. Buckley, 1733. 7 vol.

Vol. 1, Book 5, p. 196, Count Buren attended by Vesalius; Vol. 2, Book 36, p. 398, brief account of Vesalius; Vol. 7, Cap. 6, pp. 13-14, and 16-17, letter and notes by L'Ecluse (no. 248) about Vesalius; Vol. 7, Cap. 11, p. 200, mentions seeing Vesalius in Paris.

390 TÖPLY, Robert von. *Aus der Renaissancezeit.* (Neue Streiflichter ueber die Florentiner Akademie und die anatomischen Zeichnungen des Vesal.) *Janus*, 1903, 8:130-140.

391 TOLLIN, Henri. *Andreas Vesal. Biol. Zbl.*, 1885, 5:242-256; 271-278; 336-349; 373-384; 404-414.

See especially p. 375 about Vesalius' connection with Charles V.

392 TOMMASINI, Jacopo Filippo. *Gymnasium Patavinum libris V comprehensum* . . . Utini, N. Schiratti, 1654. [16] 497 [45] pp.

See pp. 75 *et seq.*; 302 *et seq.* Illustration of anatomical theatre, p. 74.

393 TORTEBAT, François. *Abrégé d'anatomie, accomodé aux arts de peinture et de sculpture, et mis dans un ordre nouveau* . . . Paris, Tortebat, 1667 (?1668). 12 *ff.* (VI.D.25.)

394 TOSONI, Pietro. *Della anatomia degli antichi e della scuola anatomica padovana memoria.* Padova, Tipogr. del Seminario, 1846. 132 pp.

See pp. 70-87.

395 TOURNEUR, Victor. *Catalogue des médailles du royaume de Belgique. Ministère de Sciences et des Arts. Bibliothèque Royale. Cabinet des Médailles.* Bruxelles, Ch. Dupriez, 1911. 2 vol.

See Vol. I, pp. xlvi-xlviii, sketch of medalist Jouvenal, plate XVIII, no. 8, Medallion with head of Vesalius; p. 161, description of medal no. 548. (Not given by Kluykens; Spielman no. 12.)

396 TRICOT-ROYER, J. *André Vésale, quatrième centenaire. Art méd.*, Anvers, 1914, 7:65-80; 81-94, portr.

397 —— *La famille des "Van Wesel." Chron. méd.*, 1914, 21:259-264.

398 TURNER, E. *Les planches anatomiques de J. Dryander et de G. H. Ryff. Gaz. hebd. Méd. Chir.*, 1876, 33:785-791; 817-823.

399 —— Les six premières planches anatomiques de Vésale et leurs contrefaçons. *Gaz. hebd. Méd. Chir.*, 1877, 24:261-271.

400 —— Le portrait d'André Vésale au Musée du Louvre. *Gaz. hebd. Méd. Chir.*, 1877, 24:437-444; 469-474. Review: *L'Art*, Paris, 1876, 5²:89.

401 —— Les planches anatomiques du grand livre d'anatomie et de l'Epitome. *Gaz. hebd. Méd. Chir.*, 1877, 24:517-525.

402 —— Ce que sont devenues les planches de Vésale publiées in 1543 dans le grand ouvrage d'anatomie et dans l'Epitome. *Gaz. hebd. Méd. Chir.*, 1878, 25:49-58; 65-78; 113-119; 129-141; 161-166; 177-194.

403 —— Loys Vassé, de Châlons-sur-Marne.—Jean Vassès, de Meaux (1486-1550), docteur régent et doyen de la Faculté de Paris.—Nicolas Vasses, du diocèse de Meaux, étudiant en médecine en 1535.—Jean Le Vasseur, de Paris (1518-1570), docteur régent.—Claude Le Vasseur, de Paris (1614-1683).—Louis Le Vasseur, de Paris, docteur de Montpellier en 1658.—David Vassé, de Paris, docteur régent en 1723. *Gaz. hebd. Méd. Chir.*, 1882, 2. s., 19:373-379; 405-410; 437-442; 457-462. Reprinted, pp. 401-545 in his: *Etudes historiques, premier fascicule*, Paris, G. Masson, 1878.

403a Two forerunners. Our debt to Copernicus and Vesalius. The passing of mediæval science. *Times Literary Supplement*, London, 1943, May 29, pp. 258; 262, portr.

404 TYE, M. Myrtle. *The published works of Vesalius. J. med. Ass. Ga.*, 1930, 19:321-324.

404a UNDERWOOD, E. Ashworth. The "Fabrica" of Andreas Vesalius. A quatercentenary tribute. *Brit. med. J.*, 1943, 1:795-796.

405 UYTTERHOEVEN, Victor. *Monument-Vésale*. Bruxelles, 25 Sept., 1841. 1 leaf.

406 —— *Monument-Vésale. Procès-verbal de l'inauguration de la statue.* Bruxelles, 1847. 7 pp.

407 *VASARI, Giorgio. *Le vite de' più excellenti pittori, scultori, et architetti, di nuovo ampliate, con i ritratti loro, et con l'aggiunta delle vite de' vivi e de' morti dall' anno 1550 insino al 1567.* Firenze, Giunti, 1568. 2 vol. in 3.   (Brunet)

See Part 3, p. 818; 858.

408 —— *Lives of the most eminent painters, sculptors and architects, translated by Mrs. Jonathan Foster.* London, G. Bell and Sons, 1885-90. 5 vol.

See Vol. 3, p. 591; Vol. 5, pp. 402-403; 459.

409 VEDRANI, Alberto. Andrea Vesalio. *Ill. med. ital.*, 1919, 1:53‑56. 2 portr.

On Vesalius and Calcar.

410 VESALE, André, vol. 2, pp. 2018‑2024 in: SEYN, E. de, *Dictionnaire des ecrivains belges*. Bruges, 1931. Portr.

411 VESALIUS, Andreas. *Penny Cyclopædia*, 1843, 26:280‑281.

412 VETH, Jan. Andreas Vesalius en de Kunst. Rede gehouden ter gelegenheid der Vesalius‑Herdenking te Leiden, op 4 Januari 1915. *De Gids*, 1915, 79 (pt. 1):264‑275.

413 VIERORDT, H. Vesalius in Tübingen. *Dtsch. med. Pr.*, 1916, 20:6‑7.

414 VILLARET, M., and MOUTIER, F. Contribution à l'étude du plagiat iconographique chez les anatomistes du XVIme siècle. *Int. Congr. Hist. Med.*, 1923, 3:117‑120.

415 VIRCHOW, H. Zum Gedächtnis des 400. jährigen Geburtstages des Anatomen Andreas Vesalius. *Berl. klin. Wschr.*, 1915, 52:39‑40.

416 WAGSTAFFE, W. W. Vesalius, the founder of modern anatomy. *Trans. Oxf. Univ. Jr. Sci. Cl.* 1907, pp. 146‑158.

416a WALKER, Louise. Exhibition of books on the history of anatomical illustration, held in the Archibald Church Library of Northwestern University Medical School. *Bull. med. Libr. Ass.*, 1943, 31:272‑278.

See especially pp. 277‑278.

417 WALLER, Erik. Eine unbekannte Ausgabe von Vesals Epitome. *Lychnos*, 1936, pp. 251‑260.

418 WALSH, James J. Andreas Vesalius (1514‑1564), pp. 17‑44 in: WINDLE, B., *Twelve Catholic men of science*, London, Catholic Truth Society, 1923.

419 WALTZ, G. Ein Holograph des Andreas Vesalius. *Virchows Arch.*, 1878, 74:553.

A short paragraph about a note found in Madrid, dated "Ratisbon XI Augusti," about the illness of Vice‑Chancellor Naves. Prof. Waltz places the date as undoubtedly 1546.

420 WASHBURN, William H. Galen, Vesalius, da Vinci—anatomists. *Bull. Soc. med. Hist. Chicago*, 1916, 4:1‑17.

421 WATTLES, Merrill. Andreas Vesalius: 1514‑1564. A sketch of his life. *J. med. Ass. Ga.*, 1930, 19:318‑321.

422 WAUTERS, Alphonse. Quelques mots sur André Vésale, ses ascendants, sa famille et sa demeure à Bruxelles nommée la maison de Vésale. *Mém. cour. Acad. Sci. Belg.*, 1898, 55:1‑74.

423 WEAVER, J. Calvin. Anatomy before Vesalius. *J. med. Ass. Ga.*, 1930, 19:315‑318.

424 WEGNER, Richard N. *Das Anatomenbildnis. Seine Entwicklung im Zusammenhang mit der anatomischen Abbildung*. Basel, B. Schwabe and Co., [1939]. 199 pp.

Tintoretto portrait of Vesalius.

425 WEINBERG, Richard. Vesals körperliche Erscheinung. *Anat. Anz.*, 1925‑6, 60:208‑225.

426 WELCH, W. H. Vesalius and the spirit of his time. *N. Y. med. J.*, 1915, 101:488‑489; *Med. Rec.*, N. Y., 1915, 87:245‑256.

427 —— The times of Vesalius. Contributions of Vesalius other than anatomical. *Johns Hopk. Hosp. Bull.*, 1915, 26:118‑120.

428 WEYNANTS, Nicolaus. Andræ Vesalii præconium, oratio quam in solemni præmiorum distributione Collegii Lit. Hum. Alticolensis. *Annu. Univ. cathol. Louvain*, 1845, 9:233‑241.

429 WHARTON, Edith. Vesalius in Zante (1564). *N. Amer. Rev.*, 1902, 175:625‑631.

429a WIBERG, J. Anatomy of the heart in the 16th, 17th and 18th centuries (Andreas Vesalius, Richard Lower and Raimond Vieussens). *Janus*, 1927, 31:279‑285.

430 WOLTMAN, A. F. G. A., and WOERMANN, K. *History of painting, translated by* Clara Bell. New York, Dodd, Mead and Co., 1880‑85. 2 vol.

Vol. 2, p. 625, reference to Calcar and Vesalius.

431 YESKO, Stephen A. Anatomy before the modern period (Vesalius). *Med. Rec.*, N. Y., 1938, 147:394‑397.

ZASIUS, Ulrich, *see* STINTZING, R. v., no. 376.

432 *ZILBOORG, G. Psychological sidelights on Andreas Vesalius. *Bull. Hist. Med.*, 1943 (Dec.).

433 ZUALLART, Jean. Il devotissimo viaggio di Gierusalemme . . . in sei libri. Roma, D. Basa, 1595. (ICN)

See p. 85 *et seq.*

434 BENJAMIN, John A. A discussion of the twenty-first illustration of the fifth book of *De humani corporis fabrica* (1543). *Bull. Hist. Med.*, 1943, *13*:(Dec.).

435 CASSIRER, Ernst A. The place of Vesalius in the culture of the Renaissance. *Yale J. Biol. Med.*, 1943, *16*:(Dec.).

436 CASTIGLIONI, Arturo. Andreas Vesalius: Professor at the Medical School of Padua. *Bull. N.Y. Acad. Med.*, 1943, *19*:766-777.

437 —— The attack of Puteus on Vesalius and the defence by Cuneus. *Yale J. Biol. Med.*, 1943, *16*:(Dec.).

438 CODELLAS, Pan S. Vesalius—Valverde—Patousas: The unpublished manuscript of the first modern anatomy in the Greek language. *Bull. Hist. Med.*, 1943, *13*:(Dec.).

439 EDELSTEIN, Ludwig. Andreas Vesalius, the humanist. *Bull. Hist. Med.*, 1943, *13*:(Dec.).

440 FRANCIS, William W. Introductory remarks: Celebration of the 400th anniversary of the *Fabrica*. *Yale J. Biol. Med.*, 1943, *13*:(Dec.).

441 METZGER, Charles. Les lettrines de l'Anatomie d'André Vésale. Scènes de la vie des anatomistes et des chirurgiens au XVIe siècles. *Hippocrate*, 1935 (Dec.):825.

442 MEYER, A. W., and WIRT, Sheldon K. The Amuscan illustrations. *Bull. Hist. Med.*, 1943, *13*:(Dec.).

443 MILLER, Genevieve. An exhibit illustrating the life and work of Vesalius. *Bull. Hist. Med.*, 1943, *13*:(Dec.).

444 MONTEIRO, Hernâni. André Vesálio no quarto centário da publição da *Fabrica*. Conferencia lida na Sala Nobre da Faculdade de Medicina do Pôrto—na noite de 18-III-1943. *J. Médico*, 1943, *3*:(nos. 58-59) [23 pp.].

445 —— Tres anatómicos célebres da Renascença italiana: Leonardo da Vinci, Berengário da Carpi, André Vesálio. *J. Médico*, 1943, *3*:(nos. 62-63) [20 pp.]. Reprinted: *Arch. Anat. Anthrop. Lisboa*, 1943, v. 22.

446 —— As letras capitulares do tratado de anatomia de Vesálio "De humani corporis fabrica" (Basileia, 1543). *Arch. Anat. Anthrop. Lisboa*, 1943, *22*:433-476.

447 ROLLINS, Carl P. Oporinus and the publication of the *Fabrica*. *Yale J. Biol. Med.*, 1943, *16*:(Dec.).

448 SIGERIST, Henry E. Albanus Torinus and the German edition of the *Epitome*. *Bull. Hist. Med.*, 1943, *13*:(Dec.).

449 STEWART, George. Benediction: Celebration of the 400th anniversary of the *Fabrica*. *Yale J. Biol. Med.*, 1943, *16*:(Dec.).

450 STRAUS, William L., Jr., and TEMKIN, Owsei. Some aspects of the anatomical material of Vesalius. *Bull. Hist. Med.*, 1943, *13*:(Dec.).

451 STREETER, Edward C. Vesalius at the University of Paris. *Yale J. Biol. Med.*, 1943, *16*:(Dec.).

APPENDIX TO CHAPTER X

A NOTE ON PROSPERO BORGARUCCI
AND THE *CHIRURGIA MAGNA*

By ARTURO CASTIGLIONI, M.D.

Among the works which were published under the name of Andreas Vesalius there is one whose authenticity was questioned in early times, and it can now be stated that the book is certainly spurious. It is the *Chirurgia magna* edited by Prospero Borgarucci and published as a fat octavo of some five hundred leaves by Vincenzo Valgrisi at Venice in 1568 under the title: *Andreæ Vessalii Bruxellensis Philippi Hispaniarum regis, medici, chirurgia magna in septem libros digesta. In qua nihil desiderari potest, quod ad perfectam, atque integram de curandis humani corporis malis, methodum pertineat. Prosperi Borgarutii Excellentissimi Philosophi, ac Medici Regii, opera, atque diligentia expolita, emendata, in ordinem digesta, comparata, & ut sua edita. Cum amplissimis Indicibus tùm capitum: tùm rerum omnium memorabilium.*

Borgarucci was appointed professor at the University of Padua in 1564, the year of Vesalius' death. Three years later he was called to Paris and appointed physician to the Queen of France, but in the following year he returned to Padua. He states in the introduction of the book that he had found the MS. of the *Chirurgia magna* in 1567 in Paris. The book contains three woodcuts that are borrowed from Tagault's *De chirurgica institutione* published by the same Valgrisi in 1544 and are bad copies of the skeletal figures of the *Tabulæ sex*; a fourth woodcut is a bad copy of the 'thinking skeleton' from the *Fabrica*. The *Chirurgia magna* had two printings in 1568 in which the dedication to Cortusio is different. The first is dated *idibus Septembris 1568*; the second, abbreviated from thirty to four pages, has the date *V. nonas Octobris* and a slightly different title. The text of the book, however, is not changed, and it may be assumed that after the first appearance of the book Borgarucci felt it necessary to suppress a part of the preface. The *Chirurgia* also had three editions in 1569. The differences between the two prefaces, in the second of which the fact of the acquisition of Vesalius' MS. in Paris is not told, is a problem which deserves further study.

Boerhaave and Albinus included the *Chirurgia magna* in their edition (VI.D.8). Haller had some doubt about the authenticity, but even so put the work under Vesalius' name. Haeser (180) and Burggraeve (62) also accepted the authorship of Vesalius.

Roth examined the contents of the *Chirurgia magna* very carefully and strongly criticised it. He is undoubtedly correct in saying that the book cannot be considered as a work of Vesalius. There are too many errors in it, too many passages which cannot be attributed to the author of the *Fabrica,* and too many quotations from books, such as the work of Fallopius, which were published after Vesalius' death. Vesalius, therefore, could not have been the author. We may only add that Roth's condemnation of Borgarucci seems to be too strong. Roth characterized him as a plagiarist who fathered the book on Vesalius only in order to give it the prestige of that name and to give the printer an opportunity to use the old blocks. We must remember, however, that Vesalius had really taught surgery in Padua, that in fact he had been officially appointed professor of surgery in charge of anatomical dissection. We know that his *magnum opus* started with the purpose of teaching anatomy for the surgeons and that he had expressed the intention of publishing a book on surgery. In the explanation of the initials E and F (*Fabrica,* Book IV, Chapter 9), speaking of luxations, he adds: "We shall treat of this subject in a book on another subject."

That the 'Surgery' edited by Borgarucci is not the work which Vesalius intended to write on surgery is absolutely certain. However, one may properly suggest that what Borgarucci bought in Paris and edited and published may have been the class notes of some pupils of Vesalius. The custom of publishing students' notes as the posthumous works of famous lecturers was very common, even in the Italy of the Renaissance. An example of it is given by the anatomical and medical works of Fallopius which we quoted above and which derived from the same source—that is, notes of students, not always accurate and exact. Borgarucci with the help of such notes and recourse to the *Fabrica* and *Epitome,* from which he largely borrowed, and of the blocks of Tagault's Surgery composed the book which he dedicated to Jacobo Antonio Cortusio, a Paduan patrician who had been a great friend of Vesalius. Borgarucci is most eloquent in his praise of Vesalius and in his belief that his work may find the approval of the "Paduan republic of letters." To-day we may pass judgment on his work as being neither correct nor opportune nor authentic, but we cannot with absolute certainty deny Borgarucci the good intention of contributing to the greater glory of Vesalius.

INDEX OF RECORDED COPIES

The numbers refer to the pages of the book

* Copies not actually cited on these pages.

218

* Copies not actually cited on these pages.

CHRONOLOGY OF EDITIONS

INDEX OF NAMES

THIS EDITION OF
A BIO⁄BIBLIOGRAPHY OF ANDREAS VESALIUS
LIMITED TO EIGHT HUNDRED COPIES
WAS DESIGNED AND PRINTED
BY THE PRESS OF A. COLISH, NEW YORK